W9-AYG-902

Test Item File

INTERNATIONAL BUSINESS

Test Item File

INTERNATIONAL BUSINESS

Second Edition

Ricky W. Griffin
Michael w. Pustay

Tracy Ryan
Virginia Commonwealth University

PEARSON
Prentice
Hall

Upper Saddle River, New Jersey 07458

Editor-in-Chief: Jeff Shelstad
Managing Editor: Jennifer Glennon
Associate Editor: Christine Genneken
Manager, Print Production: Christy Mahon
Production Editor & Buyer: Phyllis Rosinsky
Printer/Binder: Technical Communication Services

Copyright © 2005 by Pearson Education, Inc., Upper Saddle River, New Jersey, 07458.
Pearson Prentice Hall. All rights reserved. Printed in the United States of America. This publication is protected by Copyright and permission should be obtained from the publisher prior to any prohibited reproduction, storage in a retrieval system, or transmission in any form or by any means, electronic, mechanical, photocopying, recording, or likewise. For information regarding permission(s), write to: Rights and Permissions Department.

This work is protected by United States copyright laws and is provided solely for the use of instructors in teaching their courses and assessing student learning. Dissemination or sale of any part of this work (including on the World Wide Web) will destroy the integrity of the work and is not permitted. The work and materials from it should never be made available to students except by instructors using the accompanying text in their classes. All recipients of this work are expected to abide by these restrictions and to honor the intended pedagogical purposes and the needs of other instructors who rely on these materials.

Pearson Prentice Hall[TM] is a trademark of Pearson Education, Inc.

10 9 8 7 6 5 4 3 2 1
ISBN 0-13-142269-3

Test Item File
Table of Contents

Multiple Choice

1. Beijing is the host of the Olympic Games in the year _____.
    a. 2000
    b. 2004
    c. 2006
    d. 2008
    e. 2012
    (d; moderate; p. 3)

2. _____ was recognized for widespread unethical behaviors in its bid for the Olympic games.
    a. Salt Lake City
    b. Beijing
    c. Atlanta
    d. Sydney
    e. None of the above
    (a; easy; p. 3)

3. The IOC is based in _____.
    a. Germany
    b. Austria
    c. Switzerland
    d. United States
    e. Greece
    (c; moderate; p. 3)

4. Which of the following is not one of the decisions made by the IOC concerning the Olympics?
    a. location
    b. selection of judges
    c. sports included
    d. selection of referees
    e. all are decisions made by the IOC
    (e; easy; p. 4)

5. The fee for "worldwide partner" sponsorship of the Olympics is _____ according to the text.
    a. $25 million
    b. $55 million
    c. $75 million
    d. $100 million
    e. more than $100 million
    (b; moderate; p. 4)

6.   Which of the following brands is not a worldwide partner in the Olympics?
        a.   Coca-Cola
        b.   Samsung
        c.   Kodak
        d.   Panasonic
        e.   Olympus
        (e; difficult; p. 4)

7.   Olympic sponsorship is best suited for which type of companies?
        a.   companies pursuing a niche market
        b.   companies selling technological goods
        c.   retailers
        d.   companies pursuing a world-wide market
        e.   companies in the field of sports
        (d; moderate; p. 4)

8.   Coca-Cola benefits from its sponsorship of the Olympics because
        a.   it pursues a niche market.
        b.   it sells high-tech products.
        c.   people drink more at sports events.
        d.   it pursues a world-wide market.
        e.   none of the above.
        (d; easy; p. 4)

9.   _____ consist(s) of business transactions between parties from more than one
        country.
        a.   Currency exports
        b.   International business
        c.   Domestic business
        d.   Global ventures
        e.   None of the above
        (b; easy; p. 5)

10.   Which of the following represent reasons that international business differs from
        domestic business?
        a.   currencies
        b.   legal systems
        c.   cultures
        d.   resources
        e.   all of the above
        (e; moderate; p. 5)

11.   _____ consist(s) of business transactions between parties from more than one country.
    a.   International business
    b.   Domestic business
    c.   Cross country negotiations
    d.   Corporate expansion
    e.   None of the above
    (a; easy; p. 5)

12.   Just-in-time systems were created in _____.
    a.   the United States
    b.   Japan
    c.   Germany
    d.   China
    e.   Great Britain
    (b; easy; p. 6)

13.   JIT stands for _____.
    a.   just-in-time
    b.   Japanese information technology
    c.   an inventory management technique
    d.   a and c
    e.   none of the above
    (a; easy; p. 6)

14.   JIT is a type of _____ system.
    a.   warehousing
    b.   computer
    c.   inventory management
    d.   manufacturing
    e.   human resource
    (c; moderate; p. 6)

15.   The term _____ means that the financial liability of the company's owners is limited to the extent of their investments if the company fails or encounters financial or legal difficulties.
    a.   LLC
    b.   TM
    c.   Inc.
    d.   CPA
    e.   LR
    (c; moderate; p. 7)

16.   Small, privately held companies in Germany use a form of limited liability called
       _____.
       a. AG
       b. KGaA
       c. GmbH
       d. KK
       e. SpA
       (c; difficult; p. 7)

17.   Large, publicly held firms in Germany with management boards and boards of
       directors utilize the _____ form of limited liability.
       a. AG
       b. KGaA
       c. GmbH
       d. KK
       e. SpA
       (a; difficult; p. 7)

18.   The limited liability form used in the Netherlands is _____.
       a. KK
       b. BV
       c. Ltd
       d. Inc
       e. GmbH
       (b; difficult; p. 7)

19.   Deutsche Bank and Volkswagen are both examples of companies using the _____
       form of limited liability.
       a. AG
       b. KGaA
       c. GmbH
       d. KK
       e. SpA
       (a; difficult; p. 7)

20.   Limited liability companies in the United Kingdom that are privately held use
       _____.
       a. AG
       b. PLC
       c. Ltd
       d. GmbH
       e. Inc
       (c; difficult; p. 7)

21.   Limited liability companies in the United Kingdom that are publicly held use
        _____.
        a. AG
        b. PLC
        c. Ltd
        d. GmbH
        e. Inc
        (b; difficult; p. 7)

22.   _____ is the selling of products made in one's own country for use or resale in
        other countries.
        a. Exporting
        b. Importing
        c. Merchandising
        d. Transporting
        c. Trading
        (a; easy; p. 7)

23.   Black and Decker produce tools at a plant in North Carolina and ship the tools to
        retailers in England. Which type of international business activity is this an
        example of?
        a. exporting
        b. importing
        c. merchandising
        d. transporting
        e. trading
        (a; moderate; p. 7)

24.   _____ is the buying of products made in other countries for use or resale in one's
        own country.
        a. Exporting
        h. Importing
        c. Merchandising
        d. Transporting
        e. Trading
        (b; easy; p. 7)

25.   Sam's Club purchases kalamata olives from Greece for sale in its stores. Which
        international business activity does this represent?
        a. exporting
        b. importing
        c. merchandising
        d. transporting
        e. trading
        (b; moderate; p. 7)

26.   The British term for the trading of tangible goods is _____.
       a. visible trade
       b. invisible trade
       c. merchandise exports/imports
       d. service exports/imports
       e. none of the above
       (a; moderate; p. 7)

27.   The British term for the trading of intangible goods is _____.
       a. visible trade
       b. invisible trade
       c. merchandise exports/imports
       d. service exports/imports
       e. none of the above
       (b; moderate; p. 7)

28.   Boeing sells commercial aircraft to Lufthansa in Germany. This is an example of
       _____.
       a. exporting
       b. importing
       c. merchandising
       d. transporting
       e. trading
       (a; moderate; p. 7)

29.   Trade in goods includes products such as _____.
       a. clothing
       b. banking
       c. travel
       d. accounting
       e. all of the above
       (a; moderate; p. 7)

30.   Trade in services includes all of the following except _____.
       a. clothing
       b. banking
       c. travel
       d. accounting
       e. all of the above
       (a; moderate; p. 7)

31.   The international business activity called _____ occurs when capital is supplied by residents of one country to residents of another country.
       a. international investment
       b. foreign direct investment
       c. portfolio investment
       d. financial insurance
       e. capitalism
       (a; moderate; p. 8)

32.   _____ are investments made for the purpose of actively controlling property, assets, or companies located in host countries.
       a. Financial assets
       b. Portfolio investments
       c. Foreign direct investments
       d. International bonds
       e. Indirect investments
       (c; easy; p. 8)

33.   _____ is where the parent company's headquarter is located.
       a. Host country
       b. Home country
       c. Parental country
       d. United States
       e. None of the above
       (b; easy; p. 9)

34.   Ford Motor Company is based in Detroit, Michigan. It also has offices in Germany, England, and China. _____ is the home country.
       a. Germany
       b. England
       c. China
       d. United States
       e. All are home countries for Ford Motor Company
       (d; moderate; p. 9)

35.   _____ is where a company operates but is not headquartered.
       a. Host country
       b. Home country
       c. Parental country
       d. European Union
       e. None of the above
       (a; easy; p. 9)

36.   Seimens is headquartered in Germany but maintains operations in the United
        States. The United States is the _____ country.
        a. home
        b. host
        c. parent
        d. subsidiary
        e. none of the above
        (b; moderate; p. 9)

37.   _____ are purchases of foreign financial assets for a purpose other than control.
        a. Foreign direct investments
        b. Bonds
        c. International stocks
        d. Portfolio investments
        e. Indirect investments
        (d; easy; p. 9)

38.   Which country has the highest level of exports as a percentage of GDP according
        to the text?
        a. United States
        b. Japan
        c. Netherlands
        d. Mexico
        e. Indonesia
        (c; difficult; p. 9)

39.   Ford Motor Company purchased all of the common stock of Sweden's Volvo
        Corporation. This is an example of _____.
        a. portfolio investment
        b. foreign direct investment
        c. international expansion
        d. corporate take over
        e. licensing
        (b; moderate; p. 9)

40.   McDonald's has licensed its brand name, operational systems, and trademarks to
        individual restaurant owners in Europe. This is called _____.
        a. leasing
        b. renting
        c. franchising
        d. contracting
        e. expanding
        (c; moderate; p. 10)

41.   _____ is a contractual arrangement in which a firm in one country licenses the use
        of its intellectual property to a firm in a second country, in return for a royalty
        payment.
        a. Leasing
        b. Renting
        c. Franchising
        d. Licensing
        e. Royalty expansion
        (d; easy; p. 10)

42.   Licensing usually involves permission to use _____.
        a. patents
        b. trademarks
        c. brand names
        d. copyrights
        e. all of the above
        (e; easy; p. 10)

43.   Walt Disney permits a German clothing manufacturer to market children's
        pajamas embroidered with Mickey Mouse in return for a percentage of company
        sales. This is an example of _____.
        a. franchising
        b. licensing
        c. royalty expansion
        d. leasing
        e. piracy
        (b; moderate; p. 10)

44.   A(n) _____ is an agreement wherein a firm in one country agrees to operate
        facilities or provide other management services to a firm in another country for an
        agreed-upon fee.
        a. franchising agreement
        b. licensing agreement
        c. management contract
        d. portfolio investment
        e. indirect investment
        (c; moderate; p. 10)

45.   KFC has restaurants in South Korea, China, and Japan. What type of arrangement
        is most likely used by KFC and the restaurant owners?
        a. franchising agreement
        b. licensing agreement
        c. management contract
        d. portfolio investment
        e. indirect investment
        (a; moderate; p. 10)

46.   McDonald's has at least _____ restaurants in China according to the text.
        a. 200
        b. 400
        c. 600
        d. 1000
        e. 1500
        (b; difficult; p. 10)

47.   In 2002, _____ was considered the world's largest corporation according to the text.
        a. Nike
        b. Ford Motor Company
        c. Coca-Cola
        d. McDonald's
        e. Wal-Mart
        (e; difficult; p. 11)

48.   The top three world-wide corporations according to revenue figures are all based in _____.
        a. Germany
        b. France
        c. United States
        d. European Union
        e. Canada
        (c; easy; p. 11)

49.   The term _____ is used to identify firms that have extensive involvement in international business.
        a. global
        b. multinational corporation
        c. international conglomerate
        d. multidomestic organization
        e. all of the above
        (b; easy; p. 11)

50.   MNC stands for _____.
        a. manufacturing news contracts
        b. multinational contracts
        c. mining national copper
        d. multinational corporation
        e. none of the above
        (d; easy; p. 11)

51.   Which of the following is not a common activity of MNCs?
        a. owning and controlling foreign assets
        b. buying resources in various countries
        c. creating goods and/or services in a variety of countries
        d. selling goods and/or services in various countries
        e. all are activities of MNCs
        (e; moderate; p. 11)

52.   The IOC is technically considered an _____.
        a. MNC
        b. MNE
        c. MNO
        d. MMM
        e. FDI
        (c; difficult; p. 11)

53.   International non-profit organizations are called _____.
        a. multinational corporations
        b. multinational organizations
        c. multinational enterprises
        d. multinational non-profits
        e. none of the above
        (b; moderate; p. 11)

54.   Which of the following is not a basic motive for firms to become more global?
        a. leverage of core competencies
        b. acquisition of resources
        c. access to new markets
        d. ability to compete
        e. all are basic motives for globalization
        (e; moderate; p. 12)

55.   Nike's use of manufacturing facilities in Asia is an example of the motive of
        _____.
        a. leverage of core competencies
        b. acquisition of resources
        c. access to new markets
        d. all of the above
        e. none of the above
        (b; difficult; p. 12)

56.   Access to cheap labor can be categorized as _____.
        a. leverage of core competencies
        b. acquisition of resources
        c. access to new markets
        d. all of the above
        e. none of the above
        (b; moderate; p. 12)

57.   Which of the following is the likely motive for Procter & Gamble's move into China?
        a. leverage of core competencies
        b. acquisition of resources
        c. access to new markets
        d. ability to compete
        e. all are basic motives for globalization
        (c; difficult; p. 13)

58.   _____ is a distinctive strength that is central to a firm's operations.
        a. Core competency
        b. Distinctive advantage
        c. Differential advantage
        d. Strategic imperative
        e. Global advantage
        (a; moderate; p. 12)

59.   Singapore Airlines' _____ is its award-winning standards of customer satisfaction.
        a. core competency
        b. distinctive advantage
        c. differential advantage
        d. strategic imperative
        e. global advantage
        (a; difficult; p. 13)

60.   Which of the following is *not* one of the benefits of acquiring resources and supplies in other countries?
        a. access to scarce items
        b. access to cheaper resources
        c. increased shipping costs
        d. access to items unavailable in home country
        e. all are benefits of acquiring resources from other countries
        (c; difficult; p. 13)

61.   Which of the following is *not* one of the benefits for seeking new markets?
        a.   access to new customers
        b.   economies of scale
        c.   diversification of revenue stream
        d.   increased dependence on sales in home country
        e.   all are benefits of seeking new markets
        (d; difficult; p. 13)

62.   After World War I, international business was restricted by _____.
        a.   import barriers
        b.   export barriers
        c.   government supply contracts
        d.   lack of transportation
        e.   all of the above
        (a; moderate; p. 13)

63.   International business was encouraged by the _____ following World War II.
        a.   improved transportation options
        b.   introduction of the Euro
        c.   minimization of high-quality Japanese goods in the marketplace
        d.   reduced tariffs and quotas
        e.   all of the above
        (d; moderate; p. 13)

64.   Influential regional trading accords include all of the following *except*?
        a.   GATT
        b.   WTO
        c.   EU
        d.   Mercosur
        e.   NAFTA
        (a; difficult; p. 13)

65.   Advances in communications technology include all of the following *except*
        _____.
        a.   information processing via computer
        b.   facsimile transmission
        c.   electronic mail
        d.   web access
        e.   none of the above
        (a; difficult; p. 14)

66.   The Internet is important to international business because it _____.
        a. facilitates international trade in services
        b. levels the playing field between small and large businesses
        c. increases efficiency of business-to-business networks
        d. enhances the speed of communication
        e. all of the above
        (e; moderate; p. 16)

67.   Which of the following does not represent technological changes important to
        improvements in international business?
        a. communications
        b. transportation
        c. information processing
        d. international standardization
        e. electronic mail
        (d; difficult; p. 14)

True/False

68.   The Olympic games obtain revenue through the sale of broadcast rights.
        (T; easy; p. 4)

69.   Hosting the Olympics creates a financial hardship on that city. (F; easy; p. 4)

70.   The highest profile level in corporate sponsorship of the Olympics is that of
        worldwide partner. (T; moderate; p. 4)

71.   Coca-Cola paid $60 million above its partnership fee for television advertising
        during the Olympics. (T; moderate; p. 4)

72.   The primary benefit of worldwide partnership is the right to use the Olympic logo
        on all advertising by the sponsor. (F; difficult; p. 4)

73.   One of the benefits of studying international business is the development of
        cultural literacy. (T; moderate; p. 6)

74.   Students in Europe and Asia often learn multiple languages during their education.
        (T; easy; p. 6)

75.   Borrowing from a bank in one country to finance operations in another is not an
        example of international business. (F; difficult; p. 4)

76.   Most large organizations have some interest in international affairs. (T; easy; p. 5)

77.   JIT was created in the United States. (F; easy; p. 6)

78.   The desire for control is the primary difference between foreign direct investments and portfolio investments. (T; moderate; p. 8)

79.   Ford's purchase of all the common stock in Volvo is an example of portfolio investment. (F; difficult; p. 9)

80.   All limited liability companies in Japan use kabuskiski kaisha. (T; difficult; p. 7)

81.   More than half of Boeing's commercial aircraft sales are to foreign customers. (T; difficult; p. 7)

82.   Management contracts are common in the upper end of the international hotel industry. (T; difficult; p. 10)

83.   The British call merchandise exports and imports visible trade. (T; easy; p. 7)

84.   The British call service exports and imports intangible trade. (F; easy; p. 7)

85.   Exporting is often critical to a country's financial health. (T; easy; p. 7)

86.   The home country is where a foreign firm operates. (F; easy; p. 9)

87.   Exports make up a significant portion of GDP for well-developed countries. (T; moderate; p. 9)

88.   A brand name is a type of intellectual property. (T; easy; p. 10)

89   Wal-Mart is the world's largest corporation. (T; moderate; p. 11)

90.   MNO stands for multinational operations. (F; moderate; p. 11)

91.   The IOC is a multinational enterprise. (F; moderate; p. 11)

92.   Pepsi has chosen not to participate in foreign markets because of Coca-Cola's aggressive marketing. (F; moderate; p. 13)

93.   Some argue that the World Trade Organization promotes interests of the rich and powerful. (T; moderate; p. 12)

94.   The World Trade Organization is the successor the General Agreement on Tariffs and Trade. (T; difficult; p. 13)

95.   Trade agreements increase trade barriers among country members. (F; easy; p. 13)

96.	*Anne of Red Hair* is the Japanese name for the book *Anne of Green Gables*. (T; easy; p. 14)

97.	The Internet makes it more difficult for small businesses to compete with larger businesses. (F; moderate; p. 16)

98.	Some believe the world will someday be a boundaryless global economy. (T; easy; p. 4)

Short Answer

99.	What is the name of the organization that governs the Olympic games? Answer: International Olympic Committee (IOC). (easy; p. 3)

100.	Explain the meaning of the term cultural literacy. Answer: Cultural literacy refers to one's knowledge of other cultures. (moderate; p. 6)

101.	Explain the meaning of the term Inc. and its benefits. Answer: Inc. stands for Incorporated and means that the financial liability of the company's owners is limited to the extent of their investments if the company fails or encounters financial or legal difficulties. (moderate; p. 7)

102.	What is the difference between exporting and importing? Answer: Exporting refers to products sent from the home country to other countries. Importing refers to products sent from other countries into the home country. (easy; p. 7)

103.	Germany uses three forms of limited liability. What is the primary characteristic that determines which form is used by a firm? Answer: The primary characteristic to determine the appropriate form of limited liability used by a firm is the firm's ownership. Large, publicly held firms with a management board and a board of directors uses the Aktiengesellschaft (AG) form. A firm that is owned by limited partners but has at least one shareholder with unlimited liability uses the Kommanditgesellschaft auf Aktien (KGaA). Smaller, privately held companies use the Gesellschaft mit beschrankter Haftung (GmbH) form. (difficult; p. 7)

104.	What is the largest corporation in the world? Answer: Wal-Mart. (moderate; p. 11)

105.	What is a portfolio investment? How does it differ from foreign direct investments? Answer: Portfolio investment refers to investments made for reasons other than control (such as for an attractive rate of return). Foreign direct investment is investment for the purpose of control. (moderate; p. 9)

106.	Into what two categories can international investments be divided? Answer: Portfolio investments and foreign direct investments. (moderate; p. 8)

107.   What is the simplest form of international business activity? Answer: Exporting. (easy; p. 7)

108.   Control is the primary difference between what two forms of international investments? Answer: Portfolio investments and foreign direct investments. (moderate; p. 8)

109.   Explain the difference between licensing and franchising. Answer: Licensing is a contractual arrangement in which a firm in one country licenses the use of its intellectual property to a firm in a second country in return for a royalty payment. Franchising is a specialized form of licensing which occurs when the franchisor authorizes the franchisee to utilize its operating system as well as its intellectual property. (easy; p. 10)

110.   Explain the difference between the terms multinational corporation, multinational enterprise, and multinational organization. Answer: The difference is in the type of organization. A multinational corporation is an international for-profit company. Some large organizations are not actually corporations (such as accounting partnerships) and these are referred to as multinational enterprises. Multinational not-for-profits are referred to as multinational organizations. (moderate; p. 11)

111.   Describe the meaning of globalization. Answer: Globalization can be defined as the inexorable integration of markets, nation-states, and technologies, in a way that is enabling individuals, corporations, and nation-states to reach around the world farther, faster, deeper, and cheaper than ever before. (moderate; p. 11)

112.   Explain the various activities undertaken by MNCs. Answer: MNCs buy resources in a variety of countries, create goods and services in a variety of countries, and sell those goods and services in a variety of countries.

        (moderate; p. 11)

113.   Where will the Olympics be held in 2008? Answer: Beijing. (easy; p. 3)

114.   Why are companies willing to pay millions of dollars to be an Olympic sponsor? Answer: Because of the visibility, publicity, and goodwill generated from the sponsorship. (moderate; p. 4)

115.   Why do cities compete for the privilege of hosting the Olympic games? Answer: Hosting the Olympics brings recognition and publicity to the city just as it does to a company brand name. In addition, the city benefits from increased travel, tourism, and investment by businesses supporting the Olympic games. (moderate; p. 3)

116. Why are small businesses becoming more involved in international business? Answer: Technology allows small businesses to have access to customers without the previous expense and investment. (moderate; p. 6)

117. Explain the meaning of the term core competency. Answer: A core competency is a distinctive strength or advantage that is central to a firm's operations. (easy; p. 12)

118. Why might Japanese women who are fans of the book *Anne of Red Hair* relate so well to the character of Anne? Answer: It could be that Anne's characteristics of rebelliousness and frankness appeal to Japanese women. (difficult; p. 14)

119. What are the primary technological changes advancing international business? Answer: Communications, transportation, and information processing. (moderate; p. 14)

Essay

120. International business differs from domestic business in several ways. Identify four sources of these differences and describe the implications that result from each difference.

Answer: The countries may use different currencies, which require currency conversion and exchange rate risk. Because the legal systems are different this forces one or more parties to adjust their practices to comply with local laws. The cultures of the countries may differ and the available resources differ from country to country. Consequently, the production of various items and the production methods may vary from country to country. (moderate; p. 5)

121.   Why is it important for business students to study international business?

Answer: Most large organizations will have international operations or be affected by the global economy. Career opportunities will be expanded and helps when dealing with other managers. Small businesses are increasingly involved in international business and students keep pace with competition from other countries. It also enables students to stay aware of the latest business techniques and tools. Importantly, it provides an opportunity to develop cultural literacy. (easy; pp. 5-6)

122.   Licensing, franchising, and management contracts are all forms of international business activity. Briefly define each form. What are the advantages and disadvantages of using these forms of activity? Provide an example.

Answer: Licensing is a contractual arrangement in which a firm in one country licenses the use of its intellectual property to a firm in a second country in exchange for royalty payments. Walt Disney allowing the use of Mickey Mouse's image on clothing by a German manufacturer is a example of licensing. Franchising is a specialized form of licensing. It occurs when a firm in one country authorizes a firm in a second country to utilize its operating system as well as its intellectual property in exchange for payments. McDonald's authorizes franchises in many different countries including China. Management contracts involve an arrangement wherein a firm in one country operates facilities or provides other management services to a firm in another country for a fee. Hilton and Marriott utilize management contracts to operate overseas hotel properties. Each firm allows a company to earn fees for its assets (intellectual property, operating systems, and management services) while allowing another firm access to those assets. However, each allows the potential to create competition in another country by providing access to those assets. (moderate; p. 10)

123.   The growth of the Internet has affected international business in several ways. Discuss the influence of the Internet on international business. How does it affect the ability for different countries to compete internationally?

Answer: The Internet affects international business in these three ways. First, it facilitates trade in services including banking, consulting, educating, retailing, and gambling. Second, it levels the playing field between large and small companies. Third, it has potential as an efficient networking mechanism among businesses. Students should include statements on the ability for companies in different countries to easily access customers in other parts of the world. However, non-English speaking countries will be limited due to the dominance of English online. Countries with poor transportation and distribution systems will also be in a difficult position for taking advantage of the benefits of the Internet for commerce.

124.   Some have argued that the World Trade Organization, the World Bank, and the
        International Monetary Fund are fundamentally undemocratic and promote the
        interests of the rich and powerful over those of the poor and dispossessed. Explain
        both sides of this issue. Who do you think is right? Why?

        Answer: Each of these organizations seeks to promote trade and financial stability
        world wide. However, some believe that international trade and development is
        not the best choice for all countries. The assumption that all countries should seek
        to produce more and export more is based on acceptance that monetary wealth is
        desirable. Further, many of the opponents of such organizations see the
        organizations as aiding rich countries in their quest to acquire cheaper resources
        of poorer countries. Students must address the opinion question. (difficult; p. 12)

125.   Name the two primary types of international investments. Describe the primary
        difference between them.

        Answer: The two types of international investments are foreign direct investment
        and portfolio investment. Foreign direct investment emphasizes control over
        assets while portfolio investment is investment for some purpose other than
        control. (moderate; p. 8)

Multiple Choice

1. Why do businesses trying to internationalize their operations sometimes fail?
    a. lack of market potential
    b. lack of capital for expansion
    c. lack of information about the international environment
    d. poor management
    e. investor limitations
    (c; moderate; p. 24)

2. Which of the factors listed below affects the patterns of trade and investment in international business?
    a. linguistics
    b. cultural ties
    c. past political associations
    d. military alliances
    e. all of the above
    (e; moderate; p. 24)

3. What is London's origin as a world financial center?
    a. military power of British Empire in the nineteenth century
    b. influence of royalty on its reputation
    c. rule over several former colonies
    d. prestige of the London Stock Exchange
    e. none of the above
    (a; difficult; p. 24)

4. In the last 21 years, the US share of the world's GDP has _____.
    a. remained the same
    b. grown by 5%
    c. grown by 10%
    d. decreased
    e. none of the above
    (d; easy; p. 24)

5. Which country or region of the world is responsible for the largest percent of the world's GDP?
    a. United States
    b. Canada
    c. Japan
    d. European Union
    e. Africa
    (a; easy; p. 24)

6.   Seventy-three percent of the world's GDP is produced by _____.
        a. the Triad
        b. the Quad
        c. the European Union
        d. the United States
        e. Japan
        (b; moderate; p. 24)

7.   The Triad includes which group of countries and regions?
        a. Japan, Korea, and China
        b. Germany, France, and Great Britain
        c. Canada, United States, and Mexico
        d. Japan, the European Union, and the United States
        e. Africa, Australia, and North America
        (d; moderate; p. 24)

8.   In which industry is global strategic thinking typical?
        a. airlines
        b. banking
        c. securities
        d. automobiles
        e. all of the above
        (e; easy; p. 24)

9.   The United States accounts for _____ of the world's GDP.
        a. one-quarter
        b. one-third
        c. one-half
        d. two-thirds
        e. more than two-thirds
        (b; moderate; p. 25)

10.   Which of the following countries is *not* part of North America according to your
        textbook?
        a. The United States
        b. Caribbean islands
        c. Iceland
        d. Greenland
        e. All of these are part of North America
        (c; difficult; p. 25)

11.   Which country has the highest per capita income in North America?
        a. The United States
        b. Caribbean islands
        c. Canada
        d. Mexico
        e. Greenland
        (a; easy; p. 25)

12.   _____ is the currency in which the sale of goods and services is denominated.
        a. Flight capital
        b. Euro
        c. Invoicing currency
        d. Capital substitution
        e. Keiretsu
        (c; moderate; p. 27)

13.   _____ is the money sent out of a politically or economically unstable country to
        one perceived as a safe haven.
        a. Invoicing currency
        b. Flight capital
        c. Capital substitution
        d. Capital investment
        e. Keiretsu
        (b; moderate; p. 27)

14.   Which country listed below commonly attracts flight capital?
        a. Germany
        b. Canada
        c. The United States
        d. Hong Kong
        e. Singapore
        (c; easy; p. 27)

15.   The acronym OECD stands for _____.
        a. Opportunities for Economic Commitment and Development
        b. Organization for Economic Cooperation and Development
        c. Oil, Exports, Commodities, and Distribution
        d. Organization for Exports, Cooperation, and Distribution
        e. None of the above
        (b; difficult; p. 25)

16.   _____ is the dominant market for Canadian goods.
a. Cuba
b. The United States
c. European Union
d. China
e. Mexico
(b; moderate; p. 27)

17.   Which of the following is *not* a benefit of investing in Canada?
a. proximity to the U.S. market
b. stability of political and legal systems
c. long-standing conflict between French-speaking Canadians and English-speaking Canadians
d. strong infrastructure
e. all of the above are benefits of investing in Canada
(c; difficult; p. 28)

18.   What percentage of Canadian residents lives within a 100-mile area along the border with the United States?
a. 20%
b. 40%
c. 60%
d. 80%
e. none of the above
(d; difficult; p. 27)

19.   NAFTA was initiated in which year?
a. 1992
b. 1994
c. 1995
d. 1997
e. 2000
(b; moderate; p. 29)

20.   Which of the following is not a member of the Triad?
a. China
b. The United States
c. The European Union
d. Japan
(a; easy; p. 2[?])

21.   Economic development in the Caribbean islands has benefited from
       a. political instability in the area.
       b. chronic U.S. military intervention.
       c. inadequate educational systems.
       d. import limitations by the U.S.
       e. none of the above.
       (e; moderate; p. 29)

22.   The European Union is comprised of _____ countries according to your text.
       a. 10
       b. 12
       c. 15
       d. 20
       e. more than 20
       (c; moderate; p. 30)

23.   The EU's most important member is _____.
       a. Germany
       b. France
       c. Great Britain
       d. Italy
       e. None of the above
       (a; easy; p. 30)

24.   Why does Germany play a major role in formulating economic policies for the
       EU?
       a. Germany has a strong economy.
       b. Germany's government is strict in its anti-inflationary policies.
       c. Germany initiated the EU.
       d. Both a and b.
       e. Both a and c.
       (d; difficult; p. 30)

25.   Which EU country listed below refused to replace its national currency with the
       Euro?
       a. Germany
       b. The United Kingdom
       c. France
       d. Italy
       e. None of the above
       (b; moderate; p. 30)

26.   Which of the following countries or regions are members of the Quad?
        a.   Japan
        b.   The United States
        c.   The European Union
        d.   Canada
        e.   All of the above
        (e; easy; p. 2)

27.   Canada's most important exports include all of the following except _____.
        a.   forest products
        b.   petroleum
        c.   minerals
        d.   grain
        e.   all of the above
        (e; moderate; p. 27)

28.   Mexico's government system is most like that of _____.
        a.   England
        b.   Germany
        c.   The United States
        d.   Canada
        e.   None of the above
        (c; moderate; p. 28)

29.   With which country listed below does Mexico have a free-trade agreement?
        a.   The United States
        b.   El Salvador
        c.   Guatemala
        d.   Honduras
        e.   All of the above
        (e; moderate; p. 29)

30.   Which of these countries is a member of the EU?
        a.   Iceland
        b.   Norway
        c.   Switzerland
        d.   Liechtenstein
        e.   None of the above
        (e; easy; p. 30)

31.   Glasnost means _____ in Russian.
        a. economic restructuring
        b. hello
        c. to your health
        d. openness
        e. none of the above
        (d; easy; p. 32)

32.   What country holds the world's largest land mass?
        a. The United States
        b. Russia
        c. China
        d. India
        e. Canada
        (b; moderate; p. 35)

33.   Who was Russia's first democratically elected president?
        a. Mikhail Baryshnikov
        b. Mikhail Gorbachev
        c. Boris Yeltsin
        d. Vladimir Putin
        e. Ayn Rand
        (c; easy; p. 35)

34.   The Newly Independent States refers to _____.
        a. the Central European countries
        b. the former Soviet republics
        c. the nations of Africa
        d. Puerto Rico and Guam
        e. the Four Tigers
        (b; difficult; p. 35)

35.   The Commonwealth of Independent States refers to _____.
        a. a free-trade area among some of the former Soviet republics
        b. a free-trade area among the Central European countries
        c. a new country in the Middle East
        d. a new country in Africa
        e. none of the above
        (a; moderate; p. 35)

36.   Russia's natural resources include all of the following except _____.
        a. oil
        b. diamonds
        c. natural gas
        d. gold
        e. grain
        (e; difficult; p. 35)

37.   In what year did the Soviet Union collapse?
        a. 1985
        b. 1989
        c. 1991
        d. 1993
        e. 1997
        (c; difficult; p. 35)

38.   Which country listed below is the most important member of the Newly
        Independent States (NIS)?
        a. Estonia
        b. Ukraine
        c. Lithuania
        d. Russia
        e. Belarus
        (d; easy; p. 35)

39.   All of the following Central European countries except _____ are classified as
        upper-middle-income countries by the World Bank.
        a. Albania
        b. the Czech Republic
        c. Hungary
        d. Poland
        e. all are classified as upper-middle-income countries
        (a; difficult; p. 35)

40.   In which country listed below are MNCs reluctant to invest in due to the
        economic problems resulting from the wars in the former Yugoslavia in the
        1990s?
        a. Kosovo
        b. Bosnia
        c. Serbia
        d. Montenegro
        e. All of the above
        (e; moderate; p. 35)

41.   For which resource is Asia a primary provider?
        a. high-quality products
        b. low-quality products
        c. highly-skilled labor
        d. low-skill labor
        e. all of the above
        (c; casy; p. 36)

42.   Which industries did Japan concentrate on immediately following World War II?
        a. steel and shipbuilding
        b. automobiles and electronics
        c. financial services
        d. apparel and footwear
        e. none of the above
        (a; difficult; p. 36)

43.   Since what time period has Japan achieved most of its economic growth?
        a. World War I
        b. World War II
        c. The Korean War
        d. The Vietnam War
        e. The Great Depression
        (b; casy; p. 36)

44.   The Japanese term, sogo sosha, refers to a(n) _____.
        a. major Japanese bank
        b. family of interrelated companies
        c. export trading company
        d. supplier
        0. none of the above
        (c; difficult; p. 36)

45.   The Japanese term, keiretsu, refers to a(n) _____.
        a. major Japanese bank
        b. family of interrelated companies
        c. export trading company
        d. supplier
        e. none of the above
        (b; easy; p. 36)

46.   Which country is the largest when measured by GDP adjusted for purchasing power parity?
       a. The United States
       b. Canada
       c. Germany
       d. Japan
       e. China
       (a; easy; p. 38)

47.   _____ is the differences in purchasing power among the local currencies.
       a. Purchase comparison
       b. Competitive parity
       c. Purchasing power parity
       d. Discretionary income
       e. Disposable income
       (c; moderate; p. 38)

48.   Which country does *not* conduct significant trade with New Zealand?
       a. Australia
       b. Japan
       c. The United States
       d. France
       e. All conduct significant amounts of trade with New Zealand
       (d; difficult; p. 39)

49.   All of the following except _____ are typical exports from New Zealand.
       a. dairy products
       b. meat
       c. wool
       d. petroleum
       e. all are typical exports from New Zealand
       (d; difficult; p. 39)

50.   The Four Tigers are also called _____.
       a. newly industrialized countries
       b. newly independent states
       c. commonwealth of independent states
       d. commonwealth of industrialized countries
       e. none of the above
       (a; moderate; p. 40)

51.   The Four Tigers refers to the countries listed below except _____.
        a. South Korea
        b. China
        c. Taiwan
        d. Hong Kong
        e. Singapore
        (b; easy; p. 39)

52.   The World Bank classifies the Four Tigers as _____.
        a. developing
        b. middle-income
        c. newly developed
        d. high-income
        e. under-developed
        (d; moderate; p. 40)

53.   Keiretsu is to Japan as _____ is to South Korea.
        a. glasnost
        b. chaebol
        c. soga sosha
        d. topda
        e. perestroika
        (b; moderate; p. 40)

54.   In what year was the Korean War cease fire declared, which effectively created
        South Korea?
        a. 1950
        b. 1951
        c. 1952
        d. 1953
        e. 1954
        (d; moderate; p. 40)

55.   The Korean term, chaebol, refers to _____.
        a. a family-based conglomerate
        b. a keiretsu
        c. harmony
        d. economic restructuring
        e. a bank
        (a; easy; p. 40)

56.   Which of the following is not an important South Korean conglomerate?
        a. Samsung
        b. Hyundai
        c. Daewoo Group
        d. LG
        e. all are South Korean conglomerates
        (e; easy; p. 40)

57.   The Republic of China is commonly known as _____.
        a. China
        b. Taiwan
        c. Vietnam
        d. Laos
        e. Singapore
        (b; easy; p. 40)

58.   Within which industry is Taiwan a primary competitor?
        a. low-wage manufacturing
        b. electronics
        c. assembly plants
        d. farming
        e. petroleum
        (b; moderate; p. 40)

59.   Singapore's economic wealth is largely due to its abilities in _____.
        a. textiles
        b. apparel
        c. high-technology industries
        d. farming
        e. automotive products
        (c; moderate; p. 41)

60.   Singapore was formerly a colony of _____.
        a. the United States
        b. France
        c. the United Kingdom
        d. Spain
        e. Singapore was never under colonial rule
        (c; moderate; p. 40)

61.   Because of its excellent port facilities, Singapore thrives on _____.
        a. shipping
        b. oil refining
        c. telecommunications
        d. re-exporting
        e. none of the above
        (d; moderate; p. 41)

62.   _____ is the world's most populous country.
        a. India
        b. China
        c. Africa
        d. The United States
        e. Australia
        (b; easy; p. 41)

63.   India was a colony of which country?
        a. The United States
        b. France
        c. Pakistan
        d. The United Kingdom
        e. None of the above
        (d; easy; p. 42)

64.   Which two countries make up the Indian subcontinent?
        a. Afghanistan and Egypt
        b. India and Pakistan
        c. Afghanistan and India
        d. Pakistan and Kazakhstan
        e. India and Iran
        (b; easy; p. 42)

65.   Which characteristic do India and Britain have in common?
        a. parliamentary system
        b. independent judiciary
        c. professional bureaucracy
        d. language
        e. all of the above
        (e; moderate; p. 42)

66.   Which country asked Coca-Cola to reveal its secret soft drink formula as a
       condition of continuing to do business in that country?
       a. Russia
       b. China
       c. India
       d. North Korea
       e. Brazil
       (c; difficult; p. 42)

67.   What region is Afghanistan a part of?
       a. Central Europe
       b. The Middle East
       c. Central Asia
       d. Western Europe
       e. Africa
       (c; difficult; p. 43)

68.   Between what geographic areas does Hong Kong traditionally serve as a bridge
       for international business exchanges?
       a. China and South Korea
       b. Laos and Taiwan
       c. China and Taiwan
       d. Taiwan and Vietnam
       e. Vietnam and Thailand
       (c; moderate; p. 41)

69.   Because of its past colonial relationship, France has a competitive advantage in
       the countries listed below except _____.
       a. Niger
       b. Chad
       c. Cote d'Ivoire
       d. Kenya
       e. Senegal
       (d; difficult; p. 45)

70.   Because of its past colonial relationship, the United Kingdom has a competitive
       advantage in the countries listed below except _____.
       a. Kenya
       b. Zimbabwe
       c. Senegal
       d. Republic of South Africa
       e. all were colonies of the United Kingdom
       (c; difficult; p. 45)

71.   What region is sometimes called the cradle of civilization?
       a. Central Asia
       b. The European Union
       c. The Middle East
       d. Far East
       e. Africa
       (c; moderate; p. 45)

72.   Which of the following religions were *not* born in the Middle East?
       a. Buddhism
       b. Christianity
       c. Judaism
       d. Islam
       e. All were born in the Middle East
       (a; difficult; p. 45)

73.   A policy that attempts to stimulate development of local industry by discouraging
       imports through tariffs and nontariff barriers is called _____.
       a. export substitution
       b. import substitution
       c. development stimulation
       d. protectionism
       e. none of the above
       (b; moderate; p. 46)

74.   A policy that encourages economic growth through export expansion is called
       _____.
       a. export expansion
       b. export substitution
       c. export promotion
       d. development stimulation
       e. none of the above
       (c; moderate; p. 46)

75.   Export promotion has been successfully applied by all the countries listed below
       except _____.
       a. Taiwan
       b. Hong Kong
       c. South Korea
       d. Brazil
       e. Singapore
       (d; easy; p. 46)

True/False

76.   The Caribbean islands are part of North America. (T; moderate; p. 25)

77.   Per capita income is usually measured by dividing a country's gross domestic product (GDP) by its population's average income. (F; difficult; p. 25)

78.   Somalia is categorized as a least developed nation by the United Nations. (T; easy; p. 25)

79.   High-income countries, as categorized by the World Bank, are countries with annual per capita incomes of at least $25,000. (F; moderate; p. 25)

80.   Mexico has trade agreements in place with El Salvador and Guatemala. (T; difficult; p. 29)

81.   High-income countries are automatically members of the OECD (Organization for Economic Cooperation and Development). (F; difficult; p. 25)

82.   Middle-income countries are not qualified to become members of OECD. (F; difficult; p. 25)

83.   Most member countries of OECD are located in Western Europe. (T; easy; p. 25)

84.   All European Union member countries share a common currency–the Euro. (F; moderate; p. 30)

85.   Financial services are among Canada's most important exports. (F; moderate; p. 27)

86.   Trade between the United States and Mexico forms the single largest bilateral trading relationship in the world. (F; easy; p. 27)

87.   Exports account for more than one-third of Canada's total GDP. (T; moderate; p. 27)

88.   International trade is a major component of the U.S. economy. (F; moderate; p. 27)

89.   The large size of the U.S. explains its lower reliance on international trade. (T; easy; p. 27)

90.   Like the U.S., Mexico's president is elected every four years. (F; difficult; p. 28)

91.   Products sold in Canada must come packaged with information in both English and French. (T; easy; p. 28)

92.   The United Kingdom is known as a strong supporter of free trade. (T; moderate; p. 30)

93.   France has advocated the restriction of free trade in certain commodities. (T; moderate; p. 30)

94.   The Russian term, glasnost, means economic restructuring. (F; difficult; p. 32)

95.   The U.S.S.R. emerged from the disintegration of the Russian Empire in World War I. (T; moderate; p. 32)

96.   Twelve of the 15 Newly Independent States established a forum called the Commonwealth of Independent States. (T; easy; p. 35)

97.   All of the countries that were aligned with the former Soviet Union are classified as lower-income countries. (F; moderate; p. 35)

98.   A sogo sosha is typically a member of a keiretsu. (T; easy; p. 36)

99.   Asia produces only 25% of the world's GDP. (T; moderate; p. 36)

100.   All four countries that are part of the Four Tigers have a Chinese heritage. (F; difficult; p. 40)

101.   The Four Tigers are the only countries that were once categorized as less developed but have now achieved high-income status. (T; difficult; p. 40)

102.   Taiwan was born when General Chiang Kai-shek fled during a civil war between the nationalist and communist forces. (T; easy; p. 40)

103.   Taiwan was once a British colony. (F; moderate; p. 40)

104.   Singapore's exports represent 133% of its GDP. (T; moderate; p. 41)

105.   Hinduism is the dominant religion in India. (T; easy; p. 42)

106.   Hinduism is the dominant religion in Pakistan. (F; moderate; p. 42)

107.   Coca-Cola turned over its secret soft drink formula to the Indian government in order to remain in the country. (F; moderate; p. 42)

108.   The Middle East is known for its oil-rich countries. (T; easy; p. 45)

109.   In Saudi Arabia, oil makes up 90% of its total export earnings.
        (T; moderate; p. 45)

Short Answer

110.   List the countries/regions of the world that make up the Triad. Why is the Triad
        such an important consideration for international businesses? Answer: Japan, the
        United States, and the European Union. Much of the world's economic activity is
        concentrated in the Triad. (easy; p. 24)

111.   What is the meaning of GDP? Answer: GDP stands for gross domestic product. It
        is the total market value of all goods and services produced in a country during
        some time period. (moderate; p. 25)

112.   Define the term per capita income. Answer: Per capita income refers to the
        income per member of the country's population. It is measured by dividing a
        country's GDP by its population. (easy; p. 27)

113.   What country is the United States' largest trading partner? Answer: Canada.
        (moderate; p. 27)

114.   Define the term invoicing currency. Answer: Invoicing currency is the currency in
        which the sale of goods and services is denominated. (difficult; p. 27)

115.   Define the term flight capital. Answer: Flight capital is money sent out of a
        politically or economically unstable country to one perceived as a safe haven.
        (difficult; p. 27)

116.   What is the purpose of the Commonwealth of Independent States? Answer: The
        CIS was formed as a forum and free-trade area for 12 of the 15 newly
        independent states formed from the former Soviet republics. (moderate; p. 35)

117.   Name the countries that compose Central Europe. Answer: Central Europe is
        made up of the Czech Republic, Hungary, Poland, Albania, Bulgaria, Romania,
        Slovenia, Croatia, Macedonia, Serbia, Montenegro, Bosnia, and Kosovo.
        (difficult; p. 32)

118.   What economic challenges face the countries of Central Europe? Answer: These
        countries had to adjust to the loss of guaranteed export markets when the Soviet
        Union broke down. They also had to restructure their own economies from
        centrally planned communist systems to decentralized market systems.
        (difficult; p. 35)

119.   Explain the meaning of the term keiretsu. Answer: A keiretsu is a large family of
        interrelated companies. (moderate; p. 36)

120.   Explain the meaning of soga sosha. Answer: Soga sosha is an export trading company used by keiretsu members to export their products. (moderate; p. 36)

121.   Explain the meaning of purchasing power parity. Answer: Purchasing power parity is the difference in purchasing power among the local currencies. (moderate; p. 38)

122.   List the countries collectively known as the Four Tigers. Answer: South Korea, Hong Kong, Singapore, and Taiwan. (moderate; p. 40)

123.   Explain the meaning of the term chaebol. Answer: A chaebol is a family of interrelated firms in South Korea. (moderate; p. 40)

124.   How is it possible that Singapore's exports total 133% of its GDP? Answer: Singapore is a major re-exporter because of its shipping ports and facilities. (difficult; p. 41)

125.   How did Hong Kong come to be ruled by the British? Answer: As a consequence of the "opium war," Hong Kong was ceded to the British. In 1860, the British obtained possession of Kowloon and later they were granted a 99-year lease on the area. (difficult; p. 41)

126.   What advantages exist for a Special Administrative Region in China? Answer: SARs enjoy a fair degree of autonomy, its own legislature, economic freedom, free-port status, and a separate taxation system. (difficult; p. 41)

127.   Which event led to the separation of Taiwan from China? Answer: In the aftermath of the civil war in China between the nationalist forces and the communist forces, General Chiang Kai-shek fled to Taiwan. He declared the island the Republic of China and himself the rightful governor. (difficult; p. 40)

128.   Why is the Middle East considered risky for international businesses? Answer: The Middle East has a long history of cont and political unrest. (moderate; p. 45)

129.   Explain the use of import substitution policies. Answer: Countries using import substitution policies attempt to stimulate the development of local industry by discouraging imports via high tariffs and nontariff barriers. (moderate; p. 46)

Essay

130.   In Japan, many industries are dominated by organizations called keiretsus. Define the meaning of a keiretsu and describe how a keiretsu operates. What are the advantages of a keiretsu? (difficult; p. 36)
       A keiretsu is a family of interrelated companies that is typically centered around a major Japanese bank. The bank meets the keiretsu's financing needs. The members act as suppliers to each other and are even shareholders for the other

member companies. This protects the Japanese market from outsiders and the member companies from hostile takeovers. (difficult; p. 36)

131.   GDP is a common measure of economic size, but some say GDP is more meaningful if it is adjusted for purchasing power parity. Explain the meaning of purchasing power parity and why it could affect measures of economic size. Do you think it should be included in country comparisons of GDP? Why or why not?

Answer: Purchasing power parity refers to the differences in purchasing power among various economies. Most sources of data compare sizes by taking a country's GDP measured in its home currency and then converting it to a standard currency (such as the U.S. dollar) using existing exchange rates. However, this figure does not take into account the fact that the local currency may go farther in its country than the U.S. dollar does in the U.S. In other words, the GDP should be adjusted for how far the money goes in terms of what it can purchase. (easy; p. 38)

132.   China has designated Hong Kong as special administrative region. How did this occur? What does this mean for Hong Kong? Be sure to address how these designation as a SAR relates to international business concerns. (moderate; p. 41)
Answer: Hong Kong was ceded to the British following the Opium War in 1842. In 1860, the British also obtained possession of Kowloon on the Chinese mainland, and in 1898 they were granted a 99-year lease. The lease expired on July 1, 1997 and China resumed political control of Hong Kong and designated it a special administrative region. As a SAR, Hong Kong has its own legislature, economic freedom, free-port status, and a separate taxation system. This status will last until 2047. From an international business perspective, China's designation of Hong Kong as a SAR went far in terms of reassuring MNCs with operations in Hong Kong. (moderate; p. 41)

133.   China has gone through three stages since communist forces took power in 1949. Name these stages and explain how each has affected China's economic power.

Answer: The three stages include the Great Leap Forward, the Cultural Revolution, and free-market policy. The Great Leap Forward sought to force industrialization through the growth of small, labor-intensive factories. Its failure led to the Cultural Revolution, which attempted to reinforce the communist doctrine. After Mao Tse-tung's death, the government adopted limited free-market policies. China continues to develop in this stage. It continues to adopt market-oriented economic policies while maintaining political control. (difficult; p. 41)

Multiple Choice

1. These are all reasons that national legal systems may vary except _____.
    a. history
    b. culture
    c. politics
    d. religion
    e. location
    (e; difficult; p. 58)

2.   Virtually all decisions by international managers are affected by _____.
    a. the home country of operations
    b. global policies and politics
    c. the country in which the transaction occurs
    d. the cost of goods and services
    e. all of the above
    (c; moderate; p. 58)

3.   Which of the following is not a foundation for legal systems?
    a. common law
    b. civil law
    c. statutory law
    d. religious law
    e. bureaucratic law
    (c; difficult; p. 60)

4.   _____ is the foundation of the legal systems in the United Kingdom and its former colonies.
    a. Common law
    b. Civil law
    c. Statutory law
    d. Religious law
    e. Bureaucratic law
    (a; moderate; p. 60)

5.   _____ is based on the cumulative wisdom of judges' decision on individual cases through history.
    a. Common law
    b. Civil law
    c. Statutory law
    d. Religious law
    e. Bureaucratic law
    (a; moderate; p. 60)

6.   The foundation of the legal system in India is _____.
        a. common law
        b. civil law
        c. religious law
        d. statutory law
        e. bureaucratic law
        (a; difficult; p. 60)

7.   Common law is the foundation of legal systems in _____.
        a. India
        b. France
        c. Germany
        d. Iran
        e. All of the above
        (a; difficult; p. 60)

8.   The foundation of the legal system in the United Kingdom is _____.
        a. common law
        b. civil law
        c. religious law
        d. bureaucratic law
        e. royal code
        (a; easy; p. 60)

9.   The foundation of the legal system in Cuba is _____.
        a. common law
        b. civil law
        c. religious law
        d. bureaucratic law
        e. royal code
        (d; easy; p. 60)

10.   _____ is based on a codification of what is and is not permissible.
        a. Common law
        b. Civil law
        c. Statutory law
        d. Religious law
        e. Bureaucratic law
        (b; moderate; p. 60)

11.   _____ is law enacted by legislative action.
         a. Common law
         b. Civil law
         c. Statutory law
         d. Religious law
         e. Bureaucratic law
         (c; easy; p. 60)

12.   The U.S. Freedom of Information Act is an example of _____.
         a. common law
         b. civil law
         c. statutory law
         d. religious law
         e. bureaucratic law
         (c; moderate; p. 60)

13.   The Official Secrets Act in Britain is an example of _____.
         a. common law
         b. civil law
         c. statutory law
         d. religious law
         e. bureaucratic law
         (c; moderate; p. 60)

14.   Civil law originated in biblical times with the _____.
         a. French
         b. Hebrews
         c. Jews
         d. Romans
         e. None of the above
         (d; difficult; p. 60)

15.   In which system is the role of judges considered neutral?
         a. common law
         b. civil law
         c. statutory law
         d. religious law
         e. bureaucratic law
         (a; difficult; p. 60)

16.   Which of these countries is considered a theocracy?
        a. United States
        b. India
        c. South Korea
        d. Iran
        e. North Korea
        (d; moderate; p. 60)

17.   _____ is based on the officially established rules governing the faith and practice
        of a particular religion.
        a. Common law
        b. Civil law
        c. Statutory law
        d. Religious law
        e. Bureaucratic law
        (d; easy; p. 60)

18.   A country that applies religious law to civil and criminal conduct is called a
        _____.
        a. democracy
        b. republic
        c. theocracy
        d. religiocracy
        e. none of the above
        (c; easy; p. 60)

19.   In Iran, the religious law is based on the teachings of the _____.
        a. Bible
        b. Koran
        c. Buddha
        d. Napoleonic Code
        e. Mullah
        (b; easy; p. 60)

20.   Which of the following countries does not have a legal system based on
        bureaucratic law?
        a. Cuba
        b. North Korea
        c. Uganda
        d. Vietnam
        e. Taiwan
        (e; difficult; p. 61)

21.   Egypt's legal system is based on _____.
       a. English common law
       b. Napoleonic Code
       c. Islamic Law
       d. All of the above
       e. None of the above
       (d; difficult; p. 61)

22.   Of the laws that may form the basis for a country's legal system, which one is considered the riskiest for international businesses?
       a. common law
       b. civil law
       c. religious law
       d. bureaucratic law
       e. statutory law
       (d; difficult; p. 62)

23.   Which of the following facets of a firm's operations are affected by laws of the countries in which the firm operates?
       a. managing its workforce
       b. financing its operations
       c. marketing its products
       d. developing technology
       e. all of the above
       (e; easy; p. 62)

24.   Which facet of a firm's domestic operations is affected by domestically-oriented laws?
       a. management
       b. marketing
       c. finance
       d. technology
       e. all of the above
       (c; easy; p. 62)

25.   A by-product of bureaucratic law is a lack of _____.
       a. predictability
       b. consistency
       c. appeal procedures
       d. all of the above
       e. none of the above
       (d; moderate; p. 62)

26.   Which country is now the world's largest market for Japanese used cars?
        a. South Korea
        b. Siberia
        c. North Korea
        d. China
        e. United States
        (b; moderate; p. 63)

27.   Restraints against commerce with another country are called _____.
        a. bans
        b. sanctions
        c. punishments
        d. trade limits
        e. none of the above
        (b; easy; p. 64)

28.   All of the following are forms of sanctions *except* _____.
        a. boycotts
        b. embargos
        c. restricted access
        d. removal of preferential tariffs
        e. all are forms of sanctions
        (e; moderate; p. 64)

29.   The United States restricts all trade with Cuba. This is an example of a(n) _____.
        a. boycott
        b. restricted access
        c. embargo
        d. preferential tariff
        e. ban
        (c; easy; p. 64)

30.   With which country has the United States unilaterally embargoed trade?
        a. China
        b. Cuba
        c. India
        d. Kuwait
        e. Afghanistan
        (b; easy; p. 64)

31.   Dual-use products are those that can be used for both_____ and _____ purposes.
        a. Civilian, military
        b. Domestic, business
        c. Wholesale, retail
        d. Domestic, international
        e. Profit, non-profit
        (a; easy; p. 64)

32.   Many countries enforced embargoes against _____ during the 1980s to protest its
        apartheid policies.
        a. Cuba
        b. South Africa
        c. China
        d. India
        e. Afghanistan
        (b; easy; p. 64)

33.   _____ may be used to induce a second country to change an undesirable policy.
        a. Threats
        b. Sanctions
        c. Restrictions
        d. Punishments
        e. All of the above
        (b; easy; p. 64)

34.   The _____ is directed against international firms that traffic in the assets of U.S.
        companies that were confiscated by the Cuban government in 1959.
        a. Bay of Pigs Declaration
        b. Anti-Castro Act
        c. Helms-Burton Act
        d. Freeport McMoRan Doctrine
        e. None of the above
        (c; easy; p. 65)

35.   Which industries are most vulnerable to nationalization?
        a. natural resource industries
        b. financial industries
        c. service industries
        d. public sector businesses
        e. all are vulnerable
        (a; moderate; p. 65)

36.   Which of the following industries is *not* vulnerable to nationalization?
       a. crude oil production
       b. mining
       c. steel
       d. oil refining
       e. all are vulnerable to nationalization
       (e; moderate; p. 65)

37.   When Cuba acquired assets owned by U.S. owners, it utilized _____.
       a. expropriation
       b. confiscation
       c. privatization
       d. repatriation
       e. none of the above
       (b; moderate; p. 65)

38.   _____ refers to the transfer of ownership of resources from the private to the public sector.
       a. Nationalization
       b. Expropriation
       c. Importation
       d. Federalization
       e. Conversion
       (a; easy; p. 65)

39.   Expropriation refers to _____.
       a. the transference of ownership of resources from private to public sector with no compensation
       b. the transference of ownership from private to public sector with compensation to private owners for their losses
       c. the conversion of state-owned property to privately-owned property
       d. the conversion of state-owned property to privately-owned property with no compensation
        (b; moderate; p. 65)

40.   The United Kingdom has privatized _____ in recent years.
       a. British Airways
       b. British Telecom
       c. British Petroleum
       d. All of the above
       e. None of the above
       (d; moderate; p. 66)

41.   Privatization stems from _____.
       a. economic pressures
       b. political ideology
       c. both a and b
       d. greed
       e. none of the above
       (c; easy; p. 66)

42.   In which industry does Mexico restrict foreign ownership?
       a. newspapers
       b. broadcasting
       c. energy
       d. automobile manufacturing
       e. telecommunications
       (c; difficult; p. 66)

43.   Telecommunications services have been privatized in _____.
       a. Argentina
       b. Chile
       c. United Kingdom
       d. Mexico
       e. All of the above
       (e; moderate; p. 66)

44.   Benefits to local economies provided by MNCs may include _____.
       a. greater selection
       b. access to national brands
       c. higher standards of quality
       d. creation of local jobs
       e. all of the above
        (e; easy; p. 66)

45.   A possible negative effect of MNCs on the local economy includes _____ as a
       result of competition with local firms.
       a. the loss of jobs
       b. lower prices
       c. increased selection
       d. quality of products
       e. none of the above
       (a; moderate; p. 67)

46.   The _____ provides that a country will honor and enforce within its own territory the judgments and decisions of foreign courts with certain limitations.
a. Helms-Burton Act
b. principle of comity
c. arbitration agreement
d. principle of fairness
e. Supreme Court
(b; easy; p. 67)

47.   Which of the following is *not* one of the conditions required for the principle of comity to apply?
a. Reciprocity is extended between the countries.
b. The defendant is given proper notice.
c. The foreign court judgment does not violate domestic statutes or treaty obligations.
d. The foreign court has less stringent punitive damages for corporations.
e. All are required conditions for the principle of comity.
(d; moderate; p. 68)

48.   _____ is the process by which both parties in a conflict agree to submit their cases to a private individual or body whose decision they will honor.
a. Negotiation
b. Repatriation
c. Arbitration
d. Resolution
e. Reciprocation
(c; easy; p. 68)

49.   The current attempt in the music industry to restrict downloads is based on the attempt to protect _____.
a. intellectual property
b. profits
c. distribution channels
d. business relationships
e. all of the above
(a; easy; p. 69)

50.   Which technique below is *not* one commonly used to resolve conflict in international business?
a. litigation
b. arbitration
c. mediation
d. negotiation
e. repatriation
(e; easy; p. 67)

51.   _____ is the process of seeking to have a case heard in the court system most favorable to a company's interests.
a. Principle of comity
b. Forum shopping
c. Mediation
d. Litigation
e. None of the above
(b; easy; p. 67)

52.   In which country are monetary awards in legal disputes usually the highest?
a. The United States
b. France
c. The United Kingdom
d. Canada
e. None of the above
(a; easy; p. 67)

53.   Which of the following is used by countries to change or shape their technological environments?
a. investment in infrastructure
b. investment in human capital
c. technology transfer
d. foreign direct investment
e. all of the above
(e; moderate; p. 69)

54.   Which of the following is a type of intellectual property?
a. patents
b. logos
c. music
d. software
e. all of the above
(e; moderate; p. 69)

55.   Which of the following products is the most frequently pirated?
a. software
b. music
c. movies
d. brand names
e. all of the above
(d; easy; p. 71)

56.   _____ is a systematic analysis of the political risks possible in foreign countries.
a. Environmental scanning
b. SWOT analysis
c. Political risk assessment
d. Operating risk
e. Micropolitical risk
(c; easy; p. 72)

57.   Which of the following is not a category of political risk?
a. transfer risk
b. exchange rate risk
c. ownership risk
d. operating risk
(b; easy; p. 72)

58.   _____ is the risk associated with the potential for the firm's property to be confiscated or expropriated.
a. Transfer risk
b. Ownership risk
c. Operating risk
d. Exchange rate risk
e. None of the above
(b; easy; p. 72)

59.   _____ is the risk associated with the potential for the employees or operations of the firm to be threatened by changes in laws, environmental standards, tax codes, and terrorism.
a. Transfer risk
b. Ownership risk
c. Operating risk
d. Exchange rate risk
e. None of the above
(c; easy; p. 72)

60.   _____ is the risk associated with the potential for the government to interfere with the firm's ability to move funds in and out of the country.
a. Transfer risk
b. Ownership risk
c. Operating risk
d. Exchange rate risk
e. None of the above
(a; easy; p. 72)

61.   Which of the following is a source of operating risk?
       a.   terrorism
       b.   confiscation
       c.   expropriation
       d.   sanctions
       e.   embargoes
       (a; moderate; p. 72)

62.   Which of the following is not a source of political risks?
       a.   expropriation
       b.   civil wars
       c.   inflation
       d.   repatriation
       e.   privatization
       (e; moderate; p. 73)

63.   All *except* _____ represent potential effects of political risks.
       a.   loss of future profits
       b.   loss of assets
       c.   destruction of property
       d.   higher after-tax profits
       e.   lower productivity
       (d; moderate; p. 73)

64.   A political risk assessment is a matter of _____.
       a.   host country laws
       b.   risk and rewards
       c.   liability
       d.   taxation
       e.   all of the above
       (b; difficult; p. 74)

65.   Which organization provides insurance against political risks?
       a.   Overseas Private Investment Corporation (OPIC)
       b.   All State
       c.   State Farm
       d.   Geico
       e.   All of the above
       (a; easy; p. 74)

66.   _____ has one of the highest levels of political risk.
         a. Saudi Arabia
         b. Australia
         c. China
         d. Egypt
         e. Brazil
         (e; difficult; p. 75)

67.   _____ has one of the lowest levels of political risk.
         a. New Zealand
         b. South Africa
         c. Japan
         d. Ireland
         e. None of the above
         (a; moderate; p. 75)

68.   What level of political risk does Russia have?
         a. highest risk
         b. high risk
         c. moderate risk
         d. low risk
         e. lowest risk
         (b; moderate; p. 75)

69.   What level of political risk does China have?
         a. highest risk
         b. high risk
         c. moderate risk
         d. low risk
         e. lowest risk
         (c; moderate; p. 75)

70.   What level of political risk exists in India?
         a. highest risk
         b. high risk
         c. moderate risk
         d. low risk
         e. lowest risk
         (c; moderate; p. 75)

71.   Most countries in the Middle East have a _____ level of political risk.
        a. highest risk
        b. high risk
        c. moderate risk
        d. low risk
        e. lowest risk
        (b; moderate; p. 75)

72.   While some countries in Africa are moderate in their levels of political risk, most
        of Africa is rated as _____.
        a. highest risk
        b. high risk
        c. moderate risk
        d. low risk
        e. lowest risk
        (a; moderate; p. 75)

73.   North America as a whole experiences _____ level of political risk.
        a. highest risk
        b. high risk
        c. moderate risk
        d. low to lowest risk
        (d; moderate; p. 75)

74.   Western European countries are rated at _____ level of political risk.
        a. highest risk
        b. high risk
        c. moderate risk
        d. low risk
        e. lowest risk
        (e; moderate; p. 75)

75.   Which continent suffers from the highest level of political risk?
        a. North America
        b. Europe
        c. Asia
        d. Africa
        e. South America
        (d; easy; p. 75)

True/False

76.   Canada's legal system is based on bureaucratic law. (F; easy; p. 60)

77.   Britain's legal system is based on religious law. (F; easy; p. 60)

78.   The United States uses a legal system based on common law. (T; easy; p. 60)

79.   Bureaucratic law is common in dictatorships. (T; easy; p. 60)

80.   Statutory laws are those enacted under the rule of a dictator. (F; easy; p. 60)

81.   The Koran is the foundation for religious law in Iran. (T; easy; p. 60)

82.   Countries with heavy populations of Muslims may be ruled by religious law. (T; moderate; p. 60)

83.   South Korea has a high supply of lawyers due to the ease of the bar exam. (F; moderate; p. 58)

84.   International businesses must adhere to the laws of its home and host countries. (T; difficult; p. 58)

85.   The United States has the greatest number of lawyers per population size in the world. (F; difficult; p. 59)

86.   Pakistan has the highest number of lawyers per population size in the world. (T; difficult; p. 59)

87.   Civil law is found primarily among the former colonies of the United Kingdom. (F; difficult; p. 60)

88.   The Napoleonic Code reinforced the use of Common Law during the early nineteenth century. (F; difficult; p. 60)

89.   Countries relying on religious law do not provide for appeals procedures. (T; moderate; p. 61)

90.   Under civil law, judges take on many tasks that lawyers would handle under common law. (T; moderate; p. 60)

91.   U.S. firms are prohibited from complying with any boycott ordered by a foreign country. (T; difficult; p. 65)

92.   The United States has enforced an embargo against Cuba since the early 1960s.
       (T; difficult; p. 64)

93.   An embargo is a type of comprehensive sanction. (T; easy; p. 64)

94.   In Saudi Arabia, all foreign firms must have a local representative or sponsor.
       (T; easy; p. 61)

95.   Under the Helms-Burton Act, the U.S. can take legal action against corporations
       that buy assets from Cuba if those assets were previously taken from U.S. owners.
       (T; easy; p. 65)

96.   Nationalization creates opportunities for international businesses. (F; easy; p. 65)

97.   Countries that provide weak protection for intellectual property are more likely to
       attract technology-intensive foreign investments. (F; moderate; p. 69)

98.   The U.S. patent policy is based on the principle, "first to file."
       (F; moderate; p. 70)

99.   In all countries, the "first to invent" is the true owner of a patent.
       (F; moderate; p. 70)

100.   The type of government in place does not influence a firm's political risk.
       (F; moderate; p. 73)

Short Answer

101.   Define the meaning of Bureaucratic Law. Answer: Bureaucratic law is whatever
       the country's bureaucrats say it is, regardless of the formal law of the land. This is
       common in dictatorships. (moderate; p. 61)

102.   What is statutory law? Answer: Statutory laws are those enacted by legislative
       action. (moderate; p. 60)

103.   What is the basis of the common law foundation? Answer: Common law is based
       on the cumulative wisdom of judges' decisions on individual cases through
       history. (moderate; p. 60)

104.   How is the role of judges different in common law as opposed to civil law?
       Answer: In a common law system, the judge serves as a neutral referee. While in
       a civil law system, the judge takes on many of the tasks of the lawyers.
       (difficult; p. 60)

105.   Provide two examples of theocracy. Answer: Iran and Saudi Arabia.
       (moderate; p. 61)

106.   What is the purpose of the Helms-Burton Act? Answer: The Helms-Burton Act
        authorizes the U.S. government and the former U.S. owners of assets confiscated
        by the Cuban government to take action against any new foreign owners.
        (difficult; p. 64)

107.   Explain the meaning of extraterritoriality. Answer: Extraterritoriality refers to a
        practice in which countries attempt to regulate business activities conducted
        outside their borders. (moderate; p. 64)

108.   What are countries concerned with monitoring sales of dual-use products?
        Answer: Because dual-use products are those used for both civilian and military
        purposes, countries restricted from purchasing the products for their military
        could secure the products through civilian channels. (difficult; p. 64)

109.   When might sanctions be used by one country against another? Answer:
        Sanctions might be used any time one country attempts to induce a second
        country to change an undesirable policy. (moderate; p. 64)

110.   Explain the relationship between the terms nationalization, expropriation, and
        confiscation. Answer: Expropriation and confiscation are both types of
        nationalization. In expropriation, a country takes control of a private asset but
        reimburses the previous owner for its value. In confiscation, no amount is paid by
        the country seizing the asset. (moderate; p. 65)

111.   Explain some causes of privatization and give an example. Answer: Countries
        may seek to privatize operations when a private firm could bring additional
        investments and manage the operations more efficiently. (difficult; p. 65)

112.   What are the benefits of privatization? Answer: For the country, it alleviates
        overhead and inefficiencies. For private firms, it offers opportunities. For
        customers, services and products may be improved and cost less. (difficult; p. 65)

113.   Why does Canada limit foreign ownership of its newspapers? Answer: This limit
        exists to protect the country's culture from influence by the United States.
        (difficult; p. 66)

114.   Define the term forum shopping. Answer: Forum shopping refers to the process of
        shopping for the best court system to hear a legal case. (moderate; p. 67)

115.   What is the purpose of the principle of comity? Answer: It determines whether a
        country will enforce a foreign court order. (moderate; p. 67)

116.   Name the four types of conflict resolution techniques commonly used
        international business. Answer: Litigation, arbitration, mediation, and negotiation.
        (easy; p. 68)

117.   What are the three categories of political risks? Answer: Ownership risk, operating risk, and transfer risk. (moderate; p. 72)

118.   What is the purpose of political risk assessment? Answer: It provides a systematic analysis of political risks a company may face in a foreign country. (easy; p. 72)

119.   What is the difference between macropolitical risk and micropolitical risk? Answer: Macropolitical risk affects all firms in a country while micropolitical risk affects only a specific firm or firms in a single industry. (easy; p. 72)

120.   Why are MNCs hesitant to invest in countries with poor protections for intellectual property rights? Answer: Because intellectual property is a source of competitive advantage, MNCs must seek to protect it. (moderate; p. 71)

Essay

121.   There are four types of laws which serve as the basis for the legal systems used by countries. Name the four types of laws and describe each.

        Answer: The four types of laws are common law, civil law, religious law, and bureaucratic law. Common law is based on judges' decisions on cases through history. The decisions create legal precedents. Civil law is based on codification of what is and is not allowed. Religious law is based on the faith and practice of a particular religion. Bureaucratic law is whatever the country's bureaucrats say it is. (moderate; pp. 60-61)

122.   Describe the purpose of the Helms-Burton Act from the U.S. point of view. How is the Act viewed by other countries?

        Answer: The purpose of the Helms-Burton Act is to ensure that foreign companies do not profit from Cuban property that was stolen from U.S. owners. Other countries, though, may view it as an attempt to force others into the U.S. anti-Castro crusade. (difficult; p. 65)

123.   Four key questions typically must be answered for an international dispute to be resolved. In fact, some business contracts address these questions upfront in order to reduce uncertainty. What are these four questions?

        Answer: 1) Which country's law applies? 2) In which country should the issue be resolved? 3) Which technique should be used to resolve the conflict? 4) How will the settlement be enforced? (difficult; p. 67)

124.   International conflicts often develop because intellectual property laws are not consistent. Compare and contrast the "first to invent" and the "first to file" systems used to award patents. Which system does the U.S. use?

Answer: The first to invent system seeks to protect the rights of the true inventor. The first to file emphasizes the importance of filing quickly to ensure one's patent rights. While the first to invent seems fair in cases where another individual or firm may have built upon the knowledge of another in developing the intellectual property, it may have limitations. First, one must be able to prove that he or she was the first to invent. Second, many innovations develop from other innovations. To whom would the patent belong in this case? Third, the first inventor may not choose to file. If others could not pursue the patent, development of the invention would be risky. However, in the first to file system, individuals or firms with more knowledge and monetary resources may be able to file faster than the actual inventor. Also, an individual or firm may have filed in one country and assumed the patent applied in other countries. Under the first to file system, another person or firm could then be the first to file in that country despite the fact that the patent was held elsewhere. The U.S. uses the first to invent system. (moderate; p. 70)

125.   What is political risk? What are the types of political risks? How can a firm protect against political risk?

Answer: Political risk is any change in the political environment that may adversely affect the value of a firm's business activities. Political risks can be divided into three categories: ownership risk, operating risk, and transfer risk. Firms can protect against political risk by purchasing insurance and by avoiding countries where the risks outweigh the benefits.
(moderate; pp. 72-74)

Multiple Choice

1.   _____ is/are the collection of values, beliefs, behaviors, customs, and attitudes that distinguish one society from another.
   a. History
   b. Culture
   c. Politics
   d. Religion
   e. Societal norms
   (b; easy; p. 85)

2.   Culture is a collection of all of the following *except* _____.
   a. values
   b. beliefs
   c. customs
   d. attitudes
   e. all of the above
   (e; easy; p. 85)

3.   Which of the following is *not* a characteristic of culture?
   a. learned
   b. interrelated
   c. adaptive
   d. unchanging
   e. shared
   (d; easy; p. 85)

4.   When parents teach their children about proper behavior, how is culture is being transferred?
   a. directly
   b. indirectly
   c. intragenerationally
   d. intergenerationally
   e. none of the above
   (d; moderate; p. 85)

5.   How is culture being transferred when seniors teach freshmen about university culture?
   a. directly
   b. indirectly
   c. intragenerationally
   d. intergenerationally
   e. none of the above
   (c; moderate; p. 85)

6.   From what source do cultural changes usually occur?
        a. internal forces
        b. external forces
        c. strengths
        d. weaknesses
        e. opportunities
        (b; moderate; p. 85)

7.   Which of the following is *not* one of the basic elements of culture?
        a. social structure
        b. language
        c. religion
        d. architecture
        e. values
        (d; moderate; p. 86)

8.   _____ is the overall framework that determines the roles of individuals within the society, the stratification of society, and individuals' mobility within the society.
        a. Social structure
        b. Language
        c. Religion
        d. Architecture
        e. Values
        (a; easy; p. 86)

9.   Which of the following is *not* a component of social structure?
        a. individual roles
        b. stratification of society
        c. individual mobility within society
        d. societal dress codes
        e. all of the above are components of social structure
        (d; moderate; p. 86)

10.   Which form of family is most emphasized in the United States?
        a. nuclear
        b. extended
        c. blended
        d. ancestral
        e. all of the above
        (a; moderate; p. 86)

11.   Which form of family is most emphasized in Somalia?
       a. nuclear
       b. extended
       c. blended
       d. ancestral
       e. all of the above
       (d; difficult; p. 86)

12.   Which form of family is most emphasized in China?
       a. nuclear
       b. extended
       c. blended
       d. ancestral
       e. all of the above
       (b; moderate; p. 86)

13.   Which country listed below is a group-focused society?
       a. The United States
       b. Japan
       c. Germany
       d. The United Kingdom
       e. Canada
       (b; moderate; p. 86)

14.   Wa is the _____ word for social harmony.
       a. Chinese
       b. French
       c. Buddhist
       d. Japanese
       e. Korean
       (d; moderate; p. 87)

15.   The key elements of Japanese culture include all of the following except _____.
       a. hierarchical structure
       b. wa
       c. devotion
       d. groupism
       e. obligation
       (c; moderate; p. 87)

16.   Lifetime employment is primarily associated with companies located in _____.
       a. the United States
       b. Brazil
       c. the United Kingdom
       d. Canada
       e. Japan
       (e; easy; p. 87)

17.   Social stratification can be based on which of the following?
       a. age
       b. occupation
       c. education
       d. wealth
       e. all of the above
       (e; moderate; p. 88)

18.   _____ is the ability of individuals to move from one stratum of society to another.
       a. Social stratification
       b. Social mobility
       c. Socialization
       d. Wa
       e. Hierarchical structure
       (b; easy; p. 88)

19.   The _____ the society, the more possible it is for individuals to move from one
       stratum to another.
       a. less stratified
       b. more stratified
       c. more open-minded
       d. smaller
       e. larger
       (a; moderate; p. 88)

20.   Which country listed below is *not* considered a more socially mobile society?
       a. The United States
       b. India
       c. Canada
       d. Singapore
       e. All are socially mobile societies
       (b; moderate; p. 88)

21.   Attitudes toward social mobility can also affect attitudes toward _____.
        a. labor relations
        b. human capital formation
        c. risk taking
        d. entrepreneurship
        e. all of the above
        (e; moderate; p. 88)

22.   The saying "the rich get richer and the poor get poorer" is a reflection of beliefs
        regarding _____.
        a. social stratification
        b. social mobility
        c. culture
        d. reality
        e. optimism
        (b; easy; p. 88)

23.   Some experts suggest that _____ different languages exist in the world.
        a. 500
        b. 1000
        c. 2000
        d. 3000
        e. 4000
        (d; moderate; p. 88)

24.   India has _____ official languages.
        a. 1
        b. 2
        c. 5
        d. 10
        e. 16
        (e; difficult; p. 90)

25.   Countries with multiple language groups tend to be _____.
        a. homogeneous
        b. heterogeneous
        c. large
        d. small
        e. group-based
        (b; moderate; p. 90)

26.   Lingua franca means _____.
        a. common language
        b. French language
        c. official language
        d. Latin language
        e. none of the above
        (a; difficult; p. 90)

27.   _____ is the lingua franca of international business.
        a. German
        b. French
        c. Spanish
        d. English
        e. American
        (d; easy; p. 90)

28.   The practice of _____ reduces the chances that a message sent in a different
        language is incorrect.
        a. translation
        b. backtranslation
        c. fundamental English
        d. proofreading
        e. pre-testing
        (b; moderate; p. 92)

29.   Which of the following instructions should be followed by individuals
        communicating to non-native speakers in the home country's language?
        a. Use common words.
        b. Use the most common meanings for words.
        c. Avoid idiomatic phrases.
        d. Speak slowly.
        e. All of the above.
        (e; easy; p. 92)

30.   In the Spanish language, manana is used to mean _____.
        a. not today
        b. some other day
        c. tomorrow
        d. all of the above
        e. none of the above
        (d; difficult; p. 92)

31.   While negotiating a contract between an American firm and a Japanese supplier,
        the Japanese manager responds with a yes. The Japanese manager probably meant
        _____.
        a.   yes
        b.   no
        c.   yes, I understand
        d.   tomorrow
        e.   none of the above
        (c; moderate; p. 92)

32.   Senders and receivers of communication both use _____ to encode or decode the
        message.
        a.   perceptions
        b.   senses
        c.   cultural filters
        d.   written tools
        e.   media
        (c; difficult; p. 93)

33.   What percentage of information is transmitted among members of a culture by
        some means other than language?
        a.   5-10%
        b.   20-30%
        c.   40-50%
        d.   60-70%
        e.   80-90%
        (e; difficult; p. 93)

34.   The signal for "okay" in the United States is a sign of _____ to the Japanese.
        a.   okay
        b.   vulgarity
        c.   money
        d.   male homosexuals
        e.   none of the above
        (c; difficult; p. 94)

35.   If you receive a gift from a Japanese businessperson, when should you open the
        gift?
        a.   right away with the gift giver present
        b.   in private
        c.   you should refuse to accept the gift
        d.   at the same time the other person opens a gift
        e.   none of the above
        (b; moderate; p. 94)

36.   Which religion below is not classified as a part of Christianity?
       a.   Catholic
       b.   Protestant
       c.   Islamic
       d.   Eastern Orthodox
       e.   None are included
       (c; easy; p. 94)

37.   The rise of capitalism has been attributed to _____.
       a.   the Protestant ethic
       b.   consumption desires
       c.   democracy
       d.   economic hardships
       e.   all of the above
       (a; moderate; p. 96)

38.   The Protestant ethic stresses all of the following except _____.
       a.   hard work
       b.   frugality
       c.   achievement
       d.   consumption
       e.   saving
       (d; moderate; p. 96)

39.   Hinduism stresses all of the following except _____.
       a.   spirituality
       b.   frugality
       c.   purity
       d.   consumption
       e.   union with universal spirit
       (d; moderate; p. 96)

40.   Mecca is located in _____.
       a.   Iran
       b.   Iraq
       c.   Saudi Arabia
       d.   Egypt
       e.   Jordan
       (c; difficult; p. 96)

41.   How many times each day are Muslims expected to pray?
       a.   1
       b.   2
       c.   3
       d.   4
       e.   5
       (e; moderate; p. 98)

42.   During Ramadan, _____ fast from sunrise to sunset.
       a.   Christians
       b.   Jews
       c.   Muslims
       d.   Hindus
       e.   Buddhists
       (c; moderate; p. 98)

43.   The Nike swoosh was thought to resemble the Arabic word for _____.
       a.   Allah
       b.   money
       c.   sport
       d.   power
       e.   spirit
       (a; difficult; p. 98)

44.   What characteristic is highly correlated with rank in Japan?
       a.   gender
       b.   age
       c.   experience
       d.   education
       e.   marital status
       (b; moderate; p. 99)

45.   Which of the following countries is *not* considered a low-context culture?
       a.   Canada
       b.   The U.S.
       c.   Australia
       d.   Korea
       e.   England
       (d; difficult; p. 100)

46.   In what type of culture do the words used by the speaker explicitly convey the
        speaker's message to the listener?
        a. verbal
        b. low context
        c. high context
        d. linguistic
        e. western
        (b; moderate; p. 100)

47.   In what type of culture does the context play a role just as important as the words
        used by the speaker in correctly conveying the speaker's message to the listener?
        a. verbal
        b. low context
        c. high context
        d. linguistic
        e. western
        (c; moderate; p. 100)

48.   Which of the following countries is considered a high-context culture?
        a. Canada
        b. Germany
        c. Australia
        d. China
        e. England
        (d; difficult; p. 100)

49.   German advertising is typically _____ oriented.
        a. fact
        b. sex
        c. emotionally
        d. visually
        e. none of the above
        (a; difficult; p. 101)

50.   Low-context cultures tend to rely upon _____ while high-context cultures rely
        more on _____.
        a. verbal communication, non-verbal communication
        b. facts, emotions
        c. visual, audio
        d. content, context
        e. both b and d
        (e; moderate; p. 101)

51.   In a high-context culture, the presence of a lawyer during business dealing would
        be considered a sign of _____.
        a. wisdom
        b. trust
        c. distrust
        d. pragmatism
        e. commitment
        (c; moderate; p. 101)

52.   A _____ comprises countries that share many cultural similarities.
        a. value cluster
        b. cultural cluster
        c. regional trading bloc
        d. region
        e. high-context cluster
        (b; easy; p. 101)

53.   Which country cluster is made up of Belgium, France, Italy, Portugal, and Spain?
        a. Anglo
        b. Nordic
        c. Germanic
        d. Latin European
        e. Latin American
        (d; moderate; p. 103)

54.   Which country cluster is made up of Greece, Iran, and Turkey?
        a. Arab
        b. Near Eastern
        c. Germanic
        d. Latin European
        e. Latin American
        (b; moderate; p. 103)

55.   Which of the following is not one of Hofstede's Five Dimensions?
        a. social orientation
        b. cultural orientation
        c. time orientation
        d. uncertainty orientation
        e. goal orientation
        (b; moderate; p. 104)

56.   _____ is a person's beliefs about the relative importance of the individual and the
        groups to which that person belongs.
        a. Social orientation
        b. Cultural orientation
        c. Time orientation
        d. Uncertainty orientation
        e. Goal orientation
        (a; easy; p. 104)

57.   _____ is the cultural belief that the person comes first.
        a. Social orientation
        b. Individualism
        c. Groupism
        d. Uncertainty orientation
        e. Goal orientation
        (b; easy; p. 104)

58.   According to Hofstede's Five Dimensions, _____ is the opposite of individualism.
        a. wa
        b. groupism
        c. collectivism
        d. uncertainty orientation
        e. goal orientation
        (c; easy; p. 104)

59.   Which of the following countries is not considered a collectivist culture?
        a. Singapore
        b. New Zealand
        c. Hong Kong
        d. Pakistan
        e. Taiwan
        (b; moderate; p. 105)

60.   Cultures emphasizing individualism may emphasize _____.
        a. self-interest
        b. self-actualization
        c. nepotism
        d. continuing education
        e. universalism
        (c; difficult; p. 105)

61.   Kim was taught to always obey her parents. This is most like _____ in the power orientation dimension.
       a. power tolerance
       b. power development
       c. power respect
       d. obligation
       e. authoritarian rule
       (c; moderate; p. 106)

62.   In Japan, a collectivist society, a CEO's pay primarily reflects _____.
       a. age
       b. performance of the group
       c. accomplishments
       d. contribution to the firm
       e. all of the above
       (b; difficult; p. 106)

63.   In a collectivist society, changing jobs may be interpreted as _____.
       a. wise
       b. disloyal
       c. impatience
       d. ambition
       e. none of the above
       (b; difficult; p. 106)

64.   In a society characterized by power tolerance, an ideal boss might be thought of as _____.
       a. a resourceful democrat
       b. a benevolent autocrat
       c. a good father
       d. a wise guru
       e. none of the above
       (a; difficult; p. 106)

65.   Which country is not characterized by power respect?
       a. France
       b. Spain
       c. Japan
       d. Germany
       e. Singapore
       (d; difficult; p. 106)

66. In cultures characterized by _____, people at all levels in a firm accept the decision of those above them because of the implicit belief that higher-level positions carry the right to make decisions.
   a. power respect
   b. power tolerance
   c. power orientation
   d. uncertainty avoidance
   e. passive goal behavior
   (a; moderate; p. 106)

67. _____ is the feeling people have regarding ambiguous situations.
   a. Power orientation
   b. Locus of control
   c. Optimism
   d. Uncertainty orientation
   e. Social orientation
   (d; easy; p. 107)

68. How might individuals from a culture high in uncertainty acceptance view uncertainty?
   a. monotonous
   b. routine
   c. exciting
   d. limiting
   e. boring
   (c; easy; p. 107)

69. Countries with cultures high in uncertainty acceptance may have higher incidences of _____.
   a. stress
   b. formalization
   c. emotional expression
   d. groupism
   e. job mobility
   (e; difficult; p. 109)

70. Formal rules and standards in the workplace are preferred by individuals from a culture high in _____.
   a. power tolerance
   b. power respect
   c. uncertainty avoidance
   d. uncertainty acceptance
   e. individualism
   (c; moderate; p. 109)

71.   What kinds of people place a high premium on material possessions, money, and
        assertiveness?
        a.   Those who are at high levels of the social hierarchy.
        b.   Those who are high in individualism.
        c.   Those who are high in power tolerance.
        d.   Those who are high in aggressive goal behavior.
        e.   Those who are high in time orientation.
        (d; moderate; p. 109)

72.   _____ refers to the extent to which members of a culture adopt a long-term versus
        a short-term outlook on work, life, and other aspects of society.
        a.   Need for immediate gratification
        b.   Need for achievement
        c.   Time orientation
        d.   Power orientation
        e.   Uncertainty orientation
        (c; easy; p. 110)

73.   _____ is the unconscious use of one's own culture to help assess new
        surroundings.
        a.   Cultural conversion
        b.   Cultural illiteracy
        c.   Cross-cultural literacy
        d.   Self-reference criterion
        e.   Acculturation
        (d; easy; p. 111)

74.   What is the first step in acculturation?
        a.   cultural conversion
        b.   travel
        c.   cross-cultural literacy
        d.   self-reference criterion
        e.   language training
        (c; moderate; p. 111)

75.   _____ is the process by which people not only understand a foreign culture but
        also modify and adapt their behavior to make it compatible with that culture.
        a.   Cultural conversion
        b.   Cultural illiteracy
        c.   Cross-cultural literacy
        d.   Culture training
        e.   Acculturation
        (e; easy; p. 111)

True/False

76.   Architecture is one of the basic elements of culture. (F; easy; p. 86)

77.   Germany shares a common culture throughout all of its regions.
         (F; moderate; p. 85)

78.   Culture is permanent; it does not change. (F; easy; p. 85)

79.   Nepotism is encouraged in the United States. (F; moderate; p. 86)

80.   Personal characteristics are more important than personal accomplishments in
         group-focused societies. (T; moderate; p. 86)

81.   The norm of lifetime employment in Japan is experiencing pressure to change.
         (T; easy; p. 87)

82.   Seeking higher education is one technique for achieving social mobility.
         (T; easy; p. 88)

83.   Social mobility tends to be lower in less stratified societies. (F; moderate; p. 88)

84.   Many languages have both formal and informal forms of the word "you."
         (T; easy; p. 88)

85.   India recognizes two official languages. (F; moderate; p. 90)

86.   Countries with multiple languages tend to be homogenous. (F; easy; p. 90)

87.   English-speaking Canadians prefer soaps that promise cleanliness.
         (T; moderate; p. 90)

88.   Spanish is the lingua franca of international business. (F; easy; p. 90)

89.   A person's cultural literacy only improves when he or she is fluent in a second
         language. (F; moderate; p. 91)

90.   KFC's slogan, "Finger Lickin Good," translates into "Eat Your Fingers Off" in
         Chinese. (T; easy; p. 91)

91.   Some companies develop their own language instruction programs to use in
         overseas operations. (T; easy; p. 92)

92.   Drum signals are a form of nonverbal communication. (T; moderate; p. 93)

93.   Facial expressions and hand gestures have universal meaning.
        (F; moderate; p. 93)

94.   Members of a culture will quickly understand nonverbal forms of
        communication. (T; easy; p. 93)

95.   The symbol for "okay" is a universal symbol. (F; moderate; p. 94)

96.   Silence communicates meaning just the same as sound does. (T; difficult; p. 94)

97.   A U.S. manager may demonstrate leadership by silence, thereby encouraging
        full participation by subordinates attending a meeting and promoting group
        consensus. (F; difficult; p. 94)

98.   In Korea, bad news is delivered at the end of the day so it will not ruin the entire
        workday. (T; moderate; p. 94)

99.   Germany is a low-context culture. (T; easy; p. 100)

100.   The term, greenfield investment, came from the saying, "The grass is greener on
        the other side." (F; difficult; p. 101)

Short Answer

101.   What are the four characteristics of culture? Answer: Culture reflects learned
        behavior and its elements are interrelated, adaptive, and shared. (easy; p. 85)

102.   Explain the meaning of social stratification. Answer: Social stratification refers
        to the categorization of people into a social hierarchy. (moderate; p. 88)

103.   What is the meaning of the term lingua franca? Answer: The term means
        common language. (easy; p. 90)

104.   How does the linguistic legacy of colonialism affect international business?
        Answer: It provides a competitive advantage to the former imperial nation
        because the nation and its former colonies share a common language.
        (difficult; p. 90)

105.   Describe the process of backtranslation. Answer: Backtranslation refers to the
        translating of words from one language to a second language and then
        translating the same words from the second language back into the first.
        (moderate; p. 92)

106.   Identify and explain the possible meanings of silence. Answer: In the United
        States, silence may reflect an inability to communicate or to empathize. In Japan,
        it may mean that someone is thinking or that the conversation is disharmonious.

In work situations in Japan, managers demonstrate leadership with silence. (difficult; p. 94)

107.   What are the primary uses of gift giving and hospitality in international business? Answer: They are means of communication that help build strong business relationships. (moderate; p. 94)

108.   Name the four religions to which 72% of the world's population adheres. Answer: Christianity, Islam, Hinduism, and Buddhism. (moderate; p. 94)

109.   What values are stressed in the Protestant ethic? Answer: Hard work, frugality, and achievement as a means of glorifying God. (moderate; p. 96)

110.   What values are stressed in the Islamic faith? Answer: While supportive of capitalism, Islam places more emphasis on an individual's contribution to society. (difficult; p. 96)

111.   In what cultures are opportunities for women restricted? Answer: Islamic cultures. (difficult, p. 96) [au: considered short answer?]

112.   What accommodations might be necessary for Muslim workers? Answer: Muslim workers must be allowed to stop work for prayer and to observe their religious holidays. It may also be appropriate to allow Muslim workers to dress in accordance with Muslim traditions. (difficult; p. 98)

113.   Describe the difference between high-context and low-context cultures. Answer: Low-context cultures are explicit in nature. What is said or written is what is meant by the communicator. High-context cultures also use context as part of the communication method. One must consider the situation and other non-verbal cues to understand the full message. (moderate; p. 100)

114.   What are cultural clusters? Answer: Cultural clusters are clusters of countries with similar cultures. (moderate; p. 101)

115.   How does a long-term outlook differ from a short-term outlook? Answer: Countries with a long-term outlook recognize that it may be necessary to delay gratification and make investments for the future. Such countries look several years out in their planning. Countries with a short-term outlook emphasize immediate changes. Investments may not be made in the long-term future. (easy; p. 110)

116.   How do passive and aggressive goal behaviors differ? Answer: People who exhibit aggressive goal behaviors place a high premium on material possessions, money, and assertiveness. People who exhibit passive goal behaviors place a higher value social relationships, quality of life, and concern for others. (moderate; p. 109)

117.   Why would nepotism be encouraged in collectivist cultures but discouraged in individualistic cultures? Answer: Collectivist cultures recognize that the most trustworthy people for the positions are likely within one's own family. Further, caring for the family is a high priority. Individualist cultures emphasize the use of achievements rather than family connections to select people for jobs. (moderate; p. 105)

118.   How might the use of lifetime employment practices in Japanese firms serve as a response to the culture of uncertainty avoidance in Japan? Answer: Because the Japanese culture as a whole seeks to avoid uncertainty, it makes sense that Japanese people would prefer to avoid the uncertainty of what one's next job might be or even whether one will have another job. Lifetime employment eliminates that uncertainty. (moderate; p. 109)

119.   Explain the meaning of self-reference criterion. Answer: Self-reference criterion is the use of one's own culture to help assess new surroundings. (easy; p. 111)

120.   How can international businesses improve the process of acculturation for its
        employees working abroad? Answer: These organizations should properly
        prepare employees who are going abroad. Preparations might include culture
        training, language training, and realistic previews of the new situation.
        (difficult; p. 111)

Essay

121.   List the four characteristics of culture and explain each one.

        Answer: Culture reflects learned behavior and its elements are interrelated,
        adaptive, and shared. (easy; p. 85)

122.   How might the view of family ties and responsibilities in the various countries
        where a company conducts business affect its operations in each country?
        Explain.

        Answer: When individuals refer to their families, they could be referring to their
        nuclear, extended, or ancestral family. The view taken of the family will affect
        how people view their responsibilities to the family. It could also affect the
        expectations for benefits at work. (moderate; p. 86)

123.   Identify the four key elements of Japanese culture and explain how it affects
        Japanese business practices.

        Answer: The four key elements are hierarchical structure, groupism, wa (social
        harmony), and obligation. Hierarchical structure affects language,
        communication patterns, and respect. In business situations, one must determine
        the relative status of the person with whom they are dealing in order to behave
        properly. Groupism means that it is important to consider the group
        consequences rather than one's individual preferences. This aids the Japanese in
        their teamwork abilities. Wa refers to social harmony. Decisions are only made
        once consensus is reached. This maintains the wa. Obligation means that once a
        person is hired, he or she becomes indebted to the firm. This debt can never be
        repaid so the individual puts the firm ahead of all other priorities. (moderate; p.
        87)

124.   Identify five forms of nonverbal communications. Why are nonverbal forms of
        communication important in international business?

        Answer: Several possible answers are listed in Table 4.1 on page 93. Some
        possibilities include hand gestures, facial expressions, posture and stance,
        clothing and hair styles, and interpersonal distances. Students should include a
        discussion of how people from different cultures might interpret nonverbals
        differently than they might be intended. (moderate; p. 93)

125.   Japanese, North Americans, and Latin Americans are thought to have very
        different styles of negotiation. Identify five differences in the negotiating styles
        of these three groups. How might these differences be overcome?

        Answer: Several possible answers to this question are highlighted in Table 4.2
        on page 102. Students should emphasize that understanding of the cultural
        differences will enable negotiators to overcome their differences. (difficult; p.
        102)

126.   Identify the five dimensions researched by Geert Hofstede. Describe each
        dimension and how it could affect international business dealings.

        Answer: The dimensions are social orientation, power orientation, uncertainty
        orientation, goal orientation, and time orientation. Social orientation refers to a
        person's beliefs about the relative importance of the individual and the groups
        to which that person belongs. Power orientation refers to the beliefs people in a
        culture hold about the appropriateness of power and authority differences in
        hierarchies. Uncertainty orientation is the feeling people have regarding
        uncertain and ambiguous situations. Goal orientation is the manner in which
        people are motivated to work toward different kinds of goals. Time orientation
        is the extent to which members of a culture adopt a long-term versus a short-
        term outlook on work, life, and other aspects of a society. Students should
        emphasize how different beliefs when working with individuals from different
        countries or when dealing with firms in other countries can affect appropriate
        human resource strategies and decisions including work assignments, rewards
        and promotions, benefits, authority in the workplace, and schedules.
        (moderate; pp. 105-108)

Multiple Choice

1.   The term _____ refers to an individual's personal beliefs about whether a decision, behavior, or action is right or wrong.
      a. value
      b. culture
      c. ethics
      d. religion
      e. expectations
      (c; easy; p. 119)

2.   Fruit juice suppliers in South America rely heavily on _____.
      a. elderly employees
      b. child labor
      c. female workers
      d. illegal immigrant workers
      e. none of the above
      (b; moderate; p. 117)

3.   What ethical abuses have independent contractors manufacturing shoes for Nike been accused of in past years?
      a. child labor abuse
      b. unsafe working conditions
      c. violations of local regulations
      d. all of the above
      (d; easy; p. 117)

4.   Ethical beliefs are _____ in nature.
      a. societal
      b. regional
      c. familial
      d. individual
      e. cultural
      (d; difficult; p. 119)

5.   Which of the following is not a factor that influences one's ethics?
      a. family
      b. peers
      c. observation of others
      d. religious beliefs
      e. all of the above influence ethical beliefs
      (e; easy; p. 119)

6.   Behavior that does not conform to generally accepted social norms is considered
        _____.
        a. ethical
        b. unethical
        c. illegal
        d. unregulated
        e. none of the above
        (b; easy; p. 119)

7.   All of the following are ethical generalizations except _____.
        a. individuals have their own belief system
        b. individuals from the same cultural contexts will tend to have similar beliefs
        c. individuals can rationalize behavior
        d. individuals may not always be consistent with their beliefs
        e. all of the above are ethical generalizations
        (e; moderate; p. 119)

8.   Perceptions of what is ethical behavior vary from _____.
        a. culture to culture
        b. individual to individual
        c. family to family
        d. country to country
        e. all of the above
        (e; easy; p. 120)

9.   Jason has been padding his expense account on business trips. However, it seems
        fair to him because the company refuses to provide him with comp time despite
        long hours he works on these business trips. Which ethical generalization is this
        an example of?
        a. Individuals have their personal belief system.
        b. Individuals from the same cultural contexts will tend to have similar beliefs.
        c. Individuals can rationalize behavior.
        d. Individuals may not always be consistent with their beliefs.
        e. All of the above are ethical generalizations.
        (c; moderate; p. 119)

10.   Janet believes in protecting the privacy of her employees. Yet, she shared a rumor
        that Alex, a co-worker, has been having an affair with another co-worker. Which
        ethical generalization is this an example of?
        a. Individuals have their personal belief system.
        b. Individuals from the same cultural contexts will tend to have similar beliefs.
        c. Individuals can rationalize behavior.
        d. Individuals may not always be consistent with their beliefs.
        e. All of the above are ethical generalizations.
        (d; moderate; p. 119)

11.   Three employees of Martin Enterprises have flown to China to meet with potential business partners there. The three employees are in a disagreement about whether to give gifts to the potential partners. James is from the U.S. office and he feels it is an ethical violation. Eun Hee (from the South Korean office) and Evan Lee (from the Japanese office) agree that the gift is appropriate given the Chinese culture. Which ethical generalization is this an example of?
a. Individuals have their personal belief system.
b. Individuals from the same cultural contexts will tend to have similar beliefs.
c. Individuals can rationalize behavior.
d. Individuals may not always be consistent with their beliefs.
e. All of the above are ethical generalizations.
(b; moderate; p. 119)

12.   Sonya and Amber work together in the Hong Kong corporate office. Despite their similar backgrounds and education, they cannot agree on whether it is appropriate to offer bribes to officials in China in order to move their business dealings along there. Which ethical generalization is this an example of?
a. Individuals have their personal belief system.
b. Individuals from the same cultural contexts will tend to have similar beliefs.
c. Individuals can rationalize behavior.
d. Individuals may not always be consistent with their beliefs.
e. All of the above are ethical generalizations.
(a; moderate; p. 119)

13.   What term best describes the things a person feels to be important?
a. values
b. beliefs
c. preferences
d. desires
e. wants
(a; easy; p. 120)

14.   Which areas of business are most susceptible to ethical variations?
a. hiring and firing practices
b. wages
c. working conditions
d. employee privacy
e. all of the above
(e; difficult; p. 121)

15.   Which ethical issue was the focus of news reports about the factories in Asia
        which Nike used to produce its footwear?
        a. hiring and firing practices
        b. wages and working conditions
        c. employee privacy
        d. conflict of interest
        e. honesty
        (b; difficult; p. 121)

16.   Some organizations read the electronic mail messages sent by its employees.
        Which ethical issue is this an example of?
        a. hiring and firing practices
        b. wages and working conditions
        c. employee privacy
        d. conflict of interest
        e. honesty
        (c; moderate; p. 121)

17.   The ethical concerns prevalent in how employees treat the organization include all
        of the following except _____.
        a. conflict of interest
        b. wages
        c. confidentiality
        d. honesty
        e. secrecy
        (b; moderate; p. 122)

18.   What ethical issue refers to the situation that occurs when a decision potentially
        benefits the individual to the possible detriment of the organization?
        a. conflict of interest
        b. wages
        c. confidentiality
        d. honesty
        e. secrecy
        (a; moderate; p. 122)

19.   Many companies have forbidden their buyers from accepting gifts from potential
        suppliers. What ethical issue is this an example of?
        a. conflict of interest
        b. wages
        c. confidentiality
        d. honesty
        e. secrecy
        (a; moderate; p. 122)

20.   In Japan, _____ gifts represent a token of gratitude for favors and loyalty shown throughout the year.
       a. wa
       b. ochugen
       c. oseibo
       d. glasnost
       e. keiretsu
       (c; difficult; p. 122)

21.   In what type of culture are gift exchanges are considered ethical and appropriate?
       a. low-context
       b. power-tolerant
       c. uncertainty accepting
       d. collectivist
       e. individualistic
       (d; difficult; p. 123)

22.   Japan has a high-context culture. Gift exchanges in a business situation are _____.
       a. common
       b. appropriate
       c. rare
       d. inappropriate
       e. both a and b
       (e; easy; p. 123)

23.   Gift exchanges are likely to be considered a conflict of interest in a(n) _____ culture.
       a. high-context
       b. collectivist
       c. low-context
       d. power-respecting
       e. uncertainty-avoiding
       (c; difficult; p. 123)

24.   Guanxi is a Chinese custom based on _____.
       a. offering a token of gratitude
       b. offering best wishes for the summer
       c. acknowledging loyalty
       d. reciprocating favors
       e. none of the above
       (d; moderate; p. 123)

25.   Ethical situations involving honesty include all of the following except _____.
        a. stealing supplies from the office
        b. making personal calls during work time
        c. padding expense accounts
        d. working overtime
        e. shopping online during work hours
        (d; easy; p. 123)

26.   Sally uses her telephone at work to call her sister long distance. Which ethical
        issue is this an example of?
        a. conflict of interest
        b. honesty
        c. confidentiality
        d. secrecy
        e. none of the above
        (b; easy; p. 123)

27.   Jason completes company work at home on the weekends. He justifies taking
        office supplies home because of the company work he completes at home. Which
        ethical issue does this scenario relate to?
        a. conflict of interest
        b. honesty
        c. confidentiality
        d. secrecy
        e. none of the above
        (b; easy; p. 123)

28.   Jack always like to place orders with Sam's Supply Company, because the
        company sends him a gift certificate for $100 each holiday season. Which ethical
        issue is this an example of?
        a. conflict of interest
        b. honesty
        c. confidentiality
        d. secrecy
        e. none of the above
        (a; easy; p. 123)

29.   Which group below is an economic agent of a firm?
        a. customers
        b. competitors
        c. stockholders
        d. suppliers
        e. all of the above
        (e; moderate; p. 123)

30.   What categories below hold the potential for ethical dilemmas between the
        organization and its economic agents?
        a. financial disclosures
        b. advertising and promotions
        c. bargaining and negotiating
        d. ordering and purchasing
        e. all of the above
        (e; easy; p. 123)

31.   Which of the following is *not* a common method for encouraging ethical behavior
        among employees?
        a. code of ethics
        b. ethics training
        c. promotion of punishment for unethical transgressions
        d. organizational practices
        e. corporate culture
        (c; easy; p. 124)

32.   Written statements of values and ethical standards that guide a firms' actions are
        called _____.
        a. manuals
        b. ethics training
        c. codes of ethics
        d. training guidebooks
        e. mission statements
        (c; moderate; p. 125)

33.   In a survey on the acceptability of bribing officials when doing business in
        foreign countries, all of the following countries except _____ found bribery
        acceptable.
        a. Russia
        b. China
        c. Austria
        d. Taiwan
        e. South Korea
        (c; difficult; p. 125)

34.   In a survey on the acceptability of bribing officials when doing business in
        foreign countries, all of the following countries except _____ found bribery
        unacceptable.
        a. Sweden
        b. Australia
        c. Switzerland
        d. South Korea
        e. Canada
        (d; difficult; p. 125)

35.   The term _____ refers to the set of obligations an organization undertakes to
        protect and enhance the society in which it functions.
        a. organizational ethics
        b. social responsibility
        c. corporate ethics
        d. social values
        e. none of the above
        (b; moderate; p. 126)

36.   Which of the following is not an area in which an organization may exercise
        social responsibility?
        a. stakeholders
        b. natural environment
        c. general social welfare
        d. local community
        e. all of the above
        (e; easy; p. 126)

37.   The term _____ refers to those people and organizations that are directly affected
        by the practices of an organization and have a stake in its performance.
        a. customers
        b. employees
        c. community
        d. organizational stakeholders
        e. suppliers
        (d; easy; p. 126)

38.   Social responsibility to customers includes all of the following except _____.
        a. provide fair treatment
        b. offer fair prices
        c. honor product warranties
        d. meet delivery commitments
        e. all are forms of customer-oriented social responsibility
        (e; easy; p. 126)

39.   Through what method can corrupt organizations be identified?
        a. governmental investigation
        b. competition
        c. whistle-blowers
        d. all of the above
        e. none of the above
        (d; easy; p. 127)

40.   What is the penalty for breaking anti-corruption laws in the United States?
       a.   incarceration
       b.   fines
       c.   disqualification from doing business with the U.S. government
       d.   all of the above
       (d; moderate; p. 127)

41.   Which of the following is *not* a penalty for breaking anti-corruption laws in South
       Korea?
       a.   A 5-year prison sentence.
       b.   A 10 million won fine.
       c.   Confiscation of ½ the profits resulting from illegal transaction.
       d.   Disqualification from doing business with the South Korean government.
       e.   All are possible penalties.
       (d; moderate; p. 127)

42.   Which of the following is the automatic penalty in France for transnational
       bribery?
       a.   A 5-year prison sentence.
       b.   A 15-year prison sentence.
       c.   A 10 million euro fine.
       d.   Confiscation of ½ the profits resulting from illegal transaction.
       e.   Disqualification from doing business with the French government.
       (b; moderate; p. 127)

43.   Which of the following strategies could be used to deal with bribe requests?
       a.   pay the bribe
       b.   say no
       c.   support a code that prohibits bribery
       d.   develop a reputation for refusing bribe requests
       e.   all of the above
       (e; moderate; p. 128)

44.   Which of the following behaviors represent social responsibility to employees?
       a.   provide fair treatment
       b.   treat everyone as part of the team
       c.   respect dignity
       d.   honor basic human needs
       e.   all of the above
       (e; easy; p. 128)

45.   The "C Principles" are principles for dealing with _____.
       a. bribe requests
       b. unsafe working conditions
       c. conflicts of interest
       d. confidentiality
       e. honesty
       (a; moderate; p. 128)

46.   Which of the following is *not* one of the "C Principles" for dealing with bribe
       requests?
       a. Company policy outlawing the use of bribes.
       b. Public reports of bribe requests.
       c. Governmental investigation of suspicious competitors.
       d. Outside auditing of any possible improper payments.
       e. All of the above are "C Principles."
       (c; difficult; p. 128)

47.   What risks are taken when a company submits to paying bribes?
       a. criminal prosecution
       b. damage to reputation
       c. degradation of markets
       d. dysfunctional relationships
       e. all of the above
       (e; moderate; p. 128)

48.   Unethical treatment of workers is most prevalent in _____.
       a. high income countries
       b. middle income countries
       c. low income countries
       d. developing countries
       e. none of the above
       (d; moderate; p. 130)

49.   Which of the following is *not* a socially responsible behavior toward investors?
       a. Follow appropriate accounting procedures.
       b. Overstate earnings to increase share prices.
       c. Manage the organization to protect shareholder interests.
       d. Avoid the appearance of improprieties.
       e. All of the above are socially responsible behaviors towards investors.
       (b; difficult; p. 128)

50.   Examples of promoting the general welfare of society include all of the following
        except _____.
        a. charitable contributions
        b. involvement in public health
        c. involvement in education
        d. promotion of human rights issues
        e. use of appropriate accounting procedures
        (e; easy; p. 129)

51.   Which of the following is the least responsible approach to social responsibility?
        a. obstructionist stance
        b. defensive stance
        c. accommodative stance
        d. proactive stance
        e. reactive stance
        (a; moderate; p. 131)

52.   Which of the following is the most responsible approach to social responsibility?
        a. obstructionist stance
        b. defensive stance
        c. accommodative stance
        d. proactive stance
        e. reactive stance
        (d; moderate; p. 131)

53.   When an organization does as little as possible to address social or environmental
        issues, it has adopted the _____ to social responsibility.
        a. obstructionist stance
        b. defensive stance
        c. accommodative stance
        d. proactive stance
        e. reactive stance
        (a; moderate; p. 131)

54.   When an organization does everything it must do from a legal standpoint but
        nothing more, it has adopted the _____ to social responsibility.
        a. obstructionist stance
        b. defensive stance
        c. accommodative stance
        d. proactive stance
        e. reactive stance
        (b; moderate; p. 131)

55.   In which of the following areas is the United States most recognized for ethical challenges?
       a. unsafe working conditions
       b. governmental corruption
       c. accounting fraud
       d. bribery
       e. environmental hazards
       (c; moderate; p. 130)

56.   Which of the following is not a common ethical issue dealt with in the United States?
       a. accounting fraud
       b. governmental corruption
       c. insider trading
       d. corporate governance scandals
       (b; moderate; p. 130)

57.   What organizational issues are shaped by a corporation's stance towards social responsibility?
       a. compliance
       b. informal dimensions of social responsibility
       c. evaluation of social responsibility efforts
       d. all of the above
       e. none of the above
       (d; easy; p. 131)

58.   When an organization meets its legal requirements and will also go beyond those requirements when approached for help, it has adopted the _____ to social responsibility.
       a. obstructionist stance
       b. defensive stance
       c. accommodative stance
       d. proactive stance
       e. reactive stance
       (c; moderate; p. 131)

59.   Firms that view themselves as citizens of society have adopted the _____ to social responsibility.
       a. obstructionist stance
       b. defensive stance
       c. accommodative stance
       d. proactive stance
       e. reactive stance
       (d; moderate; p. 131)

60.   Philip Morris follows the regulations regarding the marketing of its products in
        the United States but markets its tobacco aggressively in countries without such
        regulations. It has adopted the _____ to social responsibility.
        a. obstructionist stance
        b. defensive stance
        c. accommodative stance
        d. proactive stance
        e. reactive stance
        (b; moderate; p. 131)

61.   The Body Shop seeks out opportunities to improve the welfare of individuals all
        over the world. It has adopted the _____ to social responsibility.
        a. obstructionist stance
        b. defensive stance
        c. accommodative stance
        d. proactive stance
        e. reactive stance
        (d; moderate; p. 131)

62.   Firms can formally implement social responsibility at the corporate level through
        _____.
        a. philanthropic giving
        b. ethical compliance
        c. legal compliance
        d. all of the above
        e. none of the above
        (d; moderate; p. 133)

63.   The term _____ refers to the disclosure by an employee of illegal or unethical
        conduct on the part of others within the organization.
        a. honesty
        b. whistle-blowing
        c. acknowledgement
        d. conflict of interest
        e. organizational communication
        (b; moderate; p. 134)

64.   Justin is aware that his supervisor used corporate funds to pay for a personal
        vacation. He reports the offense. This is called _____.
        a. honesty
        b. whistle-blowing
        c. acknowledgement
        d. conflict of interest
        e. organizational communication
        (b; moderate; p. 134)

65.   The Japanese principle of _____ makes whistle-blowing uncommon.
        a. guanxi
        b. wa
        c. obligation
        d. groupism
        e. devotion
        (b; difficult; p. 135)

66.   What is the purpose of the Foreign Corrupt Practices Act (FCPA)?
        a. It prohibits the offering of bribes to any foreign government official.
        b. It protects individuals from human rights abuses.
        c. It eliminates bribery in international business transactions.
        d. It inspects working conditions of factories in developing countries.
        e. It prohibits conflicts of interest among employees of international businesses.
        (a; difficult; p. 135)

67.   What is the purpose of the Alien Tort Claims Act?
        a. It prohibits the offering of bribes to any foreign government official.
        b. It protects individuals from human rights abuses.
        c. It eliminates bribery in international business transactions.
        d. It inspects working conditions of factories in developing countries.
        e. It prohibits conflicts of interest among employees of international businesses.
        (b; difficult; p. 135)

68.   What is the purpose of the Anti-Bribery Convention of the Organization for
        Economic Cooperation and Development?
        a. It prohibits the offering of bribes to any foreign government official.
        b. It protects individuals from human rights abuses.
        c. It eliminates bribery in international business transactions.
        d. It inspects working conditions of factories in developing countries.
        e. It prohibits conflicts of interest among employees of international businesses.
        (c; difficult; p. 135)

69.   What is the purpose of the International Labor Organization (ILO)?
        a. It prohibits the offering of bribes to any foreign government official.
        b. It protects individuals from human rights abuses.
        c. It eliminates bribery in international business transactions.
        d. It inspects working conditions of factories in developing countries.
        e. It prohibits conflicts of interest among employees of international businesses.
        (d; difficult; p. 135)

70.   Which regulation prohibits the offering of bribes to any foreign government official in order to influence official actions or policies of that official or to gain or retain business?
      a.   Foreign Corrupt Practices Act
      b.   Helms-Burton Act
      c.   Alien Tort Claims Act
      d.   The Anti-Bribery Convention of the OECD
      e.   Disclosure of Conflict Act
      (a; difficult; p. 135)

71.   Which regulation seeks to protect individuals from human rights abuses and holds MNCs accountable for such abuses?
      a.   Foreign Corrupt Practices Act
      b.   Helms-Burton Act
      c.   Alien Tort Claims Act
      d.   The Anti-Bribery Convention of the OECD
      e.   Disclosure of Conflict Act
      (c; difficult; p. 135)

72.   Which regulation attempts to eliminate bribes in international business transactions?
      a.   Foreign Corrupt Practices Act
      b.   Helms-Burton Act
      c.   Alien Tort Claims Act
      d.   The Anti-Bribery Convention of the OECD
      e.   Disclosure of Conflict Act
      (d; difficult; p. 135)

73.   What organization is the major watchdog for monitoring working conditions in factories in developing countries?
      a.   International Labor Organization
      b.   Human Rights Campaign
      c.   Organization for Economic Cooperation and Development
      d.   World Trade Organization
      e.   Organization for the Protection of Under-privileged Employees
      (a; difficult; p. 136)

74.   What organization systematically inspects factories in countries like Cambodia to monitor working conditions of employees?
      a.   International Rights Organization
      b.   Human Rights Campaign
      c.   Organization for Economic Cooperation and Development
      d.   World Trade Organization
      e.   International Labor Organization
      (e; moderate; p. 136)

75.   A major company is suspected of human rights violations in factories in less developed countries. Which organization should be contacted to investigate?
        a. International Labor Organization
        b. Human Rights Campaign
        c. Organization for Economic Cooperation and Development
        d. World Trade Organization
        e. Organization for the Protection of Under-privileged Employees
        (a; difficult; p. 136)

True/False

76.   In San Miguelito, Mexico, workers receive $1.00 for every two hours they work sewing soccer balls. (T; moderate; p. 117)

77.   Forty percent of Mexico's children work each day. (F; difficult; p. 117)

78.   Child labor is legal in Mexico. (F; difficult; p. 117)

79.   An individual's ethics are determined by many factors. (T; easy; p. 119)

80.   Formal laws typically reflect the prevailing ethical standards. (T; easy; p. 119)

81.   In Japan, a junior employee cannot leave the office until the more senior person departs. (T; moderate; p. 119)

82.   Norms of behavior can be more powerful than the existence of a law. (T; moderate; p. 119)

83.   It is a privacy issue that is faced when an organization gives preferential treatment based on gender. (F; easy; p. 121)

84.   Outsourcing which results in domestic layoffs is considered unethical in Japan. (T; difficult; p. 122)

85.   Accepting gifts in a business relationship is unethical behavior in any country. (F; easy; p. 122)

86.   Low-context cultures are more likely to exchange gifts in a business context. (F; moderate; p. 123)

87.   Codes of ethics are one of the most common methods of addressing appropriate ethical behavior within organizations. (T; easy; p. 125)

88.   In a survey about the acceptability of bribery, the United States indicated that bribery is absolutely unacceptable. (F; difficult; p. 125)

89.   Bribery is common in China and Russia. (T; moderate; p. 125)

90.   Ethics training focuses only on the acceptable behaviors in the home country. (F; moderate; p. 125)

91.   Ethics training sessions include a confession component to allow employees to move beyond past unethical behavior. (F; easy; p. 125)

92.   Bribery in China may have eliminated the equivalent of 15% of the country's GDP. (T; difficult; p. 125)

93.   Paying bribes creates risk for an organization's reputation. (T; moderate; p 127)

94.   Starbucks will pay its coffee suppliers a premium when they demonstrate their commitment to the environment. (T; moderate; p. 129)

95.   There is only one right approach to social responsibility. (F; easy; p. 131)

96.   In Japan, whistle-blowing is uncommon because such an act could disturb the harmony in the group. (T; difficult; p. 135)

97.   A corporate social audit is used to analyze a firm's financial performance with regard to its stockholders. (F; moderate; p. 135)

98.   A corporate social audit is usually conducted by outside consultants. (F; difficult; p. 135)

99.   The rationalization that some employees use to justify stealing at work is based on cultural context and the interdependence of the three types of ethical situations. (T; difficult; p. 121)

100.   Employees are not one of the areas of social responsibility for international firms. (F; easy; p. 126)

Short Answer

101.   What is the fundamental reason for the existence of a business? Answer: To create value for its owners. (easy; p. 118)

102.   Explain the meaning of social responsibility. Answer: Social responsibility is the set of obligations an organization undertakes to protect and enhance the society in which it functions. (moderate; p. 126)

103.   What are the three main groups a corporation will focus on in its social responsibility efforts? Answer: Stakeholders, natural environment, and general social welfare. (moderate; p. 126)

104.   What is meant by the obstructionist approach to social responsibility? Answer: The obstructionist approach means that the organization does as little as possible to address social or environmental concerns. (moderate; p. 131)

105.   What is meant by the defensive approach to social responsibility? Answer: The defensive approach refers to an approach in which an organization does only what is legally required. (moderate; p. 131)

106.   What is meant by the accommodative approach to social responsibility? Answer: The accommodative approach refers to an approach whereby an organization does what is legal and does more when asked. (moderate; p. 132)

107.   What is meant by the proactive approach to social responsibility? Answer: The proactive approach is an approach taken by organizations who seek out opportunities to make positive social and environmental change. (moderate; p. 132)

108.   How does cultural context affect the ethics of a behavior of an organization towards its employees? Answer: Different cultures promote different norms of behavior. Because generally accepted norms of behavior are considered ethical behaviors, the culture ultimately determines a component of what is or is not ethical. (difficult; p. 120)

109.   How does cultural context affect the ethicality of the behavior of an organization toward other economic agents? Answer: What is culturally acceptable in a country may justify the behavior of an organization toward its stakeholders. For instance, drug companies charge more in the U.S. than in other areas. Part of the reason is cultural context. (difficult; p. 120)

110.   What is the difference between the gift-giving seasons of Ochugen and Oseibo in Japan? Answer: Ochugen is the gift-giving season in July which reflects one's best wishes for summer. Oseibo is the season in December when a gift is meant to reflect gratitude and loyalty. (difficult; p. 122)

111.   What is the meaning of the Chinese word, guanxi? Answer: Reciprocal exchanges of favors. (moderate; p. 123)

112.   What characteristics should a good code of ethics have? Answer: It should be clear and in writing. It should address the major elements of ethical conduct relevant to the environment and business operations. It must be adhered to when a problem arises. (moderate; p. 125)

113.   What individuals or groups make up an organization's stakeholders? Answer: Customers, employees, and investors. (moderate; p. 126)

114.   What is whistle-blowing? What risks might a whistle-blower face? Answer: Whistle-blowing means to report an unethical or illegal behavior of another employee or of the company to the proper officials. Whistle-blowers risk being penalized for their lack of loyalty. (moderate; p. 134)

115.   Why is organizational leadership important in encouraging ethical behavior throughout an organization? Answer: Employees will follow the actions of their leadership. (easy; p. 134)

116.   What is meant by legal compliance? Answer: Legal compliance is the extent to which the organization conforms to regional, national, and international laws. (easy; p. 133)

117.   What is the purpose of the Foreign Corrupt Practices Act? Answer: It prohibits U.S. firms, their employees, and agents acting on their behalf from paying or offering to pay bribes to any foreign government official in order influence the official actions or policies of that official to gain or retain business. (moderate; p. 135)

118.   What is the purpose of the Alien Tort Claims Act? Answer: This law holds MNCs responsible for human rights violations. (moderate; p. 135)

119.   What is the mission of the International Labor Organization? Answer: The ILO is a watchdog for monitoring working conditions in factories in developing countries. (moderate; p. 135)

120.   Explain the purpose of a corporate social audit. Answer: It assesses the effectiveness of a firm's social performance. (moderate; p. 135)

Essay

121.   What are the four general approaches a firm can take with regard to social responsibility? Explain each approach.

Answer: The possible approaches to social responsibility are the obstructionist stance, the defensive stance, the accommodative stance, and the proactive stance. Firms taking an obstructionist stance do as little as possible to address social or environmental problems. Firms that take a defensive approach will do all that is required legally, but nothing more. Firms that take an accommodative approach will do all that is required legally and will do more when approached with some opportunity. Firms that take a proactive stance view themselves as citizens of society. They seek out opportunities to be socially responsible. (moderate; p. 131)

122.   Why is gift exchange in business relationships more common in high-context, power-respecting cultures than in low-context, power-tolerant cultures? Answer: The gift exchange is not viewed in high-context cultures as a bribe. Rather it is viewed as a token of appreciation for past loyalty or favors or as an expression of gratitude or loyalty. Consequently, the act of gift exchange works to develop the relationship between the businesses. Because high-context cultures emphasize strong and loyal relationships in business, gift exchange is more common. (difficult; p. 123)

123.   What are the primary regulations that attempt to address issues of international ethics and social responsibility? Summarize the purpose of each regulation.

Answer: The Foreign Corrupt Practices Act prohibits the offering of bribes to any foreign government official in order to influence the official actions or policies of that official to gain or retain business. The Alien Tort Claims Act seeks to protect individuals from human rights abuses. The Anti-Bribery Convention of the Organization for Economic Cooperation and Development seeks to eliminate bribery in international business transactions. (difficult; p. 135)

124.   What risks are created when firms pay bribe requests?

Answer: Firms risk their reputation among the public in the country where it pays the bribe. It means the bureaucrats in that country also recognize the firm as a bribe payer. Consequently, bribe requests could become a regular expectation worldwide. Third, using bribes abroad threatens the firm's domestic reputation. Bribery can also cause a degradation of markets. (moderate; p. 128)

125   What methods can a firm use to encourage compliance with its ethical guidelines? Include both formal and informal methods.

Answer: Firms can use legal compliance, ethical compliance, and philanthropic giving on a formal basis. Informally, the organizational leadership and culture will play an important role as can encouragement of whistle-blowing. (moderate; p. 133)

126.   What activities are undertaken by an organization when it performs a corporate social audit?

Answer: During a corporate social audit, a firm will clearly define its social goals, analyze the resources it devotes to each goal, determine how well it is achieving the various goals, and make recommendations about which areas need additional attention. (moderate; p. 135)

Multiple Choice

1.   The term _____ refers to the voluntary exchange of goods, services, assets, or
        money between one person or organization and another.
        a. sales
        b. transaction
        c. trade
        d. business relationship
        e. relationship management
        (c; easy; p. 146)

2.   Which of the following is included in the term residents?
        a. individuals
        b. firms
        c. not-for-profit organizations
        d. governmental groups
        e. all of the above
        (e; easy p. 146)

3.   Why must both parties to a transaction believe they will gain from it to ensure that
        the transaction is completed?
        a. Because it is voluntary.
        b. Because they are greedy.
        c. Because of choices available in the marketplace.
        d. Because of the cost of the transaction.
        e. None of the above.
        (a; easy; p. 146)

4.   Who uses international trade theories?
        a. government policy makers
        b. managers
        c. economists
        d. scholars of international business
        e. all of the above
        (e; moderate; p. 147)

5.   How might managers use international trade theories?
        a. To lobby for governmental policy changes.
        b. To identify promising markets.
        c. To determine profitable internationalization strategies.
        d. Both a and b.
        e. Both b and c.
        (e; moderate; p. 147)

6.   Which region of the Quad is responsible for most of the world's merchandise
        exports?
        a. The European Union
        b. Japan
        c. The United States
        d. China
        e. Canada
        (a; difficult; p. 147)

7.   Which industry makes up the largest component of the annual trade in
        international services?
        a. financial services
        b. tourism and travel
        c. management consulting
        d. entertainment
        e. education
        (b; moderate; p. 148)

8.   What services are typically included in the travel and tourism sector?
        a. lodging
        b. dining
        c. souvenir purchases
        d. transportation
        e. all of the above
        (e; easy; p. 148)

9.   During which century were the first theories of international trade developed?
        a. Sixteenth
        b. Seventeenth
        c. Eighteenth
        d. Nineteenth
        e. Twentieth
        (a; difficult; p. 148)

10.   On what unit of analysis did the first theories of international trade focus?
        a. individual countries
        b. country clusters
        c. regions
        d. continents
        e. all of the above
        (a; difficult; p. 148)

11.   What type of trade were the early country-based theories of international trade most useful in understanding?
        a.   services
        b.   brand name goods
        c.   commodities
        d.   high tech goods
        e.   software
        (c; moderate; p. 148)

12.   The first theories of international trade are referred to as _____.
        a.   country-based theories
        b.   firm-based theories
        c.   classic theories
        d.   investment theories
        e.   none of the above
        (a; easy; p. 148)

13.   When did the firm-based theories of international trade begin to develop?
        a.   after World War I
        b.   after the Great Depression
        c.   after World War II
        d.   after the Vietnam War
        e.   after Desert Storm
        (c; easy; p. 148)

14.   What type of trade are firm-based theories of international trade most useful in understanding?
        a.   services
        b.   differentiated goods
        c.   commodities
        d.   natural resources
        e.   labor
        (b; moderate; p. 148)

15.   Differentiated goods might include _____.
        a.   automobiles
        b.   sugar
        c.   lumbar
        d.   oil
        e.   tobacco
        (a; easy; p. 148)

16.   Which of the following is an important component of a customer's purchase
       decision for differentiated goods?
       a. price
       b. brand name
       c. competition
       d. resources
       e. all of the above
       (b; easy; p. 148)

17.   _____ maintains that a country's wealth is measured by its holdings of gold and
       silver.
       a. Mercantilism
       b. Neomercantilism
       c. Country-based theory
       d. Protectionists
       e. Comparative advantages
       (a; moderate; p. 148)

18.   According to mercantilism, what should a country's primary goal be?
       a. To protect its borders from illegal aliens.
       b. To encourage a high savings rate amongst its citizens.
       c. To promote the creation of new retail stores.
       d. To enlarge holdings of gold and silver by promoting exports and discouraging
           imports.
       e. To ensure sufficient labor for low-wage jobs.
       (d; moderate; p. 148)

19.   What are modern supporters of mercantilism called?
       a. neomercantilists
       b. protectionists
       c. cosmopolites
       d. both a and b
       e. both a and c
       (d; moderate; p. 148)

20.   Who supported the economic policies of mercantilism?
       a. monarchs
       b. export-oriented manufacturers
       c. domestic manufacturers
       d. employees
       e. all of the above
       (e; difficult; p. 149)

21.   How did imperial governments use their colonies to support the goals of
       mercantilism?
       a. Shipping restrictions.
       b. Prohibition of exports that might compete with the imperial governments
           exports.
       c. Restrictions on sales to some countries.
       d. Export requirements of low-cost supplies to the imperial government.
       e. All of the above.
       (e; moderate; p. 149)

22.   Which group listed below is a modern supporter of mercantilist policies?
       a. American Federation of Labor-Congress of Industrial Organizations
       b. textile manufacturers
       c. steel companies
       d. peanut farmers
       e. all are supporters of mercantilist policies
       (e; moderate; p. 149)

23.   What economic policy of the United Kingdom ultimately led to its overthrow by
       the American colonies?
       a. mercantilism
       b. trickle-down economics
       c. econometrics
       d. Heckscher-Ohlin theory
       e. relative factor endowments
       (a; moderate; p. 149)

24.   What country or region listed below does *not* support any neomercantilist policy
       today?
       a. Japan
       b. The European Union
       c. The United States
       d. China
       e. Nearly all countries have some neomercantilist policies
       (e; difficult; p. 149)

25.   According to Adam Smith, what is the primary basic problem with mercantilism?
       a. It believes gold is treasure.
       b. It confuses the acquisition of treasure with the acquisition of wealth.
       c. It is old-fashioned.
       d. It cannot function in a global economy.
       e. It produces too many efficiencies.
       (b; easy; p. 149)

26.   What did Adam Smith believe about the ultimate effects of mercantilist policies on the health of a country's economic situation?
      a.   Mercantilist policy ultimately strengthened an economy by protecting it from competitive imports.
      b.   Mercantilist policy results in strong rates of unemployment.
      c.   Mercantilist policy reduces the wealth of a country as a whole.
      d.   Mercantilist policies harm special interest groups.
      e.   Both b and c.
      (c; difficult; p. 149)

27.   Which theory suggests that a country should export those goods and services for which it is more productive than other countries and import those goods and services for which other countries are more productive?
      a.   mercantilism
      b.   comparative advantage
      c.   absolute advantage
      d.   relative factor endowments
      e.   specialization of countries
      (c; moderate; p. 150)

28.   What flaw exists in the theory of absolute advantage?
      a.   It has no flaws.
      b.   It confuses the acquisition of treasure with the acquisition of wealth.
      c.   It looks only at relative productivity differences.
      d.   It suggests that no trade will occur in situations in which one country has an absolute advantage in multiple products.
      e.   It incorporates the concept of opportunity cost in determining which good a country should produce.
      (d; difficult; p. 150)

29.   Which theory suggests that a country should produce and export those goods and services for which it is relatively more productive than other countries are and import those goods and services for which other countries are relatively more productive?
      a.   relative advantage
      b.   comparative advantage
      c.   absolute advantage
      d.   relative factor endowments
      e.   specialization of countries
      (b; difficult; p. 150)

30.   The _____ of a good is the value of what is given up to get the good.
       a. relative cost
       b. opportunity cost
       c. absolute cost
       d. discount cost
       e. in-kind value
       (b; easy; p. 150)

31.   Which theory answers the question, "What determines the products for which a
       country will have a comparative advantage"
       a. relative advantage
       b. comparative advantage
       c. absolute advantage
       d. relative factor endowments
       e. specialization of countries
       (d; difficult; p. 153)

32.   Which theory listed below is also called the Heckscher-Ohlin Theory?
       a. relative advantage
       b. comparative advantage
       c. absolute advantage
       d. relative factor endowments
       e. specialization of countries
       (d; difficult; p. 153)

33.   The _____ theory states that a country will have a comparative advantage in
       producing products that intensively use resources it has in abundance.
       a. relative advantage
       b. comparative advantage
       c. absolute advantage
       d. relative factor endowments
       e. specialization of countries
       (d; difficult; p. 153)

34.   The _____ theory suggests that most trade in manufactured goods should be
       between countries with similar per capita incomes.
       a. relative advantage
       b. country similarity
       c. absolute advantage
       d. relative factor endowments
       e. competitive rivalry
       (b; moderate; p. 155)

35.   _____ is the exchange of goods produced by one industry in one country.
      a. Exports
      b. Imports
      c. International trade
      d. Interindustry trade
      e. Intraindustry trade
      (d; easy; p. 155)

36.   _____ is the trade between two countries of goods produced by the same industry.
      a. Exports
      b. Imports
      c. International trade
      d. Interindustry trade
      e. Intraindustry trade
      (e; easy; p. 155)

37.   In what functional field of business did product life cycle theory originate?
      a. marketing
      b. operations
      c. finance
      d. economics
      e. manufacturing
      (a; easy; p. 155)

38.   Who developed the product life cycle theory?
      a. Adam Smith
      b. Steffan Linder
      c. Raymond Vernon
      d. Michael Porter
      e. Eli Heckscher
      (c; difficult; p. 155)

39.   Which of the following is not one of the stages in the international product life
          cycle theory?
      a. new product
      b. discarded product
      c. maturing product
      d. standardized product
      e. all are stages in the theory
      (b; difficult; p. 155)

40.   In which stage of the international product life cycle, does the innovating firm's
        country become a net importer of the product?
        a.   new product stage (stage 1)
        b.   maturing product stage (stage 2)
        c.   standardized product stage (stage 3)
        d.   both b and c
        e.   never
        (c; difficult; p. 157)

41.   Which theory suggests that trade flows can be determined by firms making the
        necessary research and development expenditures?
        a.   global strategic rivalry theory
        b.   national competitive advantage theory
        c.   international product life cycle theory
        d.   internalization theory
        e.   country similarity theory
        (a; moderate; p. 158)

42.   With which method listed below can firms develop a sustainable competitive
        advantage?
        a.   owning intellectual property
        b.   investing in research and development
        c.   achieving economies of scale or scope
        d.   exploiting the experience curve
        e.   all of the above
        (e; moderate; p. 158)

43.   Which theory of international trade explains that success in international trade
        comes from the interaction of four country and firm-specific elements?
        a.   national competitive advantage
        b.   country similarity
        c.   absolute advantage
        d.   relative factor endowments
        e.   competitive rivalry
        (a; moderate; p. 159)

44.   Who developed the theory of national competitive advantage?
        a.   Adam Smith
        b.   Steffan Linder
        c.   Raymond Vernon
        d.   Michael Porter
        e.   Eli Heckscher
        (d; moderate; p. 159)

45.   Which of the following is not one of the four elements discussed in the theory of national competitive advantage?
        a. factor conditions
        b. opportunity cost
        c. firm strategy, structure, and rivalry
        d. related and supporting industries
        e. demand conditions
        (b; moderate; p. 160)

46.   Which geometric shape does Porter use to represent the elements affecting the success of international trade?
        a. square
        b. triangle
        c. rectangle
        d. diamond
        e. octagon
        (d; easy; p. 160)

47.   Which of the following factors are *not* included in Porter's view of factor endowments?
        a. land
        b. labor
        c. capital
        d. work ethic of workforce
        e. educational level of workforce
        (d; moderate; p. 160)

48.   Porter's theory of national competitive advantage can best be described as _____.
        a. a country-based theory
        b. a firm based theory
        c. a hybrid of country-based and firm-based theories
        d. a government focused theory
        e. none of the above
        (c; difficult; p. 161)

49.   Investments into which of the following are important to success in international markets as well as domestic markets?
        a. research and development
        b. quality control
        c. brand image
        d. employee training
        e. all of the above
        (e; easy; p. 161)

50.   What type of trade is explained by firm-based theories?
        a. interindustry trade
        b. intraindustry trade
        c. extraterritorially trade
        d. exports
        e. imports
        (b; moderate; p. 162)

51.   Which theory of international trade is capable of explaining all trade flows among
        countries?
        a. no theory can do that
        b. mercantilism
        c. national competitive advantage
        d. international product life cycle theory
        e. competitive rivalry
        (a; easy; p. 162)

52.   _____ represents passive holdings of securities such as foreign stocks, bonds, or
        other financial assets.
        a. Foreign direct investment
        b. Portfolio investment
        c. Labor investment
        d. Capital investment
        e. Controlling ownership
        (b; easy; p. 163)

53.   _____ is acquisition of foreign assets for the purpose of controlling them.
        a. Foreign direct investment
        b. Portfolio investment
        c. Labor investment
        d. Capital investment
        e. Controlling ownership
        (b; easy; p. 163)

54.   Which of the following is a form of foreign direct investment?
        a. foreign stock ownership
        b. foreign bond ownership
        c. participation in a joint venture
        d. mutual fund ownership
        e. none of the above
        (c; easy; p. 163)

55.   Which of the following is not a form of foreign direct investment?
       a.   new investment in property, plant, and equipment
       b.   purchasing existing assets in a foreign country
       c.   participation in a joint venture with a local partner
       d.   foreign stock ownership
       e.   all are forms of FDI
       (d; easy; p. 163)

56.   Foreign direct investments are motivated by the desire for _____.
       a.   an attractive rate of return
       b.   control
       c.   variety
       d.   achievement
       e.   globalization
       (b; moderate; p. 163)

57.   Portfolio investments are motivated by the desire for _____.
       a.   an attractive rate of return
       b.   control
       c.   variety
       d.   achievement
       e.   globalization
       (a; moderate; p. 163)

58.   Why are Bermuda, Bahamas, and other small Caribbean islands such an important
       destination of FDI from the United States?
       a.   Because of their close proximity.
       b.   Because they serve as offshore financial centers.
       c.   Because of a special agreement between them and the U.S.
       d.   Because the U.S. seeks to provide additional aid to needy nations.
       e.   None of the above.
       (b; difficult; p. 164)

59.   The _____ suggests that a firm owning a valuable asset that creates a competitive
       advantage domestically can use that advantage to penetrate foreign markets
       through FDI.
       a.   national competitive advantage
       b.   comparative advantage
       c.   absolute advantage
       d.   relative factor endowments
       e.   ownership advantage theory
       (e; easy; p. 165)

60.   Which theory explains why a firm would choose to enter a foreign market via FDI rather than exploit its ownership advantages internationally through other means?
       a. ownership advantage theory
       b. internalization theory
       c. eclectic theory
       d. relative factor endowments
       e. national competitive advantage
       (b; moderate; p. 166)

61.   _____ are the costs of negotiating, monitoring, and enforcing a contract.
       a. Compliance costs
       b. Opportunity costs
       c. Transaction costs
       d. Indirect costs
       e. Direct costs
       (c; easy; p. 166)

62.   _____ suggest(s) that FDI will be more likely to occur when transaction costs with a second firm are high.
       a. Ownership advantage theory
       b. Internalization theory
       c. Eclectic theory
       d. Relative factor endowments
       e. National competitive advantage
       (b; moderate; p. 166)

63.   Which theory fails to address the question of why production should be located abroad?
       a. ownership advantage theory
       b. internalization theory
       c. eclectic theory
       d. relative factor endowments
       e. national competitive advantage
       (b; moderate; p. 166)

64.   Who developed the eclectic theory of international investment?
       a. Adam Smith
       b. Steffan Linder
       c. Raymond Vernon
       d. Michael Porter
       e. John Dunning
       (e; moderate; p. 166)

65.   Which of the following is *not* one of the conditions specified in eclectic theory for
        the occurrence of foreign direct investment?
        a.   ownership advantage
        b.   location advantage
        c.   home country advantage
        d.   internalization advantage
        e.   all are conditions specified in eclectic theory
        (c; difficult; p. 166)

66.   Examples of ownership advantage include all of the following *except* _____.
        a.   brand name
        b.   proprietary technology
        c.   benefits of economies of scale
        d.   intellectual property
        e.   benefits of outsourcing
        (e; easy; p. 166)

67.   For the _____ advantage to accrue, undertaking the business activity must be
        more profitable in a foreign location than undertaking it in a domestic location.
        a.   ownership
        b.   location
        c.   home country
        d.   internalization
        e.   all are conditions specified in eclectic theory
        (b; moderate; p. 166)

68.   Which of the factors below do not influence a firm's decision to undertake foreign
        direct investment?
        a.   supply factors
        b.   relative endowment factors
        c.   demand factors
        d.   political factors
        e.   all affect a firm's decision to undertake FDI
        (b; moderate; p. 167)

69.   Supply factors affecting the decision to undertake FDI include all of the following
        except _____.
        a.   production costs
        b.   logistics
        c.   availability of natural resources
        d.   market demand
        e.   access to key technology
        (d; moderate; p. 167)

70.   Demand factors affecting the decision to undertake FDI include all of the
        following *except* _____.
        a. customer access
        b. marketing advantages
        c. exploitation of competitive advantages
        d. customer mobility
        e. resource mobility
        (e; moderate; p. 167)

71.   Why might foreign locations enable a firm to achieve lower production costs?
        a. lower land prices
        b. tax rates
        c. real estate rents
        d. lower cost of supplies
        e. all of the above
        (e; easy; p. 167)

72.   Marketing advantages of FDI include all of the following except _____.
        a. firm visibility
        b. buy local attitudes
        c. improved customer service
        d. quick product improvements
        e. all of the above are marketing advantages of FDI
        (e; easy; p. 169)

73.   A primary benefit of building foreign facilities is the ability for a firm to _____.
        a. avoid trade barriers
        b. promote economic welfare
        c. achieve an attractive rate of return
        d. improve customer service
        e. all of the above
        (a; moderate; p. 170)

74.   Which of the following is not a government incentive for foreign direct
        investment?
        a. reduced utility rates
        b. additions to infrastructure
        c. increases in tax burden
        d. tax holidays
        e. employee training programs
        (c; moderate; p. 170)

75.   Which of the following incentives were offered to Toyota to encourage Toyota to
       build a factory in San Antonio, Texas?
       a.   construction of a new rail line
       b.   worker training
       c.   site preparation expenses
       d.   tax abatements
       e.   all of the above
       (e; moderate; p. 170)

True/False

76.   The early theories of international trade focused on the patterns of exports and
       imports in individual countries. (T; moderate; p. 148)

77.   The first theories of international trade focused on country clusters.
       (F; moderate; p. 148)

78.   Adam Smith attacked the intellectual basis of mercantilism in 1776.
       (T; moderate; p. 149)

79.   No countries continue to use neomercantilist policies today. (F; easy; p. 149)

80.   North Americans and Europeans have long applauded Japan's open door policy
       with regard to imports. (F; moderate; p. 149)

81.   Adam Smith developed the theory of comparative advantage
       (F; difficult; p. 150)

82.   The theory of absolute advantage considers relative productivity differences
       between countries. (F; moderate; p. 150)

83.   Hechscher-Ohlin Theory is another name for the product life cycle theory.
       (F; easy; p. 155)

84.   There are three stages in the international product life cycle. (T; easy; p. 155)

85.   According to the international product life cycle theory, domestic production
       peaks in stage two. (T; moderate; p. 157)

86.   According to the international product life cycle theory, the innovating firm's
       country is primarily an exporter of the product in all three stages.
       (F; difficult; p. 157)

87.   The elements of Porter's national competitive advantage theory can be
       illustrated in the shape of a star. (F; easy; p. 160)

88.   Demand conditions refer to the conditions necessary for foreign direct investment to take place. (F; moderate; p. 160)

89.   Internalization theory suggests that FDI will be more likely to occur when transaction costs with a second firm are high. (T; easy; p. 166)

90.   Foreign direct investment is acquisition of foreign assets for the purpose of controlling them. (T; easy; p. 163)

91.   China is one of the primary recipients of FDI from the United States. (F; difficult; p. 164)

92.   More foreign direct investment in the United States originates in the United Kingdom than any other country. (T; moderate; p. 164)

93.   Outward foreign direct investment has been larger than inward foreign direct investment during the last decade for the United States. (T; moderate; p. 165)

94.   International investment theories answer the question, "Why does foreign direct investment occur?" (T; easy; p. 165)

95.   The ownership advantage theory is an explanation for occurrence of portfolio investments. (F; moderate; p. 165)

96.   Internalization theory holds that when transaction costs are high, firms are more likely to contract with outsiders. (F; easy; p. 166)

97.   McDonald's is an expert at reducing transaction costs between itself and its franchisees. (T; moderate; p. 166)

98.   Internalization theory ignores the question of why production should be located in the country's home country. (F; difficult; p. 166)

99.   Political factors do not affect a firm's decision to undertake foreign direct investment. (F; easy; p. 167)

100.   Avoidance of trade barriers is a political factor considered when firms decide whether to undertake foreign direct investment. (T; easy; p. 167)

Short Answer

101.   What is the basic goal of mercantilist policies? Answer: Under mercantilism, a country seeks to maximize exports and minimize imports. (difficult; p.148)

102.   According to Adam Smith why does free trade among countries actually enlarge a country's wealth? Answer: Free trade enables a country to expand the amount

of goods and services available to it by specializing in the production of some goods and services and trading for others. (difficult; p. 150)

103.   Explain the basic premise of the theory of absolute advantage. Answer: Absolute advantage suggests that a country should export those goods and services for which it is more productive than other countries and import those goods and services for which other countries are more productive. (moderate; p. 150)

104.   Who developed the theory of absolute advantage? Answer: Adam Smith. (easy; p. 150)

105.   Why is opportunity cost an important consideration when determining what a country should export and import? Answer: Opportunity cost acknowledges that a country should also consider how its efforts are best spent. While a country may absolutely be more productive than another country, it must consider that productivity relative to other things that the country could be producing. (difficult; p. 150)

106.   What is the difference between interindustry trade and intraindustry trade?
         Answer: Interindustry trade is the exchange of goods produced by one industry
         in country A for goods produced by a different industry in country B.
         Intraindustry trade is trade between two countries of goods produced by the
         same industry. (easy; p. 155)

107.   What theories are categorized as country-based trade theories? Answer:
         Mercantilism, absolute advantage, comparative advantage, and relative factor
         endowments. (moderate; p. 162)

108.   What theories are categorized as firm-based trade theories? Answer: Country
         similarity theory, product life cycle, global strategic rivalry, national
         competitive advantage. (moderate; p. 162)

109.   What finding is known as the Leontief paradox? Answer: Leontief investigated
         the predictions of the Heckscher-Ohlin theory. However, rather than what was
         predicted, Leontief found that U.S. imports were nearly 30% more capital-
         intensive than were U.S. exports. (difficult; p. 154)

110.   What are the three stages in the international product life cycle? Answer: New
         product, maturing product, and standardized product. (moderate; p. 155)

111.   Explain the view advocated by the global strategic rivalry theory. Answer:
         Firms struggle to develop some sustainable competitive advantage that can then
         be exploited to dominate the global marketplace. (moderate; p. 158)

112.   What form of international business occurs when residents of one country
         supply capital to a second country? Answer: International investment.
         (easy; p. 163)

113.   What are the two types of international investments? Answer: Foreign direct
         investments and portfolio investments. (easy; p. 163)

114.   From which five countries does FDI primarily flow into the United States?
         Answer: The United Kingdom, France, Netherlands, Japan, and Germany.
         (difficult; p. 164)

115.   To which five countries does FDI from the United States primarily flow?
         Answer: The United Kingdom, Canada, Netherlands, the Caribbean islands
         (namely Bermuda and the Bahamas), and Switzerland. (difficult; p. 164)

116.   Given the growth of the Chinese economy, why is FDI in China by the United
         States lower than FDI in Canada and Japan? Answer: It may be lower because
         China has a higher level of political risk than do Canada and Japan.
         (difficult; p. 164)

117.   List the theories of international investment. Answer: Ownership advantage theory, internalization theory, and Dunning's eclectic theory. (moderate; p. 165)

118.   What are the three conditions that must be satisfied in order for foreign direct investment to occur according to Dunning's eclectic theory? Answer: Ownership advantage, location advantage, and internalization advantage. (moderate; p. 166)

119.   What supply factors are relevant when firms consider whether to undertake foreign direct investment? Answer: Production costs, logistics, resource availability, and access to technology. (easy; p. 167)

120.   What demand factors are relevant when firms consider whether to undertake foreign direct investment? Answer: Customer access, marketing advantages, exploitation of competitive advantages, and customer mobility. (easy; p. 167)

Essay

121.   What is meant by the Lincoln Fallacy? Was Abraham Lincoln a supporter of mercantilism or free-trade? Explain. What considerations did Lincoln overlook in developing his position on international trade?

        Answer: The Lincoln Fallacy refers to consideration of this statement by Abraham Lincoln: "I know this much. When we buy manufactured goods abroad, we get the goods and the foreigner gets the money. When we buy the manufactured goods at home, we get both the goods and the money." This statement suggests that Lincoln adhered to the approach suggested by mercantilism. Lincoln's argument fails to take into consideration the resources used to produce those goods at home. Buying abroad frees up domestic resources that could be used in a more productive manner. In other words, specialization allows for greater wealth in the long run. (difficult; p. 152)

122.   Why did firm-based trade theories develop?

        Answer: Firm-based theories developed for these reasons: 1) the growing importance of MNCs in the postwar international economy; 2) the inability of the country-based theories to explain and predict the existence and growth of intraindustry trade, and 3) the failure of Leontief and others to empirically validate the country-based Heckscher-Ohlin theory. (moderate; p. 155)

123.   What are the three stages in the international product life cycle theory? Explain what happens in each stage.

Answer: Stage 1) New Product Stage. In stage 1, a firm develops and introduces an innovative product. Because of the need for fast feedback, the product may only be produced in the country where the research and development occurred. Stage 2) Maturing Product Stage. In stage 2, demand for the product expands dramatically as consumers recognize its value. The innovating firm may build new factories to expand its capacity and satisfy domestic and foreign demand. Stage 3) Standardized Product Stage. In stage 3, the market for the product stabilizes. The product becomes more of a commodity and the firm shifts production to countries with lower labor costs. As a result, the innovating firm's home country becomes an importer of the product, rather than an exporter. (moderate; pp. 156-157)

124.   How can a firm develop a sustainable competitive advantage? Describe four methods a firm could use.

Answer: Owning intellectual property, investing in research and development, achieving economies of scale or scope, and exploiting the experience curve. (moderate; pp. 158-159)

125.   Explain the four elements of Porter's national competitive advantage theory.

Answer: The four elements are 1) factor conditions, 2) firm strategy, structure, and rivalry, 3) demand conditions, and 4) related and supporting industries. Factor conditions refer to the basic factors that enable a country to compete internationally. These include land, labor, capital, education of the workforce, and the quality of the country's infrastructure. Firm strategy, structure, and rivalry refers to how the firm has developed its strategy and structure to compete against competition in both the domestic and international environments. Demand conditions refer to the strength of the consumer base domestically and abroad. Related and supporting industries refer to the development of local suppliers in response to a firm's needs. (moderate; p. 160)

Multiple Choice

1.   Why is the international monetary system necessary for international business?
      a. Because it is a historically significant institution.
      b. Because it controls interest rates on international business loans.
      c. Because it establishes the rules by which countries value and exchange
          currencies.
      d. Because it sets the price of a given currency.
      e. None of the above.
      (c; moderate; p. 179)

2.   The _____ establishes the rules by which countries value and exchange their
      currencies.
      a. international monetary system
      b. OECD
      c. Triad
      d. IMF
      e. Federal Reserve
      (a; moderate; p. 179)

3.   The _____ provides a mechanism for correcting imbalances between a country's
      international payments and its receipts.
      a. international accounting standards
      b. internationally accepted standards of bookkeeping
      c. international monetary system
      d. IMF
      e. OECD
      (c; moderate; p. 179)

4.   What is the international monetary system's accounting system called?
      a. IMF
      b. balance of payments
      c. international accounting standards
      d. gold standard
      e. ISO 9000
      (b; easy; p. 179)

5.   The _____ records international transactions.
      a. IMF
      b. balance of payments
      c. international accounting standards
      d. gold standard
      e. ISO 9000
      (b; easy; p. 179)

6.   The _____ supplies vital information about the health of national economies.
    a.   IMF
    b.   exchange rate
    c.   international accounting standards
    d.   gold standard
    e.   balance of payments
    (e; easy; p. 179)

7.   What changes in the international business environment can BOP statistics identify?
    a.   governmental trade restrictions
    b.   higher interest rates
    c.   accelerated inflation
    d.   reduced aggregate demand
    e.   all of the above
    (e; moderate; p. 179)

8.   What precious metal was used in ancient times as an international medium of exchange?
    a.   platinum
    b.   sterling silver
    c.   steel
    d.   gold
    e.   all of the above
    (d; easy; p. 179)

9.   Which country was the first to adopt the gold standard?
    a.   The United States
    b.   The United Kingdom
    c.   Egypt
    d.   France
    e.   Germany
    (b; difficult; p. 179)

10.   The _____ refers to an international monetary system in which countries agreed to buy or sell their paper currencies in exchange for gold on the request of any individual or firm and to allow the free export of gold.
    a.   free exchange system
    b.   free market system
    c.   gold standard
    d.   mercantilism
    e.   none of the above
    (c; easy; p. 179)

11.   Of which system is the gold standard essentially the opposite?
        a. mercantilism
        b. silver standard
        c. econometrics
        d. Heckscher-Ohlin theory
        e. relative factor endowments
        (a; difficult; p. 179)

12.   In addition to the United Kingdom, which other important trading country
        adopted the gold standard?
        a. Russia
        b. Germany
        c. France
        d. The United States
        e. All of the above
        (e; easy; p. 179)

13.   What was created by the gold standard?
        a. a fixed exchange rate system
        b. a floating exchange rate system
        c. an accounting system
        d. a export system
        e. none of the above
        (a; moderate; p. 179)

14.   A(n) _____ is the price of one currency in terms of a second currency.
        a. export rate
        b. exchange rate
        c. excise tax rate
        d. interest payment
        e. monetary value
        (b; easy; p. 179)

15.   Under the _____ the price of a given currency does not change relative to other
        currency.
        a. free trade agreement
        b. currency union
        c. fixed exchange rate system
        d. floating exchange rate system
        e. balance of payments
        (c; easy; p. 179)

16.   Under the _____, each country pegged the value of its currency to gold.
       a. mercantilism
       b. gold standard
       c. econometrics
       d. Heckscher-Ohlin theory
       e. relative factor endowments
       (b; easy; p. 179)

17.   A _____ refers the official price of a currency in terms of gold.
       a. fixed exchange rate
       b. pegged rate
       c. par value
       d. currency rate
       e. none of the above
       (c; easy; p. 179)

18.   When firms had faith in a country's pledge to exchange its currency for gold, how
       did they prefer to be paid?
       a. in gold
       b. in paper currency
       c. in a combination of gold and paper currency
       d. in credit
       e. in U.S. dollars
       (b; moderate; p. 179)

19.   Which of the following was *not* a cost of accepting payment in gold?
       a. transportation
       b. security
       c. insurance
       d. lost interest payments
       e. all of the above were costs of accepting payment in gold
       (e; moderate; p. 180)

20.   Which was the most important currency in international commerce from 1821 to
       1918?
       a. the U.S. dollar
       b. the British pound sterling
       c. gold
       d. the German deutschmark
       e. the French franc
       (b; moderate; p. 180)

21.   During the gold standard, what else was the international monetary system called?
        a. a sterling-based gold standard
        b. a dollar-based gold standard
        c. a silver-based gold standard
        d. a deutschmark-based gold standard
        e. none of the above
        (a; moderate; p. 180)

22.   Which of the following countries was ruled by the British Empire during the gold standard?
        a. Canada
        b. Australia
        c. Pakistan
        d. Belize
        e. All of the above
        (e; moderate; p. 180)

23.   Which of the following countries was *not* ruled by the British Empire during the gold standard?
        a. Kenya
        b. Singapore
        c. New Zealand
        d. Hong Kong
        e. Korea
        (e; difficult; p. 180)

24.   Which of the following British firms did *not* establish its international reputation and strength from the role of the pound sterling in the nineteenth-century gold standard?
        a. Barclays Bank
        b. Thomas Cook
        c. Harrod's
        d. Lloyd's of London
        e. All of the above
        (c; moderate; p. 180)

25.   When did the sterling-based gold standard begin to unravel?
        a. during World War I
        b. during World War II
        c. during the Vietnam War
        d. during the Korean War
        e. during the Opium War
        (a; easy; p. 180)

26.   Why was the gold standard suspended during World War I?
        a. It was no longer safe to transport gold.
        b. Economic pressures of war caused countries to suspend pledges to buy and
            sell gold at their currencies' par values.
        c. Countries were angry at opposing countries and refused to trade with them.
        d. The Bank of England could not maintain the pound's value.
        e. All of the above.
        (b; moderate; p. 180)

27.   What caused some countries to switch from the gold standard to the "sterling
        area" in 1931?
        a. The British pound sterling had become more valuable than gold.
        b. The Bank of England allowed the pound to float rather than be pegged to gold.
        c. An economic conference in Genoa concluded that a sterling standard should
            be used.
        d. Several countries increased the values of their currency in the international
            market.
        e. None of the above.
        (b; difficult; p. 180)

28.   The term _____ means that a currency's value is determined by the forces of
        supply and demand.
        a. fixed exchange rate
        b. par value
        c. float
        d. market exchange
        e. gold standard
        (c; easy; p. 180)

29.   When the gold standard ended in 1931, what currency was used as the new
        standard?
        a. British pound sterling
        b. U.S. dollar
        c. French franc
        d. All of the above
        e. None of the above
        (d; difficult; p. 180)

30.   Which political leader did *not* gain leadership advantage from the political
        instability following the breakdown of the international monetary system and
        international trade after World War I?
        a. Hitler
        b. Mussolini
        c. Stalin
        d. Churchill
        e. All of the above gained advantage
        (d; moderate; p. 182)

31.   What situation contributed to political instability prior to World War II?
        a. inflation
        b. unemployment
        c. costs of rebuilding after World War I
        d. poor economic conditions
        e. all of the above
        (e; moderate; p. 180)

32.   What did the Bretton Woods conferees agree to do in 1944?
        a. to end World War II
        b. to renew the gold standard
        c. to adhere to the sterling standard
        d. to promote world peace
        e. none of the above
        (b; easy; p. 182)

33.   Which of the following is *not* one of the possible references to Bretton Woods?
        a. a resort in New Hampshire
        b. a meeting among 44 countries in 1944
        c. a town in New Hampshire
        d. a ski resort in Colorado
        e. all of the above
        (d; easy; p. 182)

34.   The Bretton Woods conference sought to do which of the following?
        a. Create a postwar economic environment that would promote world peace.
        b. Renew the gold standard.
        c. Create the International Monetary Fund.
        d. Create the International Bank for Reconstruction and Development.
        e. All of the above.
        (e; moderate; p. 182)

35.   The International Bank for Reconstruction and Development is also known as
        _____.
        a. the World Bank
        b. the IMF
        c. the Organization for Economic Cooperation and Development
        d. the Bretton Woods
        e. none of the above
        (a; moderate; p. 182)

36.   What was the initial goal of the World Bank?
        a. To administer the gold standard.
        b. To hold financial reserves for all countries.
        c. To finance reconstruction of war-torn economies.
        d. To provide capital for corporate expansion activities.
        e. To promote international commerce.
        (c; moderate; p. 182)

37.   How many affiliated organizations are a part of the World Bank?
        a. 0
        b. 1
        c. 2
        d. 3
        e. 4
        (d; moderate; p. 182)

38.   Which country holds the largest bloc of votes in the World Bank?
        a. Japan
        b. The United Kingdom
        c. The United States
        d. Germany
        e. Russia
        (c; moderate; p. 183)

39.   Loans from the World Bank may *not* be used to finance _____.
        a. new railroads
        b. harbor facilities
        c. national highways
        d. trade deficits
        e. loans from the World Bank could finance all of the above
        (d; easy; p. 183)

40.   Which organization is authorized to make soft loans to countries?
        a.   World Bank
        b.   International Bank for Reconstruction and Development
        c.   International Development Association
        d.   International Monetary Fund
        e.   Multilateral Investment Guarantee Agency
        (c; moderate; p. 183)

41.   _____ are those that bear significant risk of not being repaid.
        a.   Hard loans
        b.   Soft loans
        c.   High-risk loans
        d.   Development loans
        e.   Reconstruction loans
        (b; easy; p. 183)

42.   The interest rate on soft loans is traditionally set at _____.
        a.   0%
        b.   5%
        c.   10%
        d.   15%
        e.   20%
        (a; moderate; p. 183)

43.   What is the target audience for loans from the International Development
        Association?
        a.   highly-developed countries
        b.   least developed countries
        c.   moderately-developed countries
        d.   multinational corporations
        e.   any country
        (b; moderate; p. 183)

44.   What is the primary purpose of the International Finance Corporation?
        a.   To make soft loans.
        b.   To make hard loans.
        c.   To promote private sector development in developing countries.
        d.   To provide political risk insurance.
        e.   All of the above.
        (c; moderate; p. 184)

45.   What is the primary purpose of the Multilateral Investment Guarantee Agency?
        a. To make soft loans.
        b. To make hard loans.
        c. To promote private sector development in developing countries.
        d. To provide political risk insurance.
        e. All of the above.
        (d; moderate; p. 184)

46.   _____ promote the economic development of the poorer countries in their
        respective regions.
        a. Regional development banks
        b. National investment banks
        c. National development banks
        d. Continental development banks
        e. Regional finance corporations
        (a; easy; p. 184)

47.   The purpose of the _____ is to oversee the functioning of the international
        monetary system.
        a. World Bank
        b. International Bank for Reconstruction and Development
        c. International Development Association
        d. International Monetary Fund
        e. Multilateral Investment Guarantee Agency
        (d; moderate; p. 185)

48.   Which country controls the largest bloc of votes in the IMF?
        a. none–all countries have an equal vote
        b. The United Kingdom
        c. The United States
        d. Germany
        e. Japan
        (c; easy; p. 185)

49.   What was created by the Bretton Woods system?
        a. a fixed exchange rate system
        b. a floating exchange rate system
        c. an accounting system
        d. a export system
        e. none of the above
        (a; moderate; p. 179)

50.   Which of the following is *not* one of the world's major currencies?
        a. American dollar
        b. Japanese yen
        c. British pound sterling
        d. Euro
        e. German deutschmark
        (e; easy; p. 188)

51.   Special Drawing Rights, SDRs, are sometimes called _____.
        a. gold
        b. paper currency
        c. paper gold
        d. credit
        e. none of the above
        (c; moderate; p. 188)

52.   The value of _____ is currently calculated daily as a weighted average of the
        market value of four major currencies.
        a. IMF's quota
        b. special drawing rights
        c. dollar averaging
        d. exchange rate standard
        e. par value
        (b; moderate; p. 188)

53.   Who was President of the United States when the marketplace learned that the
        United States did not have enough gold on hand to meet demand?
        a. John F. Kennedy
        b. Richard Nixon
        c. Franklin Roosevelt
        d. Benjamin Franklin
        e. None of the above
        (b; easy; p. 188)

54.   Which two countries are added to the Group of Five to make it the Group of
        Seven?
        a. The United States and Japan
        b. Italy and Canada
        c. Germany and France
        d. Russia and Sweden
        e. France and Canada
        (b; difficult; p.188)

55.   How many countries are members of the Group of Ten?
        a. 10
        b. 11
        c. 20
        d. 21
        e. 30
        (b; easy; p. 188)

56.   Together, the Group of Ten make up approximately what percentage of the
        world's GDP?
        a. 10%
        b. 25%
        c. 50%
        d. 70%
        e. 75%
        (d; easy; p. 188)

57.   Which of the following is not one of the four countries that, in addition to the
        Group of Seven countries, make up the Group of Ten?
        a. Netherlands
        b. Switzerland
        c. Austria
        d. Belgium
        e. Sweden
        (c; difficult; p. 188)

58.   At which conference did the Group of Ten agree to restore the fixed exchange rate
        system in 1971?
        a. Bretton Woods
        b. Smithsonian
        c. Brussels
        d. Genoa
        e. Jamaica
        (b; easy; p. 188)

59.   What term recognizes that in addition to private sector market forces, exchange
        rates are also affected by central banks buying or selling currencies on the
        foreign-exchange market?
        a. float
        b. flexible
        c. managed float
        d. special drawing rights
        e. clean float
        (c; moderate; p. 189)

60.   Dirty float is another term for _____.
        a. flexible float
        b. managed float
        c. illegal exchange
        d. par value
        e. convertible currency
        (b; easy; p. 189)

61.   Under a floating exchange rate system, what determines the exchange rate for
        each currency?
        a. a currency's par value
        b. the gold standard
        c. its pegged value
        d. the forces of supply and demand
        e. its central bank
        (d; easy; p. 189)

62.   Which agreement resulted in each country adopting its own exchange rate
        system?
        a. Bretton Woods
        b. Smithsonian
        c. Jamaica
        d. Genoa
        e. Brussels
        (c; moderate; p. 189)

63.   The _____ was created to manage currency relationships within the European
        Union.
        a. European Monetary System
        b. International Monetary System
        c. Louvre Accord
        d. Plaza Accord
        e. None of the above
        (a; easy; p. 190)

64.   The _____ is a double-entry bookkeeping system designed to measure and record
        all economic transactions between residents of one country and residents of all
        during a particular time period.
        a. managerial accounting
        b. international accounting
        c. balance of payments
        d. global books
        e. none of the above
        (c; easy; p. 196)

65.   Which of the following is *not* one of the major accounts in the BOP accounting system?
a. current account
b. capital account
c. debt account
d. official reserves account
e. errors and omissions
(c; moderate; p. 197)

66.   The _____ records exports and imports of goods and services, investment income, and gifts.
a. current account
b. capital account
c. debt account
d. official reserves account
e. errors and omissions
(a; moderate; p. 197)

67.   The _____ records the purchases and sales of assets between residents of one country and those of another country.
a. current account
b. capital account
c. debt account
d. official reserves account
e. errors and omissions
(b; moderate; p. 197)

68.   The _____ records the levels of gold, convertible currencies, special drawing rights, and reserve positions at the IMF held by a national government.
a. current account
b. capital account
c. debt account
d. official reserves account
e. errors and omissions
(d; moderate; p. 197)

69.   The _____ is used to make the BOP balance despite measurement errors.
a. current account
b. capital account
c. debt account
d. official reserves account
e. errors and omissions
(e; easy; p. 197)

70.   All of the following are typical short-term portfolio investments included in the capital account *except* _____.
       a. government bonds
       b. checking account balances
       c. time deposits
       d. commercial paper
       e. bank loans
       (a; difficult; p. 198)

71.   All of the following are typical long-term portfolio investments included in the capital account except _____.
       a. government bonds
       b. checking account balances
       c. government bills
       d. corporate stocks and bonds
       e. government notes
       (b; difficult; p. 198)

72.   The _____ measures the net balance resulting from merchandise trade, service trade, investment income, and unilateral transfers.
       a. current account balance
       b. capital account balance
       c. official reserves account balance
       d. balance of payments
       e. trade deficit
       (a; easy; p. 198)

73.   Which of the following is *not* a form of assets included in the official reserves account?
       a. gold
       b. convertible currencies
       c. special drawing rights
       d. reserve positions at the IMF
       e. all are assets included in the official reserves account
       (e; moderate; p. 200)

74.   The _____ records the net impact of the central bank's interventions in the foreign exchange market in support of the local currency.
       a. official reserves balance
       b. official settlements balance
       c. current account balance
       d. capital account balance
       e. balance of payments
       (b; moderate; p. 205)

75.   Which balance listed below is *the* balance of payments?
        a. official reserves balance
        b. official settlements balance
        c. current account balance
        d. capital account balance
        e. all are components of the balance of payments
        (e; moderate; p. 205)

True/False

76.   The international monetary system provides a means of exchanging currencies
        in international business transactions. (T; moderate; p. 179)

77.   The BOP can be useful in detecting signs of trouble that could lead to
        governmental trade restrictions. (T; easy; p. 179)

78.   International transactions are recorded by the World Trade Organization.
        (F; moderate; p. 179)

79.   Ancient reliance on gold as a medium of international exchange led to the
        adoption of an international monetary system known as the gold standard.
        (T; easy; p. 179)

80.   Platinum was used as a medium of international exchange in ancient times
        because of its strength and value. (F; easy; p. 179)

81.   The gold standard effectively created a floating exchange rate system.
        (F; moderate; p. 179)

82.   During the gold standard, most firms preferred their payment in gold rather than
        in currency. (F; moderate; p. 180)

83.   When firms accepted payment by check, they ultimately also benefited from the
        increased time the currency spent in an interest-bearing account.
        (T; moderate; p. 180)

84.   During the gold standard, the international monetary system was also called the
        dollar-based gold standard. (F; moderate; p. 180)

85.   London became a major international financial center because of the
        international trust in the British currency. (T; easy; p. 180)

86.   Once the gold standard was suspended, it was never considered again for use in
        the international monetary system. (F; difficult; p. 180)

87.   In the 1920s, most countries suffered from high levels of inflation and unemployment. (T; easy; p. 180)

88.   The gold standard was readopted after the end of the Great Depression. (F; difficult; p. 180)

89.   China has been accused of devaluing its currency just as nations did after the end of the gold standard in order to keep its exports inexpensive in world markets. (T; difficult; p. 180)

90.   The breakdown of the international monetary system created economic conditions that helped bring about World War II. (T; moderate; p. 182)

91.   Hitler's rise to power can be attributed in part to the breakdown of the international monetary system. (T; difficult; p. 182)

92.   The communist dictator, Winston Churchill, seized control of his country's government after the breakdown of the international monetary system. (F; easy; p. 182)

93.   Japan holds the largest bloc of votes in the World Bank. (F; easy; p. 183)

94.   The country members of the World Bank each have one, equal vote in decisions. (F; moderate; p. 183)

95.   The World Bank follows what is called a soft loan policy. (F; moderate; p. 183)

96.   A member country of the IMF may borrow up to 25% of its quota from the IMF. (T; easy; p. 185)

97.   Members of the IMF all have an equal vote within the IMF. (F; moderate; p. 185)

98.   The Bretton Woods system did not allow for the adjustment of a currency's par value. (F; moderate; p. 186)

99.   Truman officially ended the Bretton Woods system when he announced that the United States would no longer redeem gold at $35 per ounce. (F; difficult; p. 188)

100.   There is no single measure of a country's global economic performance. (T; easy; p. 205)

Short Answer

101.   Why might the gold standard and mercantilism be considered opposites?
Answer: The gold standard and mercantilism are opposites because the gold
standard advocated the free export of gold while mercantilism advocated
hoarding gold. (difficult; p. 179)

102.   Explain why the gold standard resulted in a fixed exchange rate system.
Answer: When one country pledged to buy or sell an ounce of gold for x
amount and another country agreed to buy or sell an ounce of gold for a par
value of y amount, then the two currencies could be freely exchanged for the
stated amount of gold, making x = 1 ounce of gold = y. (moderate; p. 179)

103.   Why did countries prefer to be paid in currency rather than in gold during the
gold standard? Answer: Because it was expensive to be paid in gold. There were
additional costs to gold payments including the costs of loading the gold into the
cargo hold of a ship, guarding the gold, transporting the gold, and insuring it.
(easy; p. 180)

104.   Why was the international monetary system also called the sterling-based gold
standard during the gold standard? Answer: The international monetary system
was also called the sterling-based gold standard because most firms were
willing to accept either British pounds or gold in settlement of transactions. The
British pound sterling was the most important currency in international
commerce during this time. This was somewhat a reflection of Britain's
economic and military power. (moderate; p. 180)

105.   Why was the claim "the sun never sets on the British Empire" made? Answer:
Because the United Kingdom ruled several countries in many parts of the world.
One could say that it was daylight in some country ruled by the United
Kingdom at any time of day. (difficult; p. 180)

106.   Why did some countries deliberately devalue their currencies following the end
of the gold standard? Answer: By deliberately and artificially lowering the
official value of its currency, each nation hoped to make its own goods cheaper
in the world markets. This would stimulate exports and reduce imports.
(difficult; p. 180)

107.   Were the countries who devalued their currencies successful in increasing
exports and decreasing imports? Why or why not? Answer: No. Because several
countries attempted the strategy, all the gains were offset when other countries
also devalued their currencies. (moderate; p. 180)

108.   How might the breakdown of the international monetary system and
international trade after World War I have influenced the occurrence of World
War II? Answer: It created inflation and unemployment combined with the costs

of rebuilding war-torn economies. This created political instability allowing dictators to seize control of their respective governments. (difficult; p. 182)

109.   What are the three organizations that are affiliated with the International Bank for Reconstruction and Development as part of the World Bank Group? Answer: International Development Association, International Finance Corporation, and Multilateral Investment Guarantee Agency. (difficult; p. 183)

110.   What is the meaning of a hard loan policy? Answer: A hard loan policy is one in which there is a reasonable expectation that the loan will be repaid. (moderate; p. 183)

111.   What complaint brought about the creation of the International Development Association? Answer: Poor countries complained that the World Bank's hard loan policy made it difficult for them to obtain World Bank loans. (moderate; p. 183)

112.   What is the mission of the International Finance Corporation (IFC)? Answer: Its mission is the development of the private sector in developing countries. (moderate; p. 183)

113.   Name four regional development banks. Answer: African Development Bank, Asian Development Bank, Inter-American Development Bank, and the European Bank for Reconstruction and Development. (moderate; p. 184)

114.   How did the United States dollar become the currency standard under the Bretton Woods system? Answer: All the Bretton Woods participants agreed to peg the value of their currencies to gold. However, only the United States pledged to redeem its currency for gold at the request of a foreign central bank. Thus, other countries accepted U.S. dollars to settle their transactions just as they had accepted British pounds in the nineteenth century. (moderate; p. 185)

115.   What was a major weakness of the Bretton Woods system? Answer: International trade needed only the U.S. dollar as a source of liquidity for expansion. This expansion depended on foreigners' willingness to continually increase their holdings of dollars as long as they trusted the integrity of the U.S. currency. However, as foreign dollar holdings increased, people began to question the ability of the United States to be able to redeem those dollars for gold. This is referred to as the Triffin paradox. (difficult; p. 187)

116.   What are the five key central banks in the world? Answer: Bank of Canada, European Central Bank, Bank of Japan, Bank of England, and the Federal Reserve Bank. (moderate; p. 189)

117.   In what two ways can capital outflows occur as debits in the BOP accounting system? Answer: Ownership of foreign assets by a country's residents increases and foreign ownership of assets in a country declines. (difficult; p. 199)

118.   In what two ways can capital inflows occur as credits in the BOP accounting system? Answer: Foreign ownership of assets in a country increases and ownership of foreign assets by a country's residents declines. (difficult; p. 199)

119.   What are the four types of assets included in the Official Reserves Account? Answer: Gold, convertible currencies, SDRs, and reserve positions at the IMF. (moderate; p. 200)

120.   With what equation is the errors and omissions account used to make the BOP balance in accordance? Answer: Current Account + Capital Account + Official Reserves Account + Errors and Omissions = O. (moderate; p. 200)

Essay

121.   The international monetary system provides three important functions in international business. What are these?

        Answer: The international monetary system establishes the rules by which countries value and exchange their currencies. It also provides a mechanism for correcting imbalances between a country's international payments and its receipts. The international monetary system's accounting system records international transactions and supplies information about the health of national economies. (moderate; p. 179)

122.   Describe the major outcomes of the Bretton Woods conference.

        Answer: The Bretton Woods conference participants sought to create a postwar economic environment that could promote world peace and prosperity. It agreed to renew the gold standard on a modified basis. It also created two new international organizations: the International Bank for Reconstruction and Development and the International Monetary Fund. (difficult; p. 182)

123.   What guidelines must the World Bank follow in making loans? Discuss at least three of these guidelines.

        Answer: The World Bank must lend for productive purposes only. Those purposes must stimulate economic growth within the recipient country. It cannot finance a trade deficit. It may lend only to national governments or for projects guaranteed by national governments. Its loans may not be tied to the purchase of goods or services from any country. It must follow a hard loan policy. (difficult; p. 183)

124.   What are the primary objectives of the International Monetary Fund?

Answer: The objectives of the IMF are to promote international monetary cooperation, facilitate the expansion and balanced growth of international trade, promote exchange stability and arrangements, assist in the establishment of a multilateral system of payments, provide confidence to members by making the general resources of the IMF temporarily available to them, and shorten the duration and lessen the degree of disequilibrium in the international balances of payments of members. (difficult; p. 185)

125.   Explain why the quota size is an important membership issue for the IMF.

Answer: The country's quota determines its voting power within the IMF. A country's quota also serves as part of its official reserves. The quota also determines the country's borrowing power from the IMF. Each IMF country has an unconditional right to borrow up to 25% of its quota from the IMF. (moderate; p. 185)

Multiple Choice

1.   The _____ refers to the twelve countries that have adopted the euro as a common currency.
a. European Union
b. euro-zone
c. customs union
d. European monetary system
e. none of the above
(b; easy; p. 211)

2.   What benefits of the euro are provided to European consumers, businesses, and visitors?
a. convenience
b. cost savings due to elimination of currency conversion
c. reduction of exchange rate risk
d. increased competitiveness of firms in international markets
e. all of the above
(e; easy; p. 211)

3.   Which European Union member country has adopted the euro as its currency?
a. Denmark
b. Sweden
c. France
d. United Kingdom
e. Switzerland
(c; moderate; p. 211)

4.   _____ is a commodity that consists of currencies issued by countries other than one's own.
a. Euro-zone
b. Foreign exchange
c. Floating exchange
d. International monetary fund
e. Special drawing rights
(b; easy; p. 212)

5.   What organization sets monetary policy for the European Union?
a. Deutsche Bank
b. European Central Bank
c. Federal Reserve Bank
d. International Monetary Fund
e. None of the above
(b; easy; p. 212)

6.   The price of foreign exchange is set by _____.
        a. the international monetary fund
        b. the gold standard
        c. demand and supply in the marketplace
        d. the World Bank
        e. none of the above
        (c; moderate; p. 212)

7.   A(n) _____ is the price of the foreign currency in terms of the home currency.
        a. direct exchange rate
        b. direct quote
        c. indirect exchange rate
        d. indirect quote
        e. both a and b
        (e; easy; p. 213)

8.   A(n) _____ is the price of the home currency in terms of the foreign currency.
        a. direct exchange rate
        b. direct quote
        c. indirect exchange rate
        d. indirect quote
        e. both c and d
        (e; easy; p. 213)

9.   Exchange rates may be quoted on a(n) _____ basis.
        a. direct
        b. indirect
        c. dollar
        d. pound
        e. both a and b
        (e; moderate; p. 214)

10.   What determines how certain exchange rates are quoted?
        a. tradition
        b. convenience
        c. regulation
        d. customer request
        e. both a and b
        (e; moderate; p. 214)

11.   Which of the following is not one of the four largest foreign-exchange markets?
       a. London
       b. New York
       c. Frankfurt
       d. Tokyo
       e. Singapore
       (c; moderate; p. 215)

12.   Which of the following is the largest foreign-exchange market in the world?
       a. London
       b. New York
       c. Frankfurt
       d. Tokyo
       e. Singapore
       (a; moderate; p. 215)

13.   Of all foreign-exchange trading, what percentage involves the U.S. dollar?
       a. 10%
       b. 25%
       c. 50%
       d. 75%
       e. 90%
       (e; moderate; p. 215)

14.   Which of the following is *not* a type of client of foreign-exchange departments of banks?
       a. commercial customers
       b. speculators
       c. arbitrageurs
       d. individuals
       e. all are clients
       (d; moderate; p. 218)

15.   _____ engage in foreign-exchange transactions as part of their normal activities of exporting and importing goods and services.
       a. Commercial customers
       b. Speculators
       c. Arbitrageurs
       d. Individuals
       e. All are clients
       (a; moderate; p. 218)

16.   Which of the following is a type of activity that commercial customers of banks normally take part in?
a. Exporting goods or services.
b. Importing goods or services.
c. Paying or receiving dividends and interest from foreign sources.
d. Purchasing or selling foreign assets and investments.
e. All of the above.
(e; moderate; p. 217)

17.   _____ assume exchange rate risks by acquiring positions in a currency and hoping that they can correctly predict changes in the currency's market value.
a. Commercial customers
b. Speculators
c. Arbitrageurs
d. Individuals
e. All are clients
(b; moderate; p. 218)

18.   _____ attempt to exploit small differences in the price of a currency between markets by buying currencies in lower-priced markets and selling in higher-priced markets.
a. Commercial customers
b. Speculators
c. Arbitrageurs
d. Individuals
e. All are clients
(c; moderate; p. 218)

19.   Currencies that are freely tradable are called _____.
a. hard currencies
b. soft currencies
c. convertible currencies
d. both a and b
e. both a and c
(e; moderate; p. 219)

20.   Which of the following is *not* considered a hard currency?
a. Swiss franc
b. German deutschmark
c. Canadian dollar
d. U.S. dollar
e. Euro
(b; moderate; p. 219)

21.   Which currency is commonly used as an intermediary currency to facilitate transactions between two currencies with no direct exchange market?
        a. Swiss franc
        b. Gold
        c. Canadian dollar
        d. U.S. dollar
        e. Euro
        (d; easy; p. 219)

22.   Suppose a Swedish knitting mill needs New Zealand dollars to pay for 100,000 pounds of merino wool, but there is no active foreign-exchange market for the direct exchange of these two currencies. What intermediary currency would they most like use?
        a. Swiss franc
        b. U.S. dollar
        c. Canadian dollar
        d. Euro
        e. Gold
        (b; easy; p. 219)

23.   The _____ consists of foreign-exchange transactions that are to be consummated immediately.
        a. soft currency market
        b. spot market
        c. hard currency market
        d. bond market
        e. forward market
        (b; easy; p. 219)

24.   The _____ consists of foreign-exchange transactions that are to occur sometime in the future.
        a. soft currency market
        b. spot market
        c. hard currency market
        d. bond market
        e. forward market
        (e; easy; p. 219)

25.   In the world of spot markets, what is the meaning of immediately?
        a. As soon as possible.
        b. Two days after the trade date.
        c. Four business days after the trade date.
        d. On the trade date.
        e. Simultaneous due to electronic transfers.
        (b; moderate; p. 219)

26.   What percentage of foreign-exchange transactions are spot transactions?
       a. 10%
       b. 20%
       c. 40%
       d. 60%
       e. 75%
       (c; moderate; p. 219)

27.   Forward market prices are published for foreign exchange that will be delivered
       _____ in the future.
       a. 30 days
       b. 90 days
       c. 180 days
       d. all of the above
       e. none of the above
       (d; moderate; p. 219)

28.   _____ transactions are common in the forward market.
       a. Swap
       b. Spot
       c. Call option
       d. Currency option
       e. None of the above
       (a; easy; p. 220)

29.   A _____ is a transaction in which the same currency is bought and sold
       simultaneously but delivery is made at two different points in time.
       a. spot transaction
       b. swap transaction
       c. call option
       d. currency option
       e. put option
       (b; easy; p. 220)

30.   What is a currency selling at if the forward price is less than the spot price?
       a. forward premium
       b. forward discount
       c. par value
       d. both a and b
       e. both a and c
       (b; moderate; p. 221)

31. What is a currency selling at if the forward price is higher than the spot price?
    a. forward premium
    b. forward discount
    c. par value
    d. both a and b
    e. both a and c
    (a; moderate; p. 221)

32. The _____ represents the marketplace's aggregate prediction of the spot price of the currency rate in the future.
    a. forward price
    b. spot price
    c. exchange rate
    d. risk assessment
    e. par value
    (a; easy; p. 221)

33. The currencies of countries suffering from BOP trade deficits or high inflation rates often sell at a _____.
    a. spot discount
    b. spot premium
    c. forward discount
    d. forward premium
    e. none of the above
    (c; moderate; p. 222)

34. If a currency is selling at a forward premium it means that the foreign-exchange market believes _____.
    a. the currency will depreciate over time
    b. the country's economy is weak
    c. the currency will appreciate over time
    d. the country's economy is strong
    e. the country suffers from a trade deficit
    (c; easy; p. 222)

35. The currencies of countries enjoying BOP trade surpluses or low inflation rates often sell at a _____.
    a. spot discount
    b. spot premium
    c. forward discount
    d. forward premium
    e. none of the above
    (d; moderate; p. 222)

36.   If a currency is selling at a forward discount it means that the foreign-exchange market believes _____.
       a. the currency will depreciate over time
       b. the country's economy is weak
       c. the currency will appreciate over time
       d. the country's economy is strong
       e. the country suffers from a trade deficit
       (a; easy; p. 222)

37.   _____ is the riskless purchase of a product in one market for immediate resale in a second market in order to profit from a price discrepancy.
       a. Commercial exchange
       b. Foreign exchange
       c. Arbitrage
       d. Gray marketing
       e. Intramarket transfer
       (c; easy; p. 222)

38.   Drug stores in Canada commonly sell prescription drugs to consumers in the United States. This is an example of _____.
       a. intercountry trade
       b. arbitrage
       c. foreign exchange
       d. speculation
       e. none of the above
       (b; easy; p. 222)

39.   Book buyers who might normally purchase books from www.amazon.com are buying from www.amazon.co.uk because of lower prices on the same books. What is this an example of?
       a. intercountry trade
       b. arbitrage
       c. foreign exchange
       d. speculation
       e. none of the above
       (b; easy; p. 222)

40.   The theory of _____ states that the prices of tradable goods, when expressed in a common currency, will tend to equalize across countries as a result of exchange rate changes.
       a. one price
       b. purchasing power parity
       c. arbitrage
       d. competitive national advantage
       e. two-point arbitrage
       (b; moderate; p. 222)

41.   When can profession traders profit through arbitraging money?
       a.   anytime
       b.   when the market is in equilibrium
       c.   when the market is not in equilibrium
       d.   when currencies as a whole are undervalued
       e.   when currencies as a whole are overvalued
       (c; moderate; p. 224)

42.   Which of the following is *not* a common form of financial arbitrage?
       a.   two-point arbitrage
       b.   three-point arbitrage
       c.   covered interest
       d.   internet arbitrage
       e.   geographic arbitrage
       (d; difficult; p. 224)

43.   Which form of arbitrage involves profiting from price differences in two distinct
       markets?
       a.   two-point arbitrage
       b.   three-point arbitrage
       c.   covered interest
       d.   internet arbitrage
       e.   arbitrage of goods
       (a; moderate; p. 224)

44.   Suppose £1 is trading for $2.00 in New York City and $1.80 in London. A foreign
       exchange trader could take $1.80 and buy £1 in London's financial exchange
       market and then sell it for $2.00 in New York's financial exchange market. What
       is this an example of?
       a.   two-point arbitrage
       b.   three-point arbitrage
       c.   covered interest
       d.   internet arbitrage
       e.   arbitrage of goods
       (a; moderate; p. 224)

45.   _____ is profitable whenever the cost of buying a currency directly differs from
       the cross rate of exchange.
       a.   Two-point arbitrage
       b.   Three-point arbitrage
       c.   Covered interest
       d.   Internet arbitrage
       e.   Arbitrage of goods
       (b; moderate; p. 224)

46.　　The _____ is an exchange rate between two currencies calculated through the use of a third currency.
　　　a.　forward rate
　　　b.　call rate
　　　c.　forward option
　　　d.　cross rate
　　　e.　covered interest rate
　　　(d; easy; p. 224)

47.　　Which country's currency is the primary third currency used in calculating cross rates?
　　　a.　Euro
　　　b.　U.S. dollar
　　　c.　Japanese yen
　　　d.　Swiss franc
　　　e.　Canadian dollar
　　　(b; easy; p. 224)

48.　　What kind of arbitrage occurs when the difference between two countries' interest rates is not equal to the forward discount/premium on their currencies?
　　　a.　two-point arbitrage
　　　b.　three-point arbitrage
　　　c.　covered interest
　　　d.　internet arbitrage
　　　e.　geographic arbitrage
　　　(c; moderate; p. 224)

49.　　Which form of arbitrage is the most important in the foreign-exchange market?
　　　a.　two-point arbitrage
　　　b.　three point arbitrage
　　　c.　covered interest
　　　d.　internet arbitrage
　　　e.　arbitrage of goods
　　　(c; moderate; p. 224)

50.　　Upon what theory is burgernomics based?
　　　a.　one price
　　　b.　purchasing power parity
　　　c.　arbitrage
　　　d.　competitive national advantage
　　　e.　two-point arbitrage
　　　(b; moderate; p. 222)

51.   When a Big Mac costs $2.71 in the United States, $1.20 in China, and $4.52 in Switzerland, what does this mean for the Swiss franc?
        a. It is in equilibrium.
        b. It is overvalued.
        c. It is undervalued.
        d. There is an opportunity for arbitrage.
        e. None of the above.
        (b; moderate; p. 226)

52.   When a Big Mac costs $2.71 in the United States, $1.20 in China, and $4.52 in Switzerland, what does this mean for the Chinese yuan?
        a. It is in equilibrium.
        b. It is overvalued.
        c. It is undervalued.
        d. There is an opportunity for arbitrage.
        e. None of the above.
        (c; moderate; p. 226)

53.   According to the Big Mac Index, in what country can one buy the cheapest Big Mac?
        a. Austria
        b. South Korea
        c. China
        d. Japan
        e. United States
        (c; moderate; p. 227)

54.   Which of the following services is *not* offered by international banks for commercial customers?
        a. financing exports and imports
        b. accepting deposits
        c. providing working capital loans
        d. offering cash management services
        e. all of the above
        (e; easy; p. 229)

55.   Which of the following countries is *not* amongst those with a large money market bank headquarters?
        a. Japan
        b. United States
        c. Germany
        d. Spain
        e. United Kingdom
        (d; moderate; p. 229)

56. Which of the following is *not* a method of establishing an overseas banking operation?
     a. subsidiary bank
     b. branch bank
     c. affiliated bank
     d. correspondent bank
     e. all are methods
     (d; moderate; p. 230)

57. When an overseas banking operation is separately incorporated from the parent bank, what is it called?
     a. subsidiary bank
     b. branch bank
     c. affiliated bank
     d. correspondent bank
     e. divisional bank
     (a; moderate; p. 230)

58. When an overseas banking operation is not separately incorporated from the parent bank, what is it called?
     a. subsidiary bank
     b. branch bank
     c. affiliated bank
     d. correspondent bank
     e. divisional bank
     (b; moderate; p. 230)

59. When an overseas banking operation is jointly owned by the parent bank and with a local or foreign partner, what is it called?
     a. subsidiary bank
     b. branch bank
     c. affiliated bank
     d. correspondent bank
     e. divisional bank
     (c; moderate; p. 230)

60. In which country is the world's largest bank in terms of assets located?
     a. United States
     b. Japan
     c. Germany
     d. United Kingdom
     e. Switzerland
     (b; moderate; p. 230)

61. What is the meaning of Eurodollars?
    a. It is another name for the euro.
    b. U.S. dollars deposited in European bank accounts.
    c. Euros deposited in U.S. bank accounts.
    d. Any currency deposited in a country other than the country of issue.
    e. None of the above.
    (b; moderate; p. 231)

62. What currencies are included in the Eurocurrency market?
    a. Eurodollars
    b. euro yen
    c. euro pounds
    d. euro mark
    e. all of the above
    (e; easy; p. 231)

63. What term refers to a currency on deposit outside its country of issue?
    a. geographic arbitrage
    b. Eurocurrency
    c. Eurodollar
    d. euro yen
    e. euro pounds
    (b; easy; p. 231)

64. The _____ is the interest rate that London banks charge each other for short-term Eurocurrency loans.
    a. foreign interest rate
    b. euro-interest rate
    c. London Interbank Offer Rate
    d. London prime interest rate
    e. none of the above
    (c; easy; p. 231)

65. Why is the euro loan market the low-cost source of loans for large, creditworthy borrowers?
    a. Euro loans are free of government banking regulations.
    b. The average cost of making Euro loans is lower.
    c. Euro loans tend to be large transactions.
    d. The risk premium charged on Euro loans is lower.
    e. All of the above.
    (e; moderate; p. 231)

66.　On the basis of which interest rate are euro loans often quoted?
    a.　United States Prime Rate
    b.　European Central Bank Offer Rate
    c.　London Interbank Offer Rate
    d.　International Monetary Fund Interest Rate
    e.　All of the above
    (c; easy; p. 231)

67.　Which types of bonds are part of the international bond market?
    a.　Foreign bonds
    b.　Eurobonds
    c.　U.S. government bonds
    d.　Both a and b
    e.　Both a and c
    (d; moderate; p. 231)

68.　A(n) _____ is an entity of a U.S. bank that is legally distinct from the bank's domestic operations and that may offer international banking services.
    a.　subsidiary bank
    b.　branch bank
    c.　affiliated bank
    d.　correspondent bank
    e.　international banking facility
    (e; moderate; p. 231)

69.　A(n) _____ is a large, liquid financial asset that can be traded anywhere at any time.
    a.　cash
    b.　American Express travelers' checks
    c.　global bond
    d.　global equity
    e.　gold
    (c; easy; p. 232)

70.　_____ focus on offering banking and other financial services to non-resident customers.
    a.　Subsidiary banks
    b.　Branch banks
    c.　Affiliated banks
    d.　Offshore financial centers
    e.　International banking facilities
    (d; moderate; p. 230)

71.   Japanese yen are on deposit in an offshore financial center located in Bermuda. In this case, what are the Japanese yen considered?
        a. offshore deposits
        b. electronic transfers
        c. Eurocurrency
        d. Eurobonds
        e. euro loans
        (c; easy; p. 231)

72.   Which of the following countries is *not* an important offshore financial center?
        a. Luxembourg
        b. Switzerland
        c. Singapore
        d. South Korea
        e. Bermuda
        (d; moderate; p. 233)

73.   Which of the following benefits are common to offshore financial centers?
        a. political stability
        b. regulatory climate that facilitates international capital transactions
        c. excellent communications links to other major financial centers
        d. legal expertise
        e. all of the above
        (e; easy; p. 233)

74.   A _____ is a mutual fund that specializes in investing in a given country's firms.
        a. country fund
        b. global equity fund
        c. high-risk fund
        d. developing markets fund
        e. localization fund
        (a; easy; p. 232)

75.   Where are offshore financial centers typically located?
        a. on island states
        b. in major financial centers
        c. in developing markets
        d. in Europe
        e. all of the above
        (a; easy; p. 233)

True/False

76.   All European Union member countries have adopted the euro as their currency. (F; moderate; p. 211)

77.   The euro reduces exchange rate risks for firms doing business in the euro-zone. (T; easy; p. 211)

78.   Switzerland is a member of the European Union. (F; moderate; p. 211)

79.   The European Central Bank is headquartered in Brussels, Belgium. (F; easy; p. 212)

80.   The euro-zone members have relinquished control of their monetary policies to the European Central Bank. (T; easy; p. 212)

81.   The price of foreign exchange is set in the same way that the prices of other commodities are set. (T; moderate; p. 212)

82.   The direct exchange rate and the indirect exchange rate are reciprocals of one another. (T; moderate; p. 214)

83.   A person normally buys things using the indirect exchange rate. (F; moderate; p. 214)

84.   Exchange rates are quoted both directly and indirectly. (T; easy; p. 213)

85.   The foreign-exchange market is the world's biggest single market. (T; easy; p. 218)

86.   Swap transactions are the only mechanism for obtaining foreign exchange in the future. (F; moderate; p. 220)

87.   Currency futures represent only 1% of the foreign-exchange market. (T; difficult; p. 220)

88.   International bankers can customize currency options for their commercial clients. (T; easy; p. 220)

89.   The forward price of a foreign currency is typically the same as its spot price. (F; moderate; p. 221)

90.   Financial arbitrage represents a major portion of the daily trading in the foreign exchange market. (T; moderate; p. 224)

91.   Three-point arbitrage is much riskier than two-point arbitrage.
       (F; moderate; p. 224)

92.   The Japanese yen is the primary third currency used in calculating cross rates.
       (F; easy; p. 224)

93.   When the direct quote and the cross quote for each possible pair of currencies
       are equal, there is no opportunity for three-point arbitrage. (T; difficult; p. 225)

94.   Changes in any one foreign-exchange market can affect prices in all other
       foreign-exchange markets. (T; easy; p. 225)

95.   The Big Mac Index has been accurate in tracking exchange rates.
       (T; moderate; p. 226)

96.   The cheapest Big Mac in the world can be purchased in Russia.
       (F; difficult; p. 227)

97.   The Japanese yen makes up the largest portion of the international bond market.
       (F; easy; p. 232)

98.   MNCs can cross-list their common stocks on multiple stock exchanges.
       (T; moderate; p. 232)

99.   Off-shore financial centers are always located on an island. (F; easy; p. 233)

100.   Deutsche Bank was eliminated when the European Central Bank became the
       organization developing monetary policy for the EU. (F; easy; p. 230)

Short Answers

101.   What steps did countries have to take in order to become members of the euro-
       zone? Answer: To be eligible to join the euro-zone, each applicant country had
       to curb its deficit spending and reduce its inflation rate. They were forced to
       stabilize the values of their currencies on the foreign-exchange market.
       (moderate; p. 211)

102.   What do the members of the euro-zone expect the common currency will
       accomplish? Answer: They believe adopting a common currency will further
       integrate their national economies into one regional economy and promote the
       competitiveness of their firms in international markets. (moderate; p. 211)

103.   What organization sets the monetary policy for the euro-zone? Answer:
       European Central Bank. (easy; p. 212)

104.   Where are the foreign-exchange markets located? Answer: Auckland, Sydney, Tokyo, Hong Kong, Singapore, Bahrain, Frankfurt, Zurich, Paris, London, New York, Chicago, and San Francisco. (moderate; p. 216)

105.   What is FXall.com? Answer: It is a joint venture designed to provide an online platform for foreign exchange. It was created by seven of the largest players in foreign-exchange market including Bank of America, Goldman Sachs, Credit Suisse First Boston, Morgan Stanley Dean Witter, UBS Warburg, and HSBC. (difficult; p. 218)

106.   What five currencies are considered hard currencies? Answer: Japanese yen, euro, U.S. dollar, Swiss franc, and Canadian dollar. (moderate; p. 219)

107.   What mechanisms can firms use to obtain foreign exchange in the future? Answer: Swap transactions, currency futures, and currency options. (moderate; p. 220)

108.   Explain the difference between a call option and a put option. Answer: A call option grants the right to buy the foreign currency in question. A put option grants the right to sell the foreign currency. (moderate; p. 220)

109.   What is the purpose of forward market, currency options, and currency futures in international trade and investment? Answer: They allow firms to hedge, or reduce, the foreign-exchange risks inherent in international transactions. (difficult; p. 220)

110.   What is the meaning of the law of one price? Answer: This law states that arbitrage will continue until the price of the good in question is identical in both markets (excluding transaction costs). (moderate; p. 222)

111.   What is the underlying logic of arbitrage? Answer: If the price of a good differs between two markets, people will tend to buy the good in the market offering the lower price and resell it in the market offering the higher price. (difficult; p. 222)

112.   Why does financial arbitrage occur? Answer: Individuals and organizations seek to profit from small differences in the price of foreign exchange in different markets. (moderate; p. 224)

113.   What is the meaning of three-point arbitrage? Answer: Three-point arbitrage is the buying and selling of three different currencies to make a riskless profit. (easy; p. 224)

114.   What limitations exist in using the Big Mac Index to understand the valuations of currencies? Answer: Big Macs are not traded across borders as the purchasing power parity theory demands. Prices are distorted by taxes, tariffs,

different profit margins, and differences in the cost of non-tradables, such as rent. (difficult; p. 226)

115.   What does the international Fisher effect predict? Answer: National differences in expected inflation rates yield differences in nominal interest rates among countries. (moderate; p. 228)

116.   What are the three ways that an overseas banking operation can be established? Answer: Subsidiary bank, branch bank, and affiliated bank. (easy; p. 230)

117.   What are Eurocurrencies? Answer: A Eurocurrency is defined as a currency on deposit outside its country of issue. (easy; p. 231)

118.   Why are the interest rates often low on international bonds? Answer: Large transaction sizes, creditworthy borrowers, and freedom from costly regulations imposed on domestic markets all help to lower interest rates charged on international bonds. (moderate; p. 232)

119.   Where are the primary offshore financial centers located? Answer: Bahamas, Bahrain, Cayman Islands, Bermuda, Netherlands Antilles, Singapore, Luxembourg, and Switzerland. (moderate; p. 233)

120.   What are the benefits available to MNCs using offshore financial centers? Answer: Political stability, positive regulatory climate for international capital transactions, excellent communication links to other major financial centers, and availability of legal, accounting, and financial expertise. (moderate; p. 233)

Essay

121.   Explain the theory of purchasing power parity. How does it affect arbitrage?

Answer: This theory states that the prices of tradable goods, when expressed in a common currency will tend to equalize across countries as a result of exchange rate changes. Purchasing power parity occurs because the process of buying goods in the cheap market and reselling them in the expensive market affects the demand for and the price of the foreign currency, as well as the market price of the good itself in the two product markets in question. When purchasing power parity occurs, there is no reason to cross borders to purchase the products. (moderate; p. 222)

122.   The per capita income in the United States in 2001 was $35,815 while the per capita income in Japan, converted into U.S. dollars, is $35,990. Does this mean that the average Japanese citizen enjoys a higher standard of living than the average American? Why or why not?

Answer: This question relates to the theory of purchasing power parity. At first glance, it does appear that the average Japanese citizen has a slightly higher income than the average American citizen. However, this does not take into account the differences in price levels between the two countries. After adjusting for purchasing power, Japan's per capita income falls to $27,430. (difficult; p. 223)

123.   Why have international banks increasingly provided their own overseas operations rather than utilizing correspondent banks?

Answer: Providing its own overseas operations enables a larger bank to compete better internationally. A bank that has its own foreign operations can access new sources of deposits and profitable lending opportunities. The bank can also better meet the needs of domestic clients with international banking needs. (moderate; p. 229)

124.   Hallmark plans to order $10 million worth of Hello Kitty merchandise from its Japanese manufacturer with a payment due in 90 days. Which international commercial banking services will Hallmark require? Answer: Hallmark will need short-term financing of the purchase, international electronic funds transfer, forward purchases of Japanese yen, and advice about proper documentation for importing and paying for the goods. (difficult; p. 230)

125.   How did the Eurocurrency Market develop?

Answer: The Eurocurrency market originated in the early 1950s when the communist-controlled governments of Central and Eastern Europe needed dollars to finance their international trade, but feared the U.S. government would confiscate or block their holdings of dollars in U.S. banks for political reasons. The communist governments solved this problem by using European banks that were willing to maintain dollar accounts for them. (difficult; p. 231)

126.   The international monetary system provides three important functions in international business. What are these?

Answer: The international monetary system establishes the rules by which countries value and exchange their currencies. It also provides a mechanism for correcting imbalances between a country's international payments and its receipts. The international monetary system's accounting system records international transactions and supplies information about the health of national economies. (moderate; p. 179)

Multiple Choice

1.   What is the primary hardship suffered by the U.S. steel industry?
        a. imports of foreign steel
        b. demanding investors
        c. lack of skilled employees
        d. protectionist legislation
        e. all of the above
        (a; moderate; p. 239)

2.   The U.S. steel industry is concentrated in all of the following states except _____.
        a. Ohio
        b. New Jersey
        c. Pennsylvania
        d. West Virginia
        e. All of the above
        (b; easy; p. 239)

3.   In which of the following consequences have the steel tariffs resulted?
        a. higher domestic prices
        b. consolidation of steel industry
        c. increased costs for steel-using firms
        d. increased unemployment
        e. all of the above
        (e; moderate; p. 240)

4.   _____ implies that the national government exerts minimal influence on the
        exporting and importing decisions of private firms and individuals.
        a. Fair trade
        b. Free trade
        c. Managed trade
        d. Equitable trade
        e. Minimalist trade
        (b; easy; p. 241)

5.   _____ suggests that the national government should actively intervene to ensure
        that domestic firms' exports receive an equitable share of foreign markets and that
        imports are controlled to minimize losses of domestic jobs ad market share in
        specific industries.
        a. Fair trade
        b. Free trade
        c. Managed trade
        d. Equitable trade
        e. Both a and c
        (e; easy; p. 241)

6.   The _____ holds that a country must be self-sufficient in critical raw materials, machinery, and technology or else be vulnerable to foreign threats.
        a. national defense argument
        b. infant industry argument
        c. industrial policy
        d. maintenance of existing jobs
        e. strategic trade theory
        (a; moderate; p. 241)

7.   Which industry receives favorable treatment for national defense reasons?
        a. steel
        b. electronics
        c. machine tools
        d. merchant marine
        e. all of the above
        (e; easy; p. 242)

8.   Which of the following industries is not protected for national defense reasons?
        a. steel
        b. farming
        c. electronics
        d. machine tools
        e. all of the above are protected for national defense reasons
        (b; moderate; p. 242)

9.   The_____ proposes that tariffs be imposed on imported manufactured goods to give U.S. firms temporary protection from foreign competition until they could fully establish themselves.
        a. national defense argument
        b. infant industry argument
        c. industrial policy
        d. maintenance of existing jobs
        e. strategic trade theory
        (b; moderate; p. 241)

10.   Who first articulated the infant industry argument?
        a. Adam Smith
        b. Alexander Hamilton
        c. Benjamin Franklin
        d. Richard Nixon
        e. None of the above
        (b; moderate; p. 242)

11.   For which industry did Alexander Hamilton propose the infant industry argument?
      a.   steel
      b.   manufacturing
      c.   electronics
      d.   merchant marine
      e.   farming
      (b; easy; p. 242)

12.   The _____ argument advocates the use of tariffs to protect high-wage jobs from imports of low-wage countries.
      a.   national defense argument
      b.   infant industry argument
      c.   industrial policy
      d.   maintenance of existing jobs
      e.   strategic trade theory
      (d; moderate; p. 241)

13.   Which U.S. industry has been protected under the maintenance of existing jobs argument?
      a.   steel
      b.   shipbuilding
      c.   electronics
      d.   both a and b
      e.   both b and c
      (d; easy; p. 242)

14.   _____ suggests that a national government can make its country better off if it adopts trade policies that improve the competitiveness of its domestic firms in oligopolistic industries.
      a.   National defense argument
      b.   Infant industry argument
      c.   Industrial policy
      d.   Maintenance of existing jobs
      e.   Strategic trade theory
      (e; moderate; p. 241)

15.   _____ actually refers to several models of international trade that provide theoretical justification for government trade intervention.
      a.   National defense argument
      b.   Infant industry argument
      c.   Industrial policy
      d.   Maintenance of existing jobs
      e.   Strategic trade theory
      (e; moderate; p. 241)

16.   Which theory best applies to those industries capable of supporting only a few
      firms worldwide?
      a.   national defense argument
      b.   infant industry argument
      c.   industrial policy
      d.   maintenance of existing jobs
      e.   strategic trade theory
      (e; moderate; p. 241)

17.   Strategic trade theory applies best to which industry identified below?
      a.   air transportation
      b.   commercial aircraft construction
      c.   farming
      d.   services
      e.   automobile manufacturing
      (b; moderate; p. 243)

18.   Which theory listed below specifically addresses the needs of individual
      industries?
      a.   strategic trade theory
      b.   economic development programs
      c.   industrial policy
      d.   public choice analysis
      e.   all address the needs of individual industries
      (a; moderate; p. 244)

19.   Which of the following theories does *not* address the needs of individual
      industries?
      a.   national defense argument
      b.   infant industry argument
      c.   industrial policy
      d.   maintenance of existing jobs
      e.   strategic trade theory
      (c; moderate; p. 241)

20.   Which theory listed below takes an economy-wide perspective on trade policy?
      a.   national defense argument
      b.   infant industry argument
      c.   industrial policy
      d.   maintenance of existing jobs
      e.   strategic trade theory
      (c; moderate; p. 241)

21.   Which of the following theories does *not* take on an economy-wide perspective?
       a. strategic trade theory
       b. economic development programs
       c. industrial policy
       d. public choice analysis
       e. all address trade policy from an economy-wide perspective
       (a; moderate; p. 244)

22.   Which strategy listed below is a type of economic development program?
       a. strategic trade
       b. export promotion strategy
       c. import substitution strategy
       d. import promotion strategy
       e. both b and c
       (e; moderate; p. 245)

23.   The _____ suggests that a country should encourage firms to compete in foreign
       markets by harnessing some advantage the country possesses.
       a. strategic trade
       b. export promotion strategy
       c. import substitution strategy
       d. import promotion strategy
       e. both b and c
       (b; moderate; p. 245)

24.   The _____ encourages the growth of domestic manufacturing industries by
       erecting high barriers to imported goods.
       a. strategic trade
       b. export promotion strategy
       c. import substitution strategy
       d. import promotion strategy
       e. both b and c
       (c; moderate; p. 245)

25.   Which country listed below did *not* adopt an export promotion strategy after
       World War II?
       a. Japan
       b. Brazil
       c. South Korea
       d. Taiwan
       e. China
       (b; difficult; p. 245)

26.   Which country listed below did *not* adopt an import substitution strategy after World War I?
        a. Australia
        b. Argentina
        c. Japan
        d. India
        e. Brazil
        (c; difficult; p. 245)

27.   When a country follows _____, the national government identifies key domestic industries critical to the country's future economic growth and then formulates programs that promote their competitiveness.
        a. strategic trade theory
        b. industrial policy
        c. export promotion strategy
        d. national competitive advantage
        e. import substitution
        (b; easy; p. 246)

28.   Which country listed below followed industrial policy to achieve economic success?
        a. Japan
        b. United States
        c. Canada
        d. Germany
        e. United Kingdom
        (a; moderate; p. 246)

29.   What Japanese organization is entrusted with setting industrial policy?
        a. Ministry of International Trade and Industry
        b. Industrial Policy Ministry
        c. Office of Strategic Trade
        d. Ministry of Industry Development
        e. None of the above
        (a; easy; p. 245)

30.   Which of the following technologies did Clinton seek to promote using industrial policy?
        a. genetics
        b. health care information systems
        c. electronics
        d. computer software
        e. all of the above
        (e; easy; p. 247)

31.   _____ suggest(s) that special interest groups will often dominate the general
        interest on any given issue because these groups are willing to work for the
        passage of laws.
        a. Strategic trade theory
        b. Economic development programs
        c. Industrial policy
        d. Public choice analysis
        e. All address trade policy from an economy-wide perspective
        (d; moderate; p. 244)

32.   According to _____, domestic trade policies that affect international business
        stem from the interaction of politicians trying to get elected.
        a. strategic trade theory
        b. economic development programs
        c. industrial policy
        d. public choice analysis
        e. all address trade policy from an economy-wide perspective
        (d; moderate; p. 244)

33.   Who said, "All politics is local."?
        a. Adam Smith
        b. Alexander Hamilton
        c. Tip O'Neill
        d. George Bush
        e. None of the above
        (c; easy; p. 248)

34.   A(n) _____ is a tax placed on a good that is traded internationally.
        a. tariff
        b. quota
        c. export substitute
        d. import substitute
        e. all of the above
        (a; easy; p. 249)

35.   What type of tariff is applied when the tax is applied as the goods leave the
        country?
        a. transit tariff
        b. ad valorem tariff
        c. specific tariff
        d. export tariff
        e. compound tariff
        (d; moderate; p. 249)

36.   What type of tariff is applied as the goods pass through one country bound for another?
a. transit tariff
b. ad valorem tariff
c. specific tariff
d. export tariff
e. compound tariff
(a; moderate; p. 249)

37.   What type of tariff is assessed as a percentage of the market value of the imported good?
a. transit tariff
b. ad valorem tariff
c. specific tariff
d. export tariff
e. compound tariff
(b; moderate; p. 249)

38.   What type of tariff is assessed as a specific dollar amount per unit of weight or other standard measure?
a. transit tariff
b. ad valorem tariff
c. specific tariff
d. export tariff
e. compound tariff
(c; moderate; p. 249)

39.   What type of tariff includes both ad valorem components and specific components?
a. transit tariff
b. ad valorem tariff
c. specific tariff
d. export tariff
e. compound tariff
(e; moderate; p. 249)

40.   Which of the following tariffs is *not* a form of import tariff?
a. transit tariff
b. ad valorem tariff
c. specific tariff
d. compound tariff
e. all of the above are import tariffs
(a; moderate; p. 249)

41.   Any government regulation, policy, or procedure other than a tariff that has the
       effect of impeding international trade may be labeled a(n) _____.
       a. specific tariff
       b. nontariff barrier
       c. ad valorem tariff
       d. compound tariff
       e. transit tariff
       (b; easy; p. 252)

42.   Which of the following is *not* a type of nontariff barrier?
       a. quotas
       b. numerical export controls
       c. voluntary export restraint
       d. regulatory controls
       e. all of the above are nontariff barriers
       (e; moderate; p. 252)

43.   A _____ is a numerical limit on the quantity of a good that may be imported into
       a country during some time period.
       a. quotas
       b. numerical export controls
       c. voluntary export restraint
       d. regulatory controls
       e. all of the above are nontariff barriers
       (a; moderate; p. 252)

44.   As a result of trade agreements, many countries have replaced quotas with _____.
       a. tariff rate quotas
       b. numerical export controls
       c. voluntary export restraints
       d. regulatory controls
       e. ad valorem tariffs
       (a; moderate; p. 252)

45.   A(n) _____ imposes a low tariff rate on a limited amount of imports of a specified
       good, but imposes a prohibitively high tariff on the good above that limited
       amount.
       a. tariff rate quota
       b. numerical export control
       c. voluntary export restraint
       d. regulatory control
       e. ad valorem tariff
       (a; moderate; p. 252)

46.   Who does *not* benefit from tariff rate quotas on sugar imports into the United
        States?
        a.   soft drink producers
        b.   domestic sugar producers
        c.   sugar substitute producers
        d.   corn farmers
        e.   sugar beet growers
        (a; difficult; p. 253)

47.   Who benefits from tariff rate quotas on sugar imports into the United States?
        a.   domestic candy producers
        b.   sugar substitute producers
        c.   soft drink producers
        d.   U.S. consumers
        e.   sugar-using U.S. companies
        (b; difficult; p. 253)

48.   A(n) _____ is a promise by a country to limit its export of a good to another
        country to a prespecified amount or percentage of the affected market.
        a.   tariff rate quota
        b.   export promise
        c.   voluntary export restraint
        d.   embargo
        e.   ad valorem tariff
        (c; moderate; p. 254)

49.   A(n) _____ is an absolute ban on the exporting and importing of goods to a
        particular destination.
        a.   voluntary export restraint
        b.   embargo
        c.   ad valorem tariff
        d.   tariff rate quota
        e.   export promise
        (b; easy; p. 254)

50.   What form of non-tariff barrier is adopted by a country to discipline another
        country?
        a.   quotas
        b.   numerical export controls
        c.   voluntary export restraint
        d.   regulatory controls
        e.   embargos
        (e; moderate; p. 252)

51.   Which of the following is a form of nonquantitative, nontariff barrier?
        a. product and testing standards
        b. restricted access to distribution networks
        c. public-sector procurement policies
        d. local-purchase requirements
        e. all of the above
        (e; easy; p. 255)

52.   Which of the following is *not* a form of nonquantitative, nontariff barrier?
        a. product and testing standards
        b. restricted access to distribution networks
        c. numerical export controls
        d. public-sector procurement policies
        e. local-purchase requirements
        (c; easy; p. 255)

53.   The federal government generally requires that international air travel purchased
        with U.S. government funds must occur on U.S. airlines. Of which nontariff
        barrier is this an example?
        a. product and testing standards
        b. restricted access to distribution networks
        c. numerical export controls
        d. public-sector procurement policies
        e. local-purchase requirements
        (d; moderate; p. 255)

54.   In Thailand, foreign banks can operate only three branches and only one of these
        can be in the city of Bangkok. Of which nontariff barrier is this an example?
        a. product and testing standards
        b. restricted access to distribution networks
        c. numerical export controls
        d. public-sector procurement policies
        e. local-purchase requirements
        (b; moderate; p. 255)

55.   Egypt requires that imported meat contain no more than 7% fat. Of which
        nontariff barrier is this an example?
        a. product and testing standards
        b. restricted access to distribution networks
        c. numerical export controls
        d. public-sector procurement policies
        e. local-purchase requirements
        (a; moderate; p. 255)

56.   In which type of country is public sector procurement policies particularly
       important?
       a.   those with extensive state ownership of industry
       b.   lesser-developed countries
       c.   high-income countries
       d.   middle-income countries
       e.   such policies are important to all countries
       (a; difficult; p. 256)

57.   Which of the following countries has employed public-sector procurement
       policies?
       a.   United States
       b.   Brazil
       c.   Belarus
       d.   Poland
       e.   All of the above
       (e; moderate; p. 256)

58.   China requires that power plants of less than 600 megawatt capacity use only
       domestically made equipment. Of which nontariff barrier is this an example?
       a.   product and testing standards
       b.   restricted access to distribution networks
       c.   numerical export controls
       d.   public-sector procurement policies
       e.   local-purchase requirements
       (e; moderate; p. 255)

59.   During prime time, at least 40% of the songs played on France's 1700 AM and
       FM stations must be written or sung by French or Francophone artists. Of which
       nontariff barrier is this an example?
       a.   product and testing standards
       b.   restricted access to distribution networks
       c.   numerical export controls
       d.   public-sector procurement policies
       e.   local-purchase requirements
       (e; moderate; p. 255)

60.   Which of the following is *not* an example of regulatory controls as a form of
       nontariff barrier?
       a.   conducting health inspections
       b.   conducting safety inspections
       c.   enforcing environmental regulations
       d.   requiring firms to receive licenses
       e.   all of the above are examples of regulatory controls
       (e; easy; p. 256)

61.   _____ make it more difficult for importers of nonessential goods to acquire foreign exchange.
a. Currency controls
b. Restricted access to distribution networks
c. Numerical export controls
d. Public-sector procurement policies
e. Quotas
(a; moderate; p. 255)

62.   _____ are common in key industries like broadcasting, utilities, air transportation, defense contracting, and financial services.
a. Currency controls
b. Restricted access to distribution networks
c. Investment controls
d. Public-sector procurement policies
e. Quotas
(c; moderate; p. 255)

63.   Which of the following industries is *not* subject to investment controls?
a. broadcasting
b. farming
c. utilities
d. financial services
e. all of the above may be subject to investment controls
(b; moderate; p. 257)

64.   _____ make it difficult for foreign firms to develop an effective presence in key industries.
a. Currency controls
b. Restricted access to distribution networks
c. Investment controls
d. Public-sector procurement policies
e. Quotas
(c; moderate; p. 255)

65.   Poland limits foreign ownership in broadcasting to 33%. Of which nontariff barrier is this an example?
a. currency controls
b. restricted access to distribution networks
c. numerical export controls
d. quotas
e. investment controls
(e; moderate; p. 255)

66.   What might countries utilize when they seek to stimulate exports?
        a. subsidies
        b. currency controls
        c. investment controls
        d. quotas
        e. all of the above
        (a; moderate; p. 258)

67.   Which of the following could be used as a subsidy to entice firms to locate or
        expand facilities in a particular community?
        a. property tax abatements
        b. free land
        c. training of workforces
        d. reduced utility rates
        e. all of the above
        (e; easy; p. 258)

68.   A(n) _____ is a geographic area where imported or exported goods receive
        preferential tariff treatment.
        a. free trade zone
        b. foreign trade zone
        c. fair trade zone
        d. special administrative region
        e. economic incentive zone
        (b; moderate; p. 259)

69.   A _____ refers to any factory located in an FTZ in Mexico.
        a. macquiladora
        b. greenfield operation
        c. keiretsu
        d. chaebol
        e. manana
        (a; easy; p. 259)

70.   What organization first investigates complaints from firms affected by alleged
        unfair trade practices in the United States?
        a. International Trade Administration
        b. International Trade Commission
        c. Department of Commerce
        d. International Trade Tribunal
        e. World Trade Organization
        (a; moderate; p. 260)

71.   A(n) _____ is calculated to offset the advantage an exporter receives from a subsidy.
       a. compound tariff
       b. export promotion
       c. ad valorem tariff
       d. countervailing duty
       e. substitution tariff
       (d; moderate; p. 260)

72.   _____ require(s) the U.S. trade representative to publicly list those countries engaging in the most flagrant unfair trade practices.
       a. Antidumping regulations
       b. Super 301
       c. International Trade Commission
       d. International Trade Administration
       e. Countervailing duties
       (b; moderate; p. 261)

73.   _____ can occur when a firm sells its goods in a foreign market at a price below what it charges in its home market.
       a. Predatory pricing
       b. International price discrimination
       c. Super 301
       d. Subsidies
       e. None of the above
       (b; easy; p. 261)

74.   What is the primary objective of promoters of laws that seek to abolish unfair trade practices?
       a. Promote global efficiency.
       b. Ensure that trade occurs on the basis of comparative advantage.
       c. Protect consumers from predatory behavior.
       d. Encourage production in countries that can produce a good the most efficiently.
       e. All of the above.
       (e; moderate; p. 262)

75.   _____ clauses exist to protect countries from sudden surges in imported goods.
       a. Fair trade
       b. Safeguard
       c. Subsidies
       d. Predatory pricing
       e. Super 301
       (b; easy; p. 262)

True/False

76.   Japan is rich in natural resources. (F; easy; p. 242)

77.   The infant industry argument has been adopted in countries worldwide.
        (T; moderate; p. 242)

78.   The strategic trade theory is more applicable than the infant industry argument.
        (F; moderate; p. 244)

79.   A country's adoption of strategic trade policies to cover a broad group of
        industries may actually reduce the country's overall international
        competitiveness because favoring certain industries inevitably hurts others.
        (T; difficult; p. 244)

80.   The export promotion strategy is generally more successful than the import
        substitution strategy. (T; moderate; p. 245)

81.   MNCs responded to export promotion strategies by locating production
        facilities within these countries to avoid the costs resulting from high barriers.
        (F; difficult; p. 245)

82.   The South Korean government patterned its economic development strategies
        after the Japanese model. (T; easy; p. 245)

83.   All the countries in the Quad follow the guidelines advocated by industrial
        policy. (F; difficult; p. 246)

84.   The United States is an ardent supporter of industrial policy.
        (F; moderate; p. 247)

85.   The Clinton administration sought to introduce industrial policy for five
        emerging technologies. (T; moderate; p. 247)

86.   Public choice analysis suggests that the general public will retain more
        influence on government policy than special interest groups. (F; easy; p. 247)

87.   Most tariffs imposed by developed countries are ad valorem
        (T; moderate; p. 249)

88.   A transit tariff is a form of import tariff. (F; easy; p. 249)

89.   A tariff applies to the product's value which is normally determined by the sales price. (T; easy; p. 249)

90.   Tariff rate quotas impose an extremely high tariff on a limited amount of imports of a specified good but a very low tariff on all goods over that limit. (F; difficult; p. 252)

91.   Export controls may be used to punish a country's political enemies. (T; moderate; p. 254)

92.   All nontariff barriers are adopted for protectionist reasons. (F; difficult; p. 255)

93.   Australia's wheat industry is harmed because that country lacks large-scale subsidies. (T; difficult; p. 258)

94.   A macquiladora system refers to foreign trade zones located in Honduras. (F; easy; p. 259)

95.   NAFTA provided many of the benefits of Mexico's foreign trade zones to factories throughout Mexico. (T; moderate; p. 259)

96.   Retail prices are irrelevant in determining whether dumping has occurred. (T; moderate; p. 261)

97.   When Japanese products are priced higher in retail stores in the United States than in Japan, this is evidence of dumping. (F; difficult; p. 261)

98.   Super 301 is not utilized by the United States any longer. (F; moderate; p. 262)

99.   Foreign firms alleged to have dumped goods in the United States must provide comprehensive documentation of their pricing and cost-accounting procedures in English and using the Generally Accepted Accounting Principles (GAAP). (T; moderate; p. 262)

100.   Safeguard clauses can permit the permanent imposition of tariffs and quotas. (F; difficult; p. 262)

Short Answers

101.   What is the primary difference between fair trade and free trade? Answer: The free trade approach suggests a minimal governmental role while the fair trade approach encourages intervention by the government. (moderate; p. 241)

102.   For which approach to trade did Adam Smith advocate? Answer: Adam Smith supported the free trade philosophy. He believed that voluntary exchange makes

both parties of the transaction better off and allocates resources to their highest valued use. (moderate; p. 241)

103.   What steps did countries have to take in order to become members of the euro-zone? Answer: To be eligible to join the euro-zone, each applicant country had to curb its deficit spending and reduce its inflation rate. They were forced to stabilize the values of their currencies on the foreign-exchange market. (moderate; p. 211)

104.   What is a primary disadvantage of industrial policy? Answer: Some experts argue that government bureaucrats cannot perfectly identify the right industries to favor under such a policy. (moderate; p. 246)

105.   Which question is at the heart of the industrial policy debate? Answer: What is the proper role of government in a market economy? (moderate; p. 247)

106.   What are the two forms of trade barriers erected through governmental intervention? Answer: Tariffs and non-tariff barriers. (easy; p. 248)

107.   What is the detailed classification scheme for imported goods called? Answer: Harmonized tariff schedule. (easy; p. 249)

108.   For what two reasons have tariffs historically been imposed? Answer: Tariffs raise revenue for the national government and act as trade barriers. (moderate; p. 250)

109.   Why do tariffs act to increase demand for domestically produced substitute goods? Answer: Because tariffs raise the prices based on domestic customers for foreign goods. (moderate; p. 251)

110.   Name five examples of nontariff barriers. Answer: Product and testing standards, restricted access to distribution networks, public-sector procurement policies, local-purchase requirements, and regulatory, currency, and investment controls. (moderate; p. 255)

111.   Why are nonquantitative, nontariff barriers more difficult to eliminate than tariffs and quotas? Answer: Because they are often embedded in bureaucratic procedures and are not quickly changeable. (difficult; p. 255)

112.   What types of regulatory controls can governments use to create nontariff barriers? Answer: Governments can conduct health and safety inspections, enforce environmental regulations, require firms to obtain licenses, and charge taxes and fees for public services. (moderate; p. 256)

113.   What effect do subsidies have on international trade? Answer: Subsidies
        artificially improve a firm's competitiveness in export markets or help domestic
        firms fight off foreign imports by reducing the cost of doing business.
        (difficult; p. 258)

114.   What is a foreign trade zone? Answer: A foreign trade zone is a geographic area
        where imported or exported goods receive preferential tariff treatment.
        (easy; p. 258)

115.   What types of unfair trade practices do organizations like the International
        Trade Commission focus on? Answer: Government subsidies that distort trade
        and unfair pricing practices. (difficult; p. 260)

116.   What is the Eximbank? Answer: The Eximbank stands for the Export-Import
        Bank of the United States. It provides financing for U.S. exports through direct
        loans and loan guarantees. (difficult; p. 260)

117.   What is a countervailing duty (CVD)? Answer: A CVD is a type of ad valorem
        tariff on an imported good that is imposed by the importing country to counter
        the impact of foreign subsidies. (moderate; p. 260)

118.   How are alleged unfair trade practice complaints handled in the United States?
        Answer: The complaints are first investigated by the International Trade
        Administration which determines whether an unfair trade practice has occurred.
        If the case is confirmed, the Department of Commerce transfers the case to the
        U.S. International Trade Commission, an independent government agency. If a
        majority of the six ITC commissioners decide that U.S. producers have suffered
        material injury, then the ITC will impose duties on the offending imports to
        counteract the unfair trade practice. (difficult; p. 260)

119.   What type of insurance does the Overseas Private Investment Corporation
        provide? Answer: Political risk insurance. (easy; p. 260)

120.   What are the two forms of dumping? Answer: International price discrimination
        and predatory pricing. (moderate; p. 261)

Essay

121.   Explain the consequences for the U.S. steel industry and steel-using U.S. firms
        if high tariffs are imposed on imports of foreign steel.

        Answer: The U.S. steel industry wanted tariffs to reduce the amount of foreign
        steel sold in the U.S. which ultimately would help protect its market. For steel-
        using U.S. firms, raising tariffs on imported steel would increase production
        costs and reduce their ability to compete against foreign firms with access to
        low-priced steel sold in the world market. (moderate; p. 239)

122.   What two principle issues have shaped the debate on appropriate trade policies? Which issue relates directly the U.S. steel industry requests for aid?

Answer: The first principle issue is whether a national government should intervene to protect the country's domestic firms by taxing foreign goods entering the domestic market or constructing other barriers against imports. The second issue is whether a national government should directly help the country's domestic firms increase their foreign sales through export subsidies, government-to-government negotiations, and guaranteed loan programs. The U.S. steel industry requested tariffs to protect domestic firms. (easy; p. 240)

123.   Explain how Japan used the Infant Industry Argument to rebuild its economic strength following World War II.

Answer: Japan eliminated tariffs on imports of raw ores and ore concentrates while imposing high tariffs on processed and fabricated metals. Consequently, Japan has developed thriving metal fabrication industries. (difficult; p. 242)

124.   List the three forms of import tariffs and explain the basis for each.

Answer: The three forms of import tariffs are ad valorem, specific, and compound. The ad valorem tariff is assessed as a percentage of the market value of the imported good. A specific tariff is assessed as a specific dollar amount per unit of weight or other standard measure. A compound tariff has both an ad valorem component and a specific component. (moderate; p. 249)

125.   Foreign firms often claim that product and testing standards discriminate against their products. Give three examples of barriers that could be discriminatory against foreign products.

Answer: Taiwan requires more extensive and costly purity testing for imported fruit juices than for domestically produced juices. Russia requires that imported telecommunications equipment be tested by two separate government agencies. Malaysia mandates that all imported meat and poultry products must undergo on-site inspection by its officials to certify that they have been prepared in accordance with Islamic practices. Egypt requires that imported meat contain no more than 7% fat but has not such requirement for domestically produced meat. (difficult; p. 255)

Multiple Choice

1.   What is the best means of promoting economic development in Mexico?
      a. trade
      b. aid
      c. mercantilism
      d. protectionism
      e. export substitutions
      (a; moderate; p. 269)

2.   What policy did Mexico rely on between the years of 1917 to 1982?
      a. high tariffs to discourage imports
      b. restrictions on foreign direct investment
      c. government ownership of key industries
      d. all of the above
      e. none of the above
      (d; moderate; p. 269)

3.   What step has Mexico taken since 1982 to encourage economic development?
      a. lowering tariffs
      b. encouraging FDI
      c. privatizing state-owned enterprises
      d. joining the WTO
      e. all of the above
      (e; moderate; p. 269)

4.   Mexico has trade agreements with all of the following countries *except* ____.
      a. United States
      b. Canada
      c. Chile
      d. European Union
      e. Australia
      (e; moderate; p. 269)

5.   Which country represents the biggest threat to Mexico's trade-driven economy?
      a. Taiwan
      b. South Korea
      c. Vietnam
      d. China
      e. Brazil
      (d; easy; p. 270)

6.   GATT is an acronym for _____.
        a. General Argument for Trade and Tariffs
        b. General Agreement on Tariffs and Trade
        c. Group Accord on Trade Tendencies
        d. Grace, Action, Trust, and Trade
        e. None of the above
        (b; easy; p. 271)

7.   What organization replaced the GATT?
        a. World Bank
        b. World Trade Organization
        c. International Trade Commission
        d. NAFTA
        e. None of the above
        (b; easy; p. 271)

8.   In what year did the WTO begin?
        a. 1990
        b. 1992
        c. 1995
        d. 1998
        e. 2000
        (c; easy; p. 271)

9.   In what city was the first GATT round conducted?
        a. Geneva
        b. Tokyo
        c. Washington
        d. Paris
        e. London
        (a; moderate; p. 272)

10.   The GATT rounds focused on decreasing _____.
        a. hostility
        b. tariffs
        c. preferential treatment
        d. subsidies
        e. all of the above
        (b; easy; p. 272)

11.   The _____ requires that any preferential treatment granted to one country must be extended to all countries.
        a. GATT
        b. WTO
        c. export promotion system
        d. most favored nation principle
        e. multifibre agreement
        (d; moderate; p. 272)

12.   What countries are granted the most favored nation status under the GATT?
        a. less developed nations
        b. any GATT member country
        c. all countries
        d. members of the WTO only
        e. members of the International Monetary Fund only
        (b; difficult; p. 274)

13.   Which of the following countries is *not* granted most favored nation status by the United States?
        a. China
        b. The Czech Republic
        c. North Korea
        d. Poland
        e. Russia
        (c; moderate; p. 274)

14.   Which of the following countries receives most favored nation status from the United States?
        a. Cuba
        b. Laos
        c. Libya
        d. Mexico
        e. Cuba
        (d; moderate; p. 274)

15.   Where is the WTO headquartered?
        a. Frankfurt
        b. Brussels
        c. Geneva
        d. London
        e. New York
        (c; easy; p. 274)

16.   The WTO seeks promote _____.
        a. trade in goods
        b. trade in services
        c. international intellectual property protection
        d. trade-related investment
        e. all of the above
        (e; moderate; p. 275)

17.   _____ refers to a nondiscriminatory approach whereby a country treats foreign
        firms the same way it treats domestic firms.
        a. Multifibre agreement
        b. Cairns Group
        c. National treatment
        d. Most favored status
        e. Domestic sales requirement
        (c; moderate; p. 275)

18.   In which industry is the inadequate enforcement of laws prohibiting illegal usage,
        copying, or counterfeiting of intellectual property a problem?
        a. music
        b. filmed entertainment
        c. computer software
        d. pharmaceuticals
        e. all of the above
        (e; easy; p. 276)

19.   Which of the following is *not* addressed by the Trade-Related Investment
        Measures Agreement (TRIMS)?
        a. trade-balancing rules
        b. foreign-exchange access
        c. domestic sales requirements
        d. protection of intellectual property rights
        e. all of the above are addressed by TRIMS
        (d; difficult; p. 276)

20.   What do human rights and environmental activists believe is missing in the
        WTO's objectives?
        a. concern for human rights abuses
        b. trade in goods
        c. trade in services
        d. trade in agricultural products
        e. none of the above
        (a; easy; p. 277)

21.   Which of the following is not an area of concern among WTO critics?
       a. human rights policies
       b. environmental protections
       c. bargaining power of labor unions
       d. job security of workers
       e. all of the above
       (e; moderate; p. 277)

22.   What is the most important regional trading bloc in the world?
       a. NAFTA
       b. Mercosur
       c. European Union
       d. APEC
       e. Andean Pact
       (c; easy; p. 280)

23.   How many member countries are a part of the European Union?
       a. 6
       b. 10
       c. 12
       d. 15
       e. 25
       (d; moderate; p. 280)

24.   Which organization or agreement was created by the desires of war-weary
       Europeans to promote peace and prosperity through economic and political
       cooperation?
       a. International Monetary Fund
       b. World Bank
       c. GATT
       d. European Union
       e. all were created by these desires
       (e; difficult; p. 280)

25.   What agreement signaled the start of the European Union?
       a. GATT
       b. Treaty of Rome
       c. WTO
       d. Uruguay Round
       e. None of the above
       (b; moderate; p. 280)

26.   Which of the following was *not* one of the first six European nations to work
        towards economic and political cooperation?
        a. France
        b. West Germany
        c. Italy
        d. United Kingdom
        e. Belgium
        (d; difficult; p. 280)

27.   Which country listed below is not included in the Benelux nations?
        a. Belgium
        b. Liechtenstein
        c. Netherlands
        d. Luxembourg
        e. All are Benelux nations
        (b; easy; p. 280)

28.   The European Union has been known under which of the following other names?
        a. European Economic Community
        b. European Community
        c. Benelux Community
        d. Both a and b
        e. Both a and c
        (d; moderate; p. 281)

29.   The 12 member countries became known as the European Union when the _____
        was signed in 1993.
        a. Treaty of Rome
        b. Treaty of Geneva
        c. Genoa Agreement
        d. Treaty of Maastricht
        e. None of the above
        (d; moderate; p. 281)

30.   After the 2004 additions to the European Union, what two major Western
        European countries will *not* belong to the European Union?
        a. United Kingdom and Denmark
        b. Norway and Switzerland
        c. Switzerland and Greece
        d. Portugal and Italy
        e. Russia and Poland
        (b; moderate; p. 281)

31.   Which of the following countries will *not* join the European Union in 2004?
      a.   Malta
      b.   Poland
      c.   Russia
      d.   Lithuania
      e.   Latvia
      (c; difficult; p. 281)

32.   Which word best describes the European Union?
      a.   intergovernmental
      b.   supranational government
      c.   intragovernmental
      d.   both a and b
      e.   both b and c
      (d; moderate; p. 282)

33.   Which of the following organizations governs the European Union?
      a.   The Council of the European Union
      b.   The European Commission
      c.   The European Parliament
      d.   The European Court of Justice
      e.   All of the above
      (e; moderate; p. 282)

34.   Where is the Council of the European Union located?
      a.   Strasbourg, France
      b.   Frankfurt, Germany
      c.   Geneva, Switzerland
      d.   Brussels, Belgium
      e.   Luxembourg
      (d; moderate; p. 282)

35.   What is the allocation of votes in the Council of the European Union based on?
      a.   population
      b.   economic importance
      c.   order of entry into the EU
      d.   both a and b
      e.   both a and c
      (d; moderate; p. 282)

36.   Where is the European Commission located?
        a. Strasbourg, France
        b. Frankfurt, Germany
        c. Geneva, Switzerland
        d. Brussels, Belgium
        e. Luxembourg
        (d; moderate; p. 282)

37.   Where is the European Parliament located?
        a. Strasbourg, France
        b. Frankfurt, Germany
        c. Geneva, Switzerland
        d. Brussels, Belgium
        e. Luxembourg
        (a; moderate; p. 282)

38.   Where is the European Court of Justice located?
        a. Strasbourg, France
        b. Frankfurt, Germany
        c. Geneva, Switzerland
        d. Brussels, Belgium
        e. Luxembourg
        (d; moderate; p. 282)

39.   Which EU organization is the most powerful?
        a. The Council of the European Union
        b. The European Commission
        c. The European Parliament
        d. The European Court of Justice
        e. All are equally powerful
        (a; moderate; p. 282)

40.   What function is served by the Council of the European Union?
        a. executive
        b. administrative
        c. legislative
        d. judicial
        e. none of the above
        (a; moderate; p. 282)

41.   How often does the European Commission meet?
        a. daily
        b. weekly
        c. monthly
        d. yearly
        e. bi-annually
        (b; moderate; p. 283)

42.   What function is served by the European Commission?
        a. executive
        b. administrative
        c. legislative
        d. judicial
        e. none of the above
        (b; moderate; p. 282)

43.   What were several programs administered by the European Commission accused
        of in 1999?
        a. fraud
        b. inept management
        c. favoritism
        d. lack of accountability
        e. all of the above
        (e; moderate; p. 283)

44.   The EU uses a _____ in areas such as health, consumer policy, and free
        movement of workers.
        a. co-decision procedure
        b. unanimous vote
        c. qualified majority
        d. consensus
        e. none of the above
        (a; moderate; p. 283)

45.   What function is performed by the European Court of Justice?
        a. administrative
        b. executive
        c. interpretation of law
        d. managerial
        e. all of the above
        (c; easy; p. 283)

46.   EU policies are implemented _____.
        a.   internationally
        b.   intranationally
        c.   nationally
        d.   supranationally
        e.   none of the above
        (c; difficult; p. 285)

47.   What percentage of programs broadcast on television stations in member
        countries must be European in origin?
        a.   10%
        b.   25%
        c.   50%
        d.   70%
        e.   100%
        (c; difficult; p. 285)

48.   How did the EU initially eliminate conflicts among member countries?
        a.   arbitration
        b.   harmonization
        c.   negotiation
        d.   legislation
        e.   all of the above
        (b; easy; p. 286)

49.   The Cassis de Dijon case brought about the concept of _____ among member
        nations in the EU.
        a.   harmonization
        b.   negotiation
        c.   arbitration
        d.   mutual recognition
        e.   free movement of goods
        (d; moderate; p.286)

50.   The _____ concept states that if one EU member state determines that a product is
        appropriate for sale, then all other EU members are also obliged to do so under
        the provisions of the Treaty of Rome.
        a.   harmonization
        b.   negotiation
        c.   arbitration
        d.   mutual recognition
        e.   free movement of goods
        (d; moderate; p.286)

51.   What rights were granted to citizens of the EU through the Maastricht Treaty?
       a. The right to live anywhere in the EU.
       b. The right to work anywhere in the EU.
       c. The right to vote anywhere in the EU.
       d. The right to run for election anywhere in the EU.
       e. All of the above.
       (e; easy; p. 287)

52.   Which organization is responsible for controlling the euro-zone's money supply, interest rates, and inflation?
       a. European Central Bank
       b. The Council of the European Union
       c. European Commission
       d. European Parliament
       e. European Court of Justice
       (a; moderate; p. 288)

53.   Euro-zone participants have agreed to limit their annual government deficits to no more than _____ of their GDPs.
       a. 3%
       b. 5%
       c. 10%
       d. 12%
       e. 15%
       (a; difficult; p. 288)

54.   The Treaty for Europe is also known as the _____.
       a. Treaty of Rome
       b. Maastricht Treaty
       c. Treaty of Amsterdam
       d. Paris Treaty
       e. Treaty of Nice
       (c; difficult; p.288)

55.   Which of the following components were an important part of the Treaty of Amsterdam?
       a. A strong commitment to address high unemployment in the EU.
       b. A plan to strengthen the role of the European Parliament.
       c. Establishment of a two-track system allowing groups of members to proceed with economic and political integration faster than the EU as a whole.
       d. Both a and b.
       e. All of the above.
       (e; moderate; p. 288)

56.   Which agreement is the latest EU integration effort?
       a.   The Treaty of Rome
       b.   The Maastricht Treaty
       c.   Treaty of Amsterdam
       d.   The Paris Treaty
       e.   The Treaty of Nice
       (e; difficult; p.288)

57.   The Treaty of Nice requires that a _____ must be met to achieve a qualified
       majority.
       a.   co-decision procedure
       b.   unanimous vote
       c.   triple majority
       d.   consensus
       e.   double majority
       (a; moderate; p. 283)

58.   Which country listed below is *not* a member of the European Free Trade
       Association?
       a.   Iceland
       b.   Liechtenstein
       c.   Norway
       d.   Switzerland
       e.   All are members of the European Free Trade Association
       (e; easy; p. 289)

59.   The European Free Trade Association has joined with the _____ to form another
       common market.
       a   NAFTA
       b.   Mercosur
       c.   European Union
       d.   Commonwealth of Independent States
       e.   Benelux nations
       (c; moderate; p. 289)

60.   The European Economic Area promotes the free movement of _____.
       a.   goods
       b.   services
       c.   labor
       d.   capital
       e.   all of the above
       (e; easy; p. 289)

61.   Which of the following is *not* a member of the European Economic Area?
      a. Switzerland
      b. Norway
      c. Liechtenstein
      d. Iceland
      e. Sweden
      (a; difficult; p. 289)

62.   Which of the following countries is *not* a part of a customs union?
      a. Russia
      b. Belarus
      c. Kazakhstan
      d. Kyrgyzstan
      e. Kuwait
      (e; difficult; p. 289)

63.   In what year was NAFTA implemented?
      a. 1985
      b. 1990
      c. 1994
      d. 1998
      e. 2000
      (c; easy; p. 290)

64.   Which of the following countries is not part of NAFTA?
      a. Mexico
      b. Canada
      c. United States
      d. Greenland
      e. All are part of NAFTA
      (d; easy; p. 290)

65.   Which industries are protected in Canada in accordance with NAFTA provisions?
      a. publishing
      b. music
      c. television
      d. film
      e. all of the above
      (e; easy; p. 290)

66.   What percentage of an automobile must be produced in the United States, Canada, and/or Mexico in order for it to be considered a North American product?
        a. 25%
        b. 37%
        c. 50%
        d. 62.5%
        e. 75.5%
        (d; difficult; p. 290)

67.   A _____ is a factory in which very little transformation of a product is undertaken.
        a. macquiladora
        b. screwdriver plant
        c. greenfield operation
        d. distribution center
        e. shipping platform
        (b; moderate; p. 290)

68.   The _____ seeks to facilitate the economic development of the countries of the countries of Central America and the Caribbean Sea.
        a. ASEAN Free Trade Area
        b. Caribbean Basin Initiative
        c. Central America Common Market
        d. Southern Cone Customs Union
        e. Andean Pact
        (b; moderate; p. 290)

69.   Which country initiated the Caribbean Basin Initiative?
        a. Venezuela
        b. The United States
        c. Colombia
        d. The Caribbean islands
        e. Bermuda
        (b; difficult; p. 290)

70.   What industry may the United States bar foreign ownership of according to NAFTA?
        a. airline industry
        b. lodging
        c. food services
        d. film
        e. music
        (a; difficult; p. 290)

71.   Which of the following countries is *not* part of the Mercosur Accord?
        a. Argentina
        b. Brazil
        c. Paraguay
        d. Uruguay
        e. All are members of the Mercosur Accord
        (e; moderate; p. 291)

72.   The _____ is an agreement to promote free trade among the five South American
        countries of Bolivia, Chile, Colombia, Ecuador, and Peru.
        a. Mercosur Accord
        b. ASEAN Free Trade Area
        c. Andean Pact
        d. Central America Common Market
        e. Southern Cone Customs Union
        (c; difficult; p. 291)

73.   Which of the following countries is not a member of the Andean Pact?
        a. Bolivia
        b. Chile
        c. Colombia
        d. Brazil
        e. Peru
        (d; difficult; p. 291)

74.   The _____ is an agreement to create a customs union among the governments of
        Argentina, Brazil, Paraguay, and Uruguay.
        a. Mercosur Accord
        b. ASEAN Free Trade Area
        c. Andean Pact
        d. Central America Common Market
        e. Southern Cone Customs Union
        (a; difficult; p. 291)

75.   Which of the following is *not* a regional trading bloc in Africa?
        a. Southern African Development Community
        b. Economic Community of Central African States
        c. Economic Community of West African States
        d. African Union
        e. All are trading blocs in Africa
        (d; moderate; p. 295)

True/False

76.   Mexico has considered that investors may abandon Mexican factories in favor
        of Chinese ones if China joins the World Trade Organization.
        (T; moderate; p. 270)

77.   The GATT is an agreement, not an organization. (T; moderate; p. 271)

78.   The GATT seeks to reduce barriers to international trade. (T; easy; p. 271)

79.   Because of the preferential treatment offered to member countries, the European
        Union actually represents an infraction against the GATT. (F; difficult; p. 272)

80.   China is a member of the World Trade Organization. (F; difficult; p. 274)

81.   Some have argued that protection of intellectual property should be more
        relaxed for pharmaceuticals than for music and film entertainment.
        (T; moderate; p. 276)

82.   One weakness of the WTO is that the enforcement of the GATT was stronger.
        (F; moderate; p. 276)

83.   The WTO enjoys strong support from companies, activist groups, and countries
        worldwide. (F; moderate; p. 277)

84.   Economic integration confers benefits on the national economy as a whole but
        often hurts specific sectors and communities within that economy.
        (T; moderate; p. 279)

85.   Switzerland was the only European nation not invited to join the European
        Union. (F; moderate; p. 281)

86.   Ten more European countries will join the European Union in 2004.
        (T; easy; p. 281)

87.   EU members are no longer sovereign nations. (F; moderate; p. 281)

88.   In decisions made by the Council of the European Union, every country has an
        equal vote. (F; difficult; p. 282)

89.   A coalition of two large countries or three smaller countries can block a
        decision by the Council of the Economic Union. (T; moderate; p. 282)

90.   The individuals appointed to the European Commission serve the European Union, not their individual country. (T; difficult; p. 282)

91.   The European Commission serves as the legislative branch of the EU. (F; difficult; p. 282)

92.   The EU has one official language. (F; easy; p. 282)

93.   Twenty percent of the employees of the European Commission are in translation services. (T; moderate; p. 282)

94.   Employees of the Council of the European Union are called eurocrats. (F; difficult; p. 282)

95.   The European Court of Justice declared Germany's 450 year old beer purity law illegal. (T; moderate; p. 283)

96.   EU policies are formulated supranationally and are also implemented supranationally. (F; difficult; p. 285)

97.   The European Constitution was established in 1999. (F; difficult; p. 289)

98.   There are other regional trading blocs within the European Union. (T; moderate; p. 289)

99.   Australia and New Zealand refuse to create a regional trading bloc because of their competition with each other. (F; moderate; p. 293)

100.   The Asia-Pacific Economic Cooperation Initiative was developed in response to the growing interdependence of the Asia-Pacific economies. (T; easy; p. 294)

Short Answers

101.   Mexico's economy continues to grow. Name five types of business that are operating in Mexico. Answer: Contract manufacturing, laundry services, call centers, data processing facilities, and automotive manufacturing. (moderate; p. 270)

102.   What are the two exceptions to the most favored nation principle? Answer: Members can lower tariffs to developing countries without lowering them for more developed countries. Regional arrangements that promote economic integration are allowed. (difficult; p. 272)

103.   What are the five core principles of the WTO's Trading System? Answer:
        Without discrimination, freer, predictable, more competitive, and beneficial for
        less developed countries. (moderate; p. 275)

104.   What is the most important characteristic of regional trading blocs? Answer:
        The extent of economic integration among the bloc's members.
        (difficult; p. 277)

105.   What is the meaning of a free trade area? Answer: A free trade area encourages
        trade among members by eliminating trade barriers. (easy; p. 278)

106.   What is the meaning of a customs union? Answer: A customs union has all the
        characteristics of a free trade area but also includes the adoption of common
        external trade policies toward nonmembers. (moderate; p. 278)

107.   What is the meaning of a common market? Answer: A common market has all
        the characteristics of a customs union but also includes the removal of barriers
        that inhibit the movement of factors of production. (moderate; p. 278)

108.   What is the meaning of an economic union? Answer: An economic union has all
        the characteristics of a common market but also includes the complete
        coordination of their economic policies in order to blend their economics into a
        single entity. (moderate; p. 278)

109.   What is a political union? Answer: A political union is the complete political as
        well as economic integration of two or more countries. (moderate; p. 279)

110.   Of all the regional trading blocs, what is the most important one? Answer:
        European Union. (easy; p. 280)

111.   The European Union creates a major advantage and disadvantage for firms
        competing there. What are they? Answer: The EU has opened up markets but
        has also created more competition. (moderate; p. 279)

112.   What are the four organizations that govern the EU? Answer: The Council of
        the European Union, The European Commission, The European Parliament, and
        The European Court of Justice. (moderate; p. 282)

113.   What functions are performed by the European Commission? Answer: It
        proposes legislation to be considered by the Council. It implements the
        provisions of the Treaty of Rome and other EU treaties; it protects the EU's
        interests in political debates; it has extensive powers in implementing the EU's
        customs union, the Common Agricultural Policy, and the completion of the
        internal market; and it administers the EU's permanent bureaucracy.
        (moderate; p. 282)

114.   What are the three pillars upon which the Maastricht Treaty rests? Answer: A new agreement to create common foreign and defense policies among members; to cooperate on police, judicial, and public safety matters; and to create an economic and monetary union among member states. (difficult; p. 287)

115.   What is the purpose of the cohesion fund in the European Union? Answer: A means of funneling economic development aid to countries whose per capita GDP is less than 90% of the EU average. (difficult; p. 287)

116.   What rights were granted to citizens of the European Union through the Maastricht Treat? Answer: The right to live, work, vote, and run for election anywhere in the EU. (difficult; p. 287)

117.   What are the conditions of the triple majority as set out in the Treaty of Nice? Answer: The Treaty of Nice states that a qualified majority can only be reached if three conditions are met. The decision must receive a specified percentage of the votes cast by Council members. A majority of the member states must approve the decision. The decision must be approved by members who represent at least 62% of the EU's population. (difficult; p. 289)

118.   What is the purpose of the European Convention? Answer: It is charged with developing a European Constitution. (moderate; p. 289)

119.   What is the purpose of the Caribbean Basin Initiative? Answer: It seeks to facilitate the economic development of the countries of Central America and the Caribbean Sea. (moderate; p. 290)

120.   What two factors lead to the creation of the ASEAN trading bloc? Answer: A decrease in government control of national economies that has stimulated local entrepreneurs and attracted FDI, and a defensive response to the growth of other regional trading blocs. (difficult; p. 294)

Essay

121.   Explain why the Clinton administration decided to adopt the term "normal trade relations" to replace the term "most favored nation."

Answer: The public reason was that normal trade relations was a more accurate description. Since almost all countries received this treatment, then the practice was normal rather than most favored. The Clinton administration also sought to secure admission into the World Trade Organization for China. President Clinton thought that this would be more easily accomplished if the United States were perceived as treating China normally rather than as favorable. (difficult; p. 274)

122.   Describe the three primary goals of the World Trade Organization.

          Answer: The goals of the WTO are to 1) promote trade flows by encouraging
          nations to adopt nondiscriminatory trade policies, 2) reduce remaining trade
          barriers through multilateral negotiations, and 3) establish impartial procedures
          for resolving trade disputes among members. (moderate; p. 274)

123.   How does the WTO differ from the GATT?

          Answer: While the GATT agreement was incorporated into the WTO agreement,
          there are two important differences. The GATT focuses on promoting trade in
          goods, whereas the WTO's mandate is broader. The WTO is responsible for
          trade in goods, trade in services, international intellectual property protection,
          and trade-related investment. AlsoSecond, the WTO's enforcement powers are
          much stronger than those of the GATT. (moderate; p. 274)

124.   Explain how violations of WTO obligations are addressed and enforced.

          Answer: A country failing to live up to the agreement may have a complaint
          filed against it. If a WTO panel finds the country in violation of the rules, the
          panel will likely ask the country to eliminate the trade barrier. If the country
          refuses, the WTO will allow the complaining country to impose trade barriers
          on the offending country equal to the damage caused by the trade barrier. The
          offending country is not allowed to counterretaliate by imposing new trade
          barriers against the complainant. (difficult; p. 276)

125.   List and explain the five forms of economic integration.

          Answer: The five forms of integration are free trade area, customs union,
          common market, economic union, and political union. The free trade area
          represents the lowest form of economic integration while the political union
          represents the highest level of economic integration. A free trade area
          encourages trade among members by eliminating trade barriers. A customs
          union combines the elimination of internal trade barriers among its members
          with the adoption of common external trade policies toward nonmembers. In a
          common market, members eliminate internal trade barriers among themselves
          and adopt a common external trade policy toward nonmembers, plus it
          eliminates barriers that inhibit the movement of factors of production among its
          members. An economic union represents full integration of the economies of
          two or more countries. In addition to all the requirements of a customs union, an
          economic union also requires its members to coordinate their economic policies
          to blend their economies into a single entity. A political union is the complete
          political as well as economic integration of two or more countries, thereby
          effectively making them one country. (moderate; p. 278)

Multiple Choice

1.   _____ is a comprehensive and ongoing management planning process aimed at formulating and implementing strategies that enable a firm to compete effectively internationally.
   a. Strategic planning
   b. International strategic management
   c. International operations management
   d. Multinational flexibility
   e. Global management
   (b; easy; p. 309)

2.   Who is primarily responsible for strategic planning in a firm?
   a. top-level executives
   b. middle-managers
   c. operational managers
   d. functional executives
   e. all of the above
   (a; easy; p. 309)

3.   _____ are comprehensive frameworks for achieving a firm's fundamental goals.
   a. Strategic business units
   b. Strategic advantages
   c. International strategies
   d. Competitive goals
   e. International operational plans
   (c; moderate; p. 310)

4.   Which of the following questions must a firm's strategic planners answer?
   a. What products does the firm intend to sell?
   b. Where and how will it make those products?
   c. Where and how will it sell them?
   d. Where and how will it acquire the necessary resources?
   e. All of the above
   (e; moderate; p. 310)

5.   Which of the following is *not* a potential difference between domestic and international operations?
   a. language
   b. culture
   c. politics
   d. advertising
   e. all are potential differences
   (e; easy; p. 310)

6.   Which of the following provides international firms with a source of global efficiency?
        a. location efficiencies
        b. economies of scale
        c. multinational flexibility
        d. both a and b
        e. both a and c
        (d; moderate; p. 311)

7.   International firms capture _____ by locating their facilities anywhere in the world that yields the lowest production or distribution costs.
        a. multinational flexibility
        b. economies of scale
        c. location efficiencies
        d. economies of scope
        e. all of the above
        (c; easy; p. 311)

8.   International firms capture _____ by building factories to serve more than one country and lowering production costs.
        a. multinational flexibility
        b. economies of scale
        c. location efficiencies
        d. economies of scope
        e. all of the above
        (b; easy; p. 311)

9.   What form of efficiency did Mercedes-Benz capture by initially producing its sport utility vehicle in Alabama?
        a. multinational flexibility
        b. economies of scale
        c. location efficiencies
        d. economies of scope
        e. all of the above
        (b; moderate; p. 311)

10.   When firms broaden their product lines in each of the countries they enter, what type of efficiency do they enjoy?
        a. multinational flexibility
        b. economies of scale
        c. location efficiencies
        d. economies of scope
        e. all of the above
        (d; moderate; p. 311)

11.   _____ occur(s) when firms broaden their product lines in each country they enter.
a. Multinational flexibility
b. Economies of scale
c. Location efficiencies
d. Economies of scope
e. All of the above
(d; easy; p. 311)

12.   _____ occur(s) when firms build factories that serve more than one country and lower their production costs.
a. Multinational flexibility
b. Economies of scale
c. Location efficiencies
d. Economies of scope
e. All of the above
(b; easy; p. 311)

13.   Nike achieved _____ by centering its manufacturing in countries where labor costs are relatively low.
a. multinational flexibility
b. economies of scale
c. location efficiencies
d. economies of scope
e. all of the above
(c; moderate; p. 311)

14.   _____ is/are enhanced when firms delegate responsibility to the managers of local subsidiaries.
a. Multinational flexibility
b. Economies of scale
c. Location efficiencies
d. Economies of scope
e. All of the above
(a; moderate; p. 312)

15.   _____ is/are minimized when too much power is centralized in one unit of the firm.
a. Multinational flexibility
b. Economies of scale
c. Location efficiencies
d. Economies of scope
e. All of the above
(a; moderate; p. 312)

16.   What effect does multinational flexibility have on a firm's global efficiencies?
       a. It reduces ability to achieve global efficiencies.
       b. It increases ability to achieve global efficiencies.
       c. It has no effect on a firm's ability to achieve global efficiencies.
       d. All of the above.
       e. None of the above.
       (a; difficult; p. 312)

17.   Pursuit of global efficiency may _____ a firm's attempts to promote worldwide
       learning.
       a. reduce
       b. increase
       c. have no impact on
       d. fluctuate with
       e. eliminate
       (a; moderate; p. 312)

18.   Which of the following steps is necessary for firms wishing to promote worldwide
       learning?
       a. Utilize an organizational structure designed to transfer knowledge.
       b. Create appropriate incentive structures.
       c. Motivate managers at headquarters to acquire, disseminate, and act upon
           worldwide learning opportunities.
       d. Motivate managers at subsidiaries to acquire, disseminate, and act upon
           worldwide learning opportunities.
       e. All of the above.
       (e; moderate; p. 313)

19.   When using a(n) _____, a firm utilizes the core competency or firm-specific
       advantage it developed at home as its main competitive weapon in the foreign
       markets it enters.
       a. multidomestic strategy
       b. home replication strategy
       c. transnational strategy
       d. global strategy
       e. international strategy
       (b; moderate; p. 313)

20.   What type of strategy is utilized when a firm takes what it does well at home and attempts to duplicate it in foreign markets?
a.   multidomestic strategy
b.   home replication strategy
c.   transnational strategy
d.   global strategy
e.   international strategy
(b; moderate; p. 313)

21.   When Mercedes-Benz relies on its brand name and reputation for well-engineered, luxurious cars to succeed in foreign markets, what strategy is it utilizing?
a.   multidomestic strategy
b.   home replication strategy
c.   transnational strategy
d.   global strategy
e.   international strategy
(b; moderate; p. 313)

22.   What type of strategy is used when a firm views itself as a collection of relatively independent operating subsidiaries, each of which focuses on a specific domestic market?
a.   multidomestic strategy
b.   home replication strategy
c.   transnational strategy
d.   global strategy
e.   international strategy
(a; moderate; p. 314)

23.   What type of strategy allows subsidiaries in each country to customize its products, communications, and operations to best suit that country's customers?
a.   multidomestic strategy
b.   home replication strategy
c.   transnational strategy
d.   global strategy
e.   international strategy
(a; moderate; p. 313)

24.   Firms using the _____ rely on its subsidiaries to be responsive to the local market.
a.   multidomestic strategy
b.   home replication strategy
c.   transnational strategy
d.   global strategy
e.   international strategy
(a; moderate; p. 313)

25.   Which approach is most appropriate when economies of scale for production, distribution, and marketing are low?
a.   multidomestic strategy
b.   home replication strategy
c.   transnational strategy
d.   global strategy
e.   international strategy
(a; difficult; p. 313)

26.   In which of the following situations is the multidomestic strategy most appropriate?
a.   Clear differences exist among national markets.
b.   Economies of scale are low.
c.   Cost of coordination between parent corporation and subsidiaries is high.
d.   All of the above.
e.   None of the above.
(d; moderate; p. 315)

27.   A firm following the _____ views the world as a single marketplace.
a.   multidomestic strategy
b.   home replication strategy
c.   transnational strategy
d.   global strategy
e.   international strategy
(d; moderate; p. 315)

28.   The primary goal of a(n) _____ is the creation of standardized goods and services that will address the needs of customers worldwide.
a.   multidomestic strategy
b.   home replication strategy
c.   transnational strategy
d.   global strategy
e.   international strategy
(d; moderate; p. 315)

29.   A global strategy is practically the exact opposite of the _____.
a.   multidomestic strategy
b.   home replication strategy
c.   transnational strategy
d.   global strategy
e.   international strategy
(a; difficult; p. 315)

30.   Firms using a global strategy tend to use a _____ structure.
        a. decentralized
        b. centralized
        c. product
        d. geographic
        e. market
        (b; moderate; p. 315)

31.   Firms using a _____ conducts business the same way anywhere in the world.
        a. home replication strategy
        b. transnational strategy
        c. global strategy
        d. both a and b
        e. both a and c
        (c; difficult; p. 315)

32.   The _____ combines the benefits of global scale efficiencies and local responsiveness.
        a. multidomestic strategy
        b. home replication strategy
        c. transnational strategy
        d. global strategy
        e. international strategy
        (c; moderate; p. 315)

33.   Microsoft locates most of its product development efforts in the United States but delegates marketing to its foreign subsidiaries. Microsoft follows a(n) _____.
        a. multidomestic strategy
        b. home replication strategy
        c. transnational strategy
        d. global strategy
        e. international strategy
        (c; difficult; p. 315)

34.   IKEA attempts to capture global efficiencies while remaining responsive to local conditions. IKEA follows a(n) _____.
        a. multidomestic strategy
        b. home replication strategy
        c. transnational strategy
        d. global strategy
        e. international strategy
        (c; moderate; p. 313)

35. Firms using a(n) _____ may locate responsibility for one product line in one country and responsibility for a second product line in another.
    a. multidomestic strategy
    b. home replication strategy
    c. transnational strategy
    d. global strategy
    e. international strategy
    (c; moderate; p. 313)

36. What factor explains the choice of strategic approach?
    a. need to achieve global integration
    b. need for local responsiveness
    c. need for centralization
    d. both a and b
    e. both a and c
    (d; moderate; p. 315)

37. The need for _____ is particularly high when local conditions vary widely across countries.
    a. global integration
    b. local responsiveness
    c. centralization
    d. both a and b
    e. both a and c
    (b; moderate; p. 316)

38. The need for _____ is particularly high when a firm is selling a standardized commodity.
    a. global integration
    b. local responsiveness
    c. centralization
    d. both a and b
    e. both a and c
    (a; moderate; p. 316)

39. Which condition is common for firms with a high need of local responsiveness?
    a. consumer preferences vary widely
    b. large differences in local laws
    c. economic conditions vary
    d. infrastructures vary
    e. all of the above
    (e; easy; p. 316)

40. The need for _____ is low when firms are able to differentiate their products.
     a. global integration
     b. local responsiveness
     c. centralization
     d. both a and b
     e. both a and c
     (a; moderate; p. 316)

41. Which of the following situations is consistent with a low need of global
     integration?
     a. differentiated products
     b. strong brand name
     c. after-sales support services
     d. high quality
     e. all of the above
     (e; easy; p. 317)

42. When firms have both low pressures of global integration and low need of local
     responsiveness, what strategy is most often adopted?
     a. multidomestic strategy
     b. home replication strategy
     c. transnational strategy
     d. global strategy
     e. international strategy
     (b; moderate; p. 317)

43. When firms experience high pressures of global integration and low pressures of
     local responsiveness, which strategy is usually adopted?
     a. multidomestic strategy
     b. home replication strategy
     c. transnational strategy
     d. global strategy
     e. international strategy
     (d; moderate; p. 317)

44. When firms experience low pressures of global integration and high pressures of
     local responsiveness, which strategy should be adopted?
     a. multidomestic strategy
     b. home replication strategy
     c. transnational strategy
     d. global strategy
     e. international strategy
     (a; moderate; p. 317)

45.   When firms experience high pressures of both global integration and local
       responsiveness, which strategy should be adopted?
       a.   multidomestic strategy
       b.   home replication strategy
       c.   transnational strategy
       d.   global strategy
       e.   international strategy
       (c; moderate; p. 317)

46.   _____ require(s) the transfer of information and experiences from the parent to
       each subsidiary, from each subsidiary to the parent and among subsidiaries.
       a.   Global efficiencies
       b.   Economies of scope
       c.   Multinational flexibility
       d.   Worldwide learning
       e.   Transnational strategies
       (d; easy; p. 318)

47.   Which strategy is likely the best for promoting global learning?
       a.   multidomestic strategy
       b.   home replication strategy
       c.   transnational strategy
       d.   global strategy
       e.   international strategy
       (c; moderate; p. 318)

48.   Which of the following is not one of the components of strategy development?
       a.   distinctive competence
       b.   differential advantage
       c.   scope of operations
       d.   resource deployment
       e.   synergy
       (b; difficult; p. 318)

49.   _____ answers the question, "What do we do exceptionally well, especially as
       compared to our competitors?"
       a.   Distinctive competence
       b.   Differential advantage
       c.   Scope of operations
       d.   Resource deployment
       e.   Core competence
       (a; difficult; p. 310)

50.   _____ answers the question, "Where are we going to conduct business?"
        a. Distinctive competence
        b. Differential advantage
        c. Scope of operations
        d. Resource deployment
        e. Synergy
        (c; moderate; p. 319)

51.   Which of the following could be a source of distinctive competence for a firm?
        a. well-respected brand name
        b. superior organizational practices
        c. cutting-edge technology
        d. efficient distribution networks
        e. all of the above
        (e; easy; p. 319)

52.   Recognition of Disney's character, Mickey Mouse, is an example of a firm's
        _____.
        a. distinctive competence
        b. differential advantage
        c. scope of operations
        d. resource deployment
        e. synergy
        (a; easy; p. 319)

53.   The compatibility of software programs with the Windows operating system is an
        example of Microsoft's _____.
        a. distinctive competence
        b. differential advantage
        c. scope of operations
        d. resource deployment
        e. synergy
        (a; moderate; p. 319)

54.   _____ may be defined in terms of geographic regions, markets, or product niches.
        a. Distinctive competence
        b. Differential advantage
        c. Scope of operations
        d. Resource deployment
        e. Synergy
        (c; moderate; p. 319)

55.   Disney operates theme parks in Japan, the United States, and France. This refers
        to Disney's _____.
        a. distinctive competence
        b. differential advantage
        c. scope of operations
        d. resource deployment
        e. synergy
        (c; moderate; p. 319)

56.   _____ answers the question "Given that we are going to compete in these markets,
        how will we allocate our resources to them?"
        a. Distinctive competence
        b. Differential advantage
        c. Scope of operations
        d. Resource deployment
        e. Synergy
        (d; moderate; p. 320)

57.   _____ determines relative priorities for a firm's limited resources.
        a. Distinctive competence
        b. Differential advantage
        c. Scope of operations
        d. Resource deployment
        e. Synergy
        (d; easy; p. 320)

58.   Although DaimlerChrysler's newest plant is in Alabama, nine out of ten Mercedes
        are still German built. This is an example of DaimlerChrysler's _____.
        a. distinctive competence
        b. differential advantage
        c. scope of operations
        d. resource deployment
        e. synergy
        (d; moderate; p. 320)

59.   _____ answers the question, "How can different elements of our business benefit
        each other?"
        a. Distinctive competence
        b. Worldwide learning
        c. Scope of operations
        d. Resource deployment
        e. Synergy
        (e; moderate; p. 321)

60.   The goal of _____ is to create a situation where the whole is greater than the sum
        of the parts.
        a. distinctive competence
        b. differential advantage
        c. scope of operations
        d. resource deployment
        e. synergy
        (e; easy; p. 321)

61.   Disney characters are seen on television and in the movies. People visit Disney
        theme parks and can buy merchandise featuring the Disney characters. What
        strategy development component is this an example of?
        a. distinctive competence
        b. differential advantage
        c. scope of operations
        d. resource deployment
        e. synergy
        (e; moderate; p. 321)

62.   _____ is deciding what to do.
        a. Strategy development
        b. Strategy formulation
        c. Strategy implementation
        d. Strategy execution
        e. Strategy evaluation
        (b; easy; p. 321)

63.   _____ is actually doing it.
        a. Strategy development
        b. Strategy formulation
        c. Strategy implementation
        d. Strategy execution
        e. Strategy evaluation
        (c; easy; p. 321)

64.   In _____, the firm establishes it goals and its strategic plan.
        a. strategy development
        b. strategy formulation
        c. strategy implementation
        d. strategy execution
        e. strategy evaluation
        (b; easy; p. 321)

65.   In _____, the firm develops the tactics for achieving the formulated international strategies.
a.   strategy development
b.   strategy formulation
c.   strategy implementation
d.   strategy execution
e.   strategy evaluation
(c; easy; p. 321)

66.   The first step in the strategic planning process is to _____.
a.   perform a SWOT analysis
b.   develop a mission statement
c.   set strategic goals
d.   develop tactical goals and plans
e.   develop a control framework
(b; moderate; p. 322)

67.   The third step in the strategic planning process is to _____.
a.   perform a SWOT analysis
b.   develop a mission statement
c.   set strategic goals
d.   develop tactical goals and plans
e.   develop a control framework
(c; moderate; p. 322)

68.   Which of the following is *not* considered during a SWOT analysis?
a.   strengths
b.   strategies
c.   weaknesses
d.   opportunities
e.   threats
(b; easy; p. 322)

69.   When firms gather data about economic, financial, political, and competitive changes in the various markets the firm serves, it is trying to identify _____.
a.   strengths
b.   opportunities
c.   threats
d.   weaknesses
e.   both b and c
(e; easy; p. 322)

70.   A(n) _____ is a systematic collection of data about all elements of the firm's external and internal environments.
        a. environmental scan
        b. strategic analysis
        c. strategic formulation
        d. situation analysis
        e. SWOT analysis
        (a; moderate; p. 322)

71.   A(n) _____ is a breakdown of the firm into its important activities.
        a. environmental scan
        b. value chain
        c. SWOT analysis
        d. situation analysis
        e. control framework
        (b; moderate; p. 323)

72.   Who developed the value chain technique?
        a. Adam Smith
        b. Michael Porter
        c. Walt Disney
        d. Bill Gates
        e. Fred Smith
        (b; moderate; p. 323)

73.   A(n) _____ calls for a firm to rely on a single business, product, or service for all its revenue.
        a. corporate strategy
        b. single-business strategy
        c. related diversification strategy
        d. functional strategy
        e. unrelated diversification strategy
        (b; moderate; p. 325)

74.   A(n) _____ calls for the firm to operate in several different but fundamentally related businesses, industries, or markets at the same time.
        a. corporate strategy
        b. single-business strategy
        c. related diversification strategy
        d. functional strategy
        e. unrelated diversification strategy
        (c; moderate; p. 325)

75. Firms using a(n) _____ operates in several unrelated industries and markets.
    a. corporate strategy
    b. single-business strategy
    c. related diversification strategy
    d. functional strategy
    e. unrelated diversification strategy
    (e; moderate; p. 325)

76. Which strategy attempts to establish and maintain the image that an SBU's product or services are fundamentally unique from other products or services in the same market segment?
    a. corporate strategy
    b. differentiation strategy
    c. related diversification strategy
    d. functional strategy
    e. unrelated diversification strategy
    (b; moderate; p. 325)

77. Firms using a(n) _____ operate in several unrelated industries and markets.
    a. corporate strategy
    b. single-business strategy
    c. related diversification strategy
    d. functional strategy
    e. unrelated diversification strategy
    (e; moderate; p. 326)

78. Which strategy calls for a firm to focus on achieving highly efficient operating procedures so that its costs are lower than its competitors?
    a. corporate strategy
    b. single-business strategy
    c. related diversification strategy
    d. overall cost leadership strategy
    e. unrelated diversification strategy
    (d; easy; p. 328)

79. Which strategy calls for a firm to target specific types of products for certain customer groups or regions?
    a. focus strategy
    b. single-business strategy
    c. related diversification strategy
    d. overall cost leadership strategy
    e. unrelated diversification strategy
    (a; moderate; p. 328)

80.   _____ attempts to answer the question, "How will we manage the functions of finance, marketing, operations, human resources, and research and development in ways consistent with our international corporate and business strategies?"
a. Corporate strategy
b. Single-business strategy
c. Related diversification strategy
d. Functional strategy
e. Unrelated diversification strategy
(d; moderate; p. 328)

True/False

81.   Tokyo Disneyland is Japan's number one tourist attraction. (T; easy; p. 307)

82.   Larger firms usually have permanent strategic planning staff to provide assistance to top managers. (T; moderate; p. 309)

83.   Nontraditional locations such as office buildings and airplanes are not considered appropriate locations for new McDonald's stores.
(F; moderate; p. 312)

84.   Global efficiencies are harder to obtain when a single unit of the firm is given world-wide responsibility for the task. (F; difficult; p. 312)

85.   BMW did not initially include cup holders in its automobiles because of the high driving speeds common in Germany. (T; moderate; p. 312)

86.   A decentralized structure is ideal for transferring learning from one subsidiary to another. (F; moderate; p. 313)

87.   The concept of the home country is irrelevant for a firm using a global strategy. (T; moderate; p. 315)

88.   In a transnational firm, all functions are heavily centralized. (F; difficult; p. 315)

89.   The first step in strategy formulation is to develop a mission statement.
(T; easy; p. 322)

90.   The second step in the strategy formulation process is to set strategic goals.
(F; moderate; p. 322)

91.   The final step in the strategy formulation process is to develop a control framework. (T; easy; p. 322)

92.   Planning team members must scan the external environment to identify weaknesses affecting the firm. (F; moderate; p. 322)

93.   Strengths and weaknesses are part of a firm's internal environment. (T; easy; p. 323)

94.   A firm's value chain is a breakdown of a firm's most important product lines. (F; moderate; p. 323)

95.   Tactics usually involve top-level managers. (F; easy; p. 324)

96.   A control framework is the set of managerial and organizational processes that keep the firm moving toward it strategic goals. (T; moderate; p. 324)

97.   There are four levels of international strategy for MNCs. (F; easy; p. 325)

98.   Related diversification is a type of business strategy. (F; easy; p. 325)

99.   Theme parks and resorts is one of Disney's SBUs. (T; moderate; p. 327)

100.   The low cost of coordinating the operations of related divisions is a primary advantage of related diversification. (F; difficult; p. 326)

101.   Differentiation strategy is the least used business strategy because it attempts to establish and maintain the image that SBU's products are fundamentally unique from other products. (F; difficult; p. 327)

102.   A conglomerate refers to the term used for firms comprising unrelated businesses. (T; easy; p. 327)

103.   Typically an international business develops a financial strategy for the overall firm as well as for each SBU. (T; moderate; p. 328)

104.   SBU stands for strategic business unit. (T; easy; p. 328)

105.   A firm's international marketing strategy is a type of business-level strategy. (F; moderate; p. 329)

106.   Short Answers
        How might advertising differ in an international operation? Answer: In a domestic operation, advertising has few restrictions and many media are available. Internationally, there may be many restrictions and limited media choices. Also, low literacy may rule out print media. (moderate; p. 310)

107.   What transportation concerns might exist in international operations? Answer: It is often inadequate internationally, but among one of the best in the United States. (moderate; p. 310)

108.   What are the three sources of competitive advantage available to international businesses? Answer: Global efficiencies, multinational flexibility, and worldwide learning. (moderate; p. 311)

109.   What global efficiencies are available to international firms? Answer: Location efficiencies, economies of scale, and economies of scope. (moderate; p. 311)

110.   Describe the meaning of a home replication strategy. Answer: A firm utilizes the core competency or firm-specific advantage it developed at home as its main competitive weapon in the foreign markets that it enters. (easy; p. 313)

111.   What need primarily affects whether a firm should choose a multidomestic strategy? Answer: The need for local responsiveness. (easy; p. 314)

112.   What similarity exists between the home replication strategy and the global strategy? Answer: Under either approach, a firm conducts business the same way anywhere in the world. (difficult; p. 315)

113.   What is an important difference between the home replication strategy and the global strategy? Answer: The home replication strategy has a home-country bias–it assumes that a firm's domestic strategy will work in foreign markets. A global strategy has no such home-country bias. (difficult; p. 315)

114.   What strategic approach seeks to achieve local responsiveness and global efficiency? Answer: Transnational strategy. (easy; p. 315)

115.   When is a global strategy most appropriate? Answer: It is most appropriate when the pressures for global integration are high, but the need for local responsiveness is low. (moderate; p. 317)

116.   What strategy is most able to promote global learning? Answer: Transnational strategy. (difficult; p. 318)

117.   What are the four basic components of strategy development? Answer: Distinctive competence, scope of operations, resource deployment, and synergy. (moderate; p. 318)

118.   What is the goal of synergy? Answer: The goal of synergy is to create a situation where the whole is greater than the sum of the parts. (easy; p. 321)

119.   What does a firm do in the strategy formulation stage? Answer: In this stage, the firm establishes its goals and the strategic plan that will lead to the achievement of those goals. (moderate; p. 321)

120.   What does a firm do during the strategy implementation stage? Answer: In this stage, the firm develops the tactics for achieving the formulated international strategics. (moderate; p. 321)

121.   Explain the purpose of a mission statement. Answer: The mission statement clarifies the organization's purpose, values, and directions. (easy; p. 321)

122.   What are the three levels of international strategy for MNCs? Answer: Corporate, business, and functional. (easy; p. 325)

123.   What are the three types of corporate strategies an MNC might choose to follow? Answer: Single-business strategy, related diversification, and unrelated diversification. (moderate; p. 325)

124.   What are the three types of business strategies an MNC might choose to follow? Answer: Differentiation, cost leadership, and focus. (moderate; p. 325)

125.   What is a single-business strategy? Answer: A single business strategy calls for a firm to rely on a single business, product, or service for all its revenue. (moderate; p. 325)

126.   What is the meaning of a related diversification strategy? Answer: A related diversification strategy calls for the firm to operate in several different but fundamentally related businesses, industries, or markets at the same time. (moderate; p. 325)

Essay

127.   What differences exist between the strategic management process for domestic operations and international operations? Identify five differences and explain each one.

        Answer: There are 15 factors students could identify for this answer. They are all listed in Table 11.1 on page 310. Some possible answers include language, culture, politics, economy, governmental interference, and labor. In domestic operations, English is universally used, while in international operation the use of local language is required in many situations. In domestic operations, culture is relatively homogeneous, while it is quite diverse in international operations. Politics are stable and somewhat unimportant domestically but could be volatile internationally. The economy is uniform domestically but varies internationally. Finally, governmental interference is extensive and subject to change in international operations but minimal in domestic operations. (moderate; p. 310)

128.   What are the advantages of pursuing a related diversification strategy?

Answer: The firm depends less on a single product or service so it is less vulnerable to competitive or economic threats. It may produce economies of scale for a firm. It may allow a firm to use technology or expertise developed in one market to enter a second market more cheaply and easily. (moderate; p. 326)

129.   Multinational corporations may adopt one of four strategic alternatives in their attempt to balance the three goals of global efficiencies, multinational flexibility, and worldwide learning. What are these four alternatives? Describe each one. What determines which strategy is appropriate?

Answer: The four strategies are home replication, multidomestic, global, and transnational. A home replication strategy means that the organization simply replicates what has worked in the home market, in its markets abroad. A multidomestic strategy suggests that a firm operates differently in its various markets based on local market characteristics. A global strategy means that the firm attempts to develop global efficiencies by standardizing its activities from country to country. A transnational strategy suggests that the firm attempts to respond to local market preferences while achieving global efficiencies. The appropriate strategy is based on a firm's need for local responsiveness and its need for global efficiencies. (moderate; pp. 313-317)

130.   What are the four basic components of strategy development? Explain the meaning of each component.

Answer: The four basic components of strategy development are distinctive competence, scope of operations, resource deployment, and synergy. Distinctive competence answers the question, "What do we do exceptionally well especially as compared to our competitors?" Scope of operations answers the question, "Where are we going to conduct business?" Resource deployment answers the question, "Given that we are going to compete in these markets, how will we allocate our resources to them?" Synergy answers the question, "How can different elements of our business benefit each other?" (moderate; p. 318)

131.   Describe the steps in the international strategic formulation process.

Answer: The steps in the process are to 1) develop a mission statement, 2) perform a SWOT analysis, 3) set strategic goals, 4) develop tactical goals and plans, and 5) develop a control framework. (easy; p. 322)

Multiple Choice

1.   Which of the following is *not* one of the three steps in increasing market share, revenue, and profits?
       a. assess alternative markets
       b. evaluate respective costs, benefits, and risks
       c. perform a situation analysis
       d. select market with most potential for entry or expansion
       e. all are relevant steps
       (c; moderate; p. 337)

2.   Which of the following factors is commonly considered when assessing alternative foreign markets?
       a. current size of market
       b. potential size of market
       c. competitive levels in market
       d. legal and political environment in market
       e. all of the above
       (e; easy; p. 337)

3.   What is the first step in selecting a foreign market?
       a. assessing market potential
       b. assessing the level of competition
       c. monitoring major markets
       d. evaluating host country's trade policies
       e. assessing general legal and political environments
       (a; moderate; p. 338)

4.   Which of the following is not a critical factor in assessing new market opportunities?
       a. product-market dimensions
       b. potential target markets
       c. success factors
       d. potential for worldwide learning
       e. product-market differences
       (d; moderate; p. 338)

5.   The second step in foreign market assessment is _____.
       a. assessing market potential
       b. assessing the level of competition
       c. evaluating costs, benefits, and risks
       d. evaluating host country's trade policies
       e. assessing general legal and political environments
       (c; moderate; p. 341)

6.   _____ refer to expenses incurred by the firm as it enters a new foreign market.
        a. Indirect costs
        b. Direct costs
        c. Opportunity costs
        d. Variable costs
        e. All of the above
        (b; easy; p. 341)

7.   Because a firm has limited resources, entering one market may preclude its entry
        into another. What type of cost is reflected in this situation?
        a. indirect costs
        b. direct costs
        c. opportunity costs
        d. variable costs
        e. all of the above
        (c; easy; p. 341)

8.   Which theory listed below is useful in deciding which mode of entry to use when
        entering foreign markets?
        a. ownership advantage theory
        b. internalization theory
        c. eclectic theory
        d. relative factor endowments
        e. national competitive advantage
        (c; moderate; p. 342)

9.   Which of the following should be considered when choosing a mode of entry?
        a. ownership advantages
        b. location advantages
        c. internalization advantages
        d. need for control
        e. all of the above
        (e; easy; p. 342)

10.   Which of the following is *not* one of the decision factors in the choice of entry
        mode?
        a. ownership advantages
        b. location advantages
        c. national competitive advantages
        d. internalization advantages
        e. resource availability
        (c; difficult; p. 342)

11.   Which of the following is not a mode of entry into foreign markets?
       a. exporting
       b. importing
       c. international licensing
       d. international franchising
       e. greenfield strategy
       (b; easy; p. 342)

12.   _____ are tangible or intangible resources owned by a firm which grant it a
       competitive advantage over its industry rivals.
       a. Ownership advantages
       b. Location advantages
       c. National competitive advantages
       d. Internalization advantages
       e. Resource availabilities
       (a; moderate; p. 343)

13.   _____ are those factors that affect the desirability of host country production
       relative to home country production.
       a. Ownership advantages
       b. Location advantages
       c. National competitive advantages
       d. Internalization advantages
       e. Resource availabilities
       (b; moderate; p. 343)

14.   Firms with a well-known brand name often utilize the _____ mode of entry.
       a. exporting
       b. international licensing
       c. international franchising
       d. both b and c
       e. both a and c
       (d; difficult; p. 343)

15.   When home country production is found to be more desirable than host country
       production, the firm will likely choose the _____ mode of entry.
       a. exporting
       b. international licensing
       c. turnkey projects
       d. greenfield strategy
       e. joint venture
       (a; difficult; p. 343)

16.   When the host country is found to be more desirable for production than the home country, which mode of entry will the firm most likely choose?
      a. exporting
      b. international licensing
      c. foreign direct investment
      d. both a and b
      e. both b and c
      (e; difficult; p. 343)

17.   Which of the following factors is important in choosing between home country and host country production?
      a. relative wage rates
      b. land acquisition costs
      c. unused capacity in existing factories
      d. political risk
      e. all of the above
      (e; easy; p. 343)

18.   Which of the following is not an important factor in choosing between home country and host country production?
      a. relative wage rates
      b. land acquisition costs
      c. internalization advantages
      d. unused capacity in existing factories
      e. political risk
      (c; moderate; p. 343)

19.   _____ are those that make it desirable for a firm to produce a good or service itself rather than contracting with another firm to produce it.
      a. Ownership advantages
      b. Location advantages
      c. National competitive advantages
      d. Internalization advantages
      e. Resource availabilities
      (d; moderate; p. 343)

20.   When transaction costs are high, which mode of entry is preferable to a firm?
      a. joint venture
      b. international licensing
      c. foreign direct investment
      d. both a and b
      e. both a and c
      (e; difficult; p. 343)

21.   When transaction costs are low, which mode of entry is preferable to a firm?
       a. exporting
       b. greenfield strategy
       c. franchising
       d. joint venture
       e. turnkey
       (c; difficult; p. 343)

22.   Which entry mode is used frequently by pharmaceutical firms?
       a. exporting
       b. licensing
       c. greenfield strategy
       d. management contract
       e. franchising
       (b; moderate; p. 344)

23.   Firms short on capital may prefer an entry mode such as _____ that economizes their financial commitments.
       a. foreign direct investment
       b. management contract
       c. licensing
       d. greenfield strategy
       e. turn key
       (c; moderate; p. 345)

24.   The choice of entry mode is a trade-off between the level of risk borne by the firm and _____.
       a. potential rewards possible
       b. magnitude of resource commitment necessary
       c. level of control sought by the firm
       d. all of the above
       e. none of the above
       (d; moderate; p. 346)

25.   _____ is the most common form of international business activity.
       a. Exporting
       b. Licensing
       c. Greenfield strategy
       d. Management contract
       e. Franchising
       (a; moderate; p. 346)

26.   Which mode of entry is the simplest mode of internationalizing a domestic business?
        a. exporting
        b. licensing
        c. greenfield strategy
        d. management contract
        e. franchising
        (a; moderate; p. 346)

27.   _____ are those that pull a firm into foreign markets as a result of opportunities available there.
        a. Reactive motivations
        b. Proactive motivations
        c. Opportunity motivations
        d. Avoidance motivations
        e. Attraction motivations
        (b; easy; p. 346)

28.   _____ for exporting are those that push a firm into foreign markets.
        a. Reactive motivations
        b. Proactive motivations
        c. Opportunity motivations
        d. Avoidance motivations
        e. Attraction motivations
        (a; easy; p. 347)

29.   Which of the following is *not* a disadvantage of exporting?
        a. vulnerability to tariffs
        b. logistical complexities
        c. potential conflicts with distributors
        d. gradual market entry
        e. vulnerability to NTBs
        (d; moderate; p. 347)

30.   Which of the following is *not* an advantage of licensing?
        a. low financial risks
        b. low-cost way to assess market potential
        c. reduced control
        d. avoidance of tariffs
        e. knowledge of local markets
        (c; moderate; p. 347)

31.   Which of the following is an advantage of licensing?
       a. low financial exposure
       b. limited market opportunities
       c. dependence on licensee
       d. potential conflicts with licensee
       e. possibility of creating future competitor
       (a; easy; p. 347)

32.   Which of the following is an advantage of franchising?
       a. limited market opportunity
       b. avoidance of tariffs
       c. dependence on franchisee
       d. potential conflicts with franchisee
       e. possibility of creating future competitor
       (b; easy; p. 347)

33.   Which of the following is an advantage of foreign direct investment?
       a. high financial investments
       b. high exposure to political risk
       c. high profit potential
       d. greater managerial complexity
       e. vulnerability to restrictions on foreign investment
       (c; easy; p. 347)

34.   Which of the following is *not* a form of exporting?
       a. indirect exporting
       b. direct exporting
       c. intercorporate transfers
       d. intracorporate transfers
       e. all are forms of exporting
       (c; difficult; p. 348)

35.   _____ occur(s) when a firm sells its products to a domestic customer, which in
       turn exports the product, in either its original form or a modified form.
       a. Indirect exporting
       b. Direct exporting
       c. Intercorporate transfers
       d. Intracorporate transfers
       e. All are forms of exporting
       (a; moderate; p. 348)

36.   _____ occur(s) through sales to customers located outside the firm's home country.
a. Indirect exporting
b. Direct exporting
c. Intercorporate transfers
d. Intracorporate transfers
e. All are forms of exporting
(b; moderate; p. 348)

37.   _____ is/are the sale of goods by a firm in one country to an affiliated firm in another country.
a. Indirect exporting
b. Direct exporting
c. Intercorporate transfers
d. Intracorporate transfers
e. All are forms of exporting
(d; moderate; p. 348)

38.   Which form of exporting is used by firms in order to lower their production costs?
a. indirect exporting
b. direct exporting
c. intercorporate transfers
d. intracorporate transfers
e. all are forms of exporting
(d; difficult; p. 348)

39.   Which of the following is *not* an important consideration in which form of exporting to use?
a. government policies
b. human resource issues
c. marketing concerns
d. logistical considerations
e. distribution issues
(b; moderate; p. 351)

40.   The imposition of _____ discourages international firms from relying on exports as an entry mode.
a. tariffs
b. export promotion policies
c. export financing programs
d. home country subsidization
e. all of the above
(a; moderate; p. 351)

41.   The use of _____ encourages international firms to rely on exports as an entry
       mode.
       a. few tariffs
       b. export promotion policies
       c. export financing programs
       d. home country subsidization
       e. all of the above
       (e; moderate; p. 351)

42.   Which of the following marketing concerns affect the decision to export?
       a. image
       b. distribution
       c. customer responsiveness
       d. need for customer feedback
       e. all of the above
       (e; moderate; p. 352)

43.   What are the third parties that specialize in facilitating imports and exports called?
       a. intermediaries
       b. wholesalers
       c. retailers
       d. exporters
       e. distributors
       (a; moderate; p. 353)

44.   _____ offer services including export management companies, Webb Pomerene
       associations, and international trading companies.
       a. Intermediaries
       b. Wholesalers
       c. Retailers
       d. Exporters
       e. Distributors
       (a; moderate; p. 353)

45.   A(n) _____ is a firm that acts as its client's export department.
       a. Webb-Pomerene association
       b. Greenfield organization
       c. export management company
       d. international trading company
       e. management broker
       (c; easy; p. 353)

46.   Which of the following duties is handled by export management companies?
       a. shipping
       b. clearing customs
       c. document preparation
       d. advice about consumer needs
       e. all of the above
       (e; easy; p. 353)

47.   A(n) _____ is a group of U.S. firms that operate within the same industry and that
       are allowed by law to coordinate their export activities without fear of violating
       U.S. antitrust laws.
       a. Webb-Pomerene association
       b. Greenfield organization
       c. export management company
       d. international trading company
       e. management broker
       (a; moderate; p. 353)

48.   Which of the following activities is commonly performed by Webb-Pomerene
       associations?
       a. market research
       b. overseas promotional activities
       c. freight consolidate
       d. contract negotiations
       e. all of the above
       (e; moderate; p. 353)

49.   A(n) _____ is a firm directly engaged in importing and exporting a wide variety
       of goods for its own account.
       a. Webb-Pomerene association
       b. Greenfield organization
       c. export management company
       d. international trading company
       e. management broker
       (d; easy; p. 353)

50.   Which of the following services is provided by international trading companies?
       a. market research
       b. customs documentation
       c. international transportation
       d. host country distribution
       e. all of the above
       (e; moderate; p. 353)

51.   Where are the most important international trading companies located?
        a. The United States
        b. Germany
        c. Japan
        d. Canada
        e. China
        (c; difficult; p. 353)

52.   To which type of export intermediary does the term soga sosha refer?
        a. Webb-Pomerene association
        b. Greenfield organization
        c. export management company
        d. international trading company
        e. management broker
        (d; moderate; p. 353)

53.   Which of the following is *not* an advantage of soga sosha?
        a. access to information about economic conditions worldwide
        b. ready access to financing
        c. built-in source of customers
        d. economies of scale in transportation
        e. all of the above are advantages
        (e; moderate; p. 353)

54.   With what legislation were Webb-Pomerene associations first authorized?
        a. Helms-Burton Act
        b. Freeport McMoRan Doctrine
        c. Export Trade Act of 1918
        d. Treaty of Rome
        e. None of the above
        (c; moderate; p. 353)

55.   How do export management companies operate?
        a. As commission agents who do not take title to the goods.
        b. As resellers who take title to the goods.
        c. As distributors who do not take title to the goods.
        d. Both a and b.
        e. Both a and c.
        (d; moderate; p. 353)

56.   Which intermediary listed below solicits domestic orders for foreign manufacturers on a commission basis?
        a. manufacturers' agent
        b. export and import broker
        c. freight forwarder
        d. manufacturers' export agent
        e. soga sosha
        (a; easy; p. 354)

57.   Which intermediary listed below acts as a foreign sales department for domestic manufacturers by selling those firms' goods in foreign markets?
        a. manufacturers' agent
        b. export and import broker
        c. freight forwarder
        d. manufacturers' export agent
        e. soga sosha
        (d; easy; p. 354)

58.   Which intermediary listed below can bring together international buyers and sellers of standardized commodities like coffee and grains?
        a. manufacturers' agent
        b. export and import broker
        c. freight forwarder
        d. manufacturers' export agent
        e. soga sosha
        (b; easy; p. 354)

59.   Which intermediary listed below specializes in the physical transportation services for their clients?
        a. manufacturers' agent
        b. export and import broker
        c. freight forwarder
        d. manufacturers' export agent
        e. soga sosha
        (c; easy; p. 355)

60.   The Mitsubishi Corporation is a firm that is directly engaged in importing and exporting a wide variety of goods for its own account and is a part of a keiretsu system. What type of export intermediary is it?
        a. export management company
        b. Webb-Pomerene association
        c. soga sosha
        d. freight forwarder
        e. export and import broker
        (c; difficult; p. 354)

61.   The Nintendo Company manufactures electronic video game players and game
       cartridges. Nintendo provides game designers with technical specifications for
       how its game players work. The design firms create the games and then pay
       Nintendo a fee to manufacture those games. What mode of entry is described in
       this example?
       a.   exporting
       b.   franchising
       c.   licensing
       d.   greenfield strategy
       e.   joint venture
       (c; difficult; p. 355)

62.   Cantab Pharmaceuticals PLC specializes in developing new immunogenic drugs
       and lacks the resources to manufacture and distribute its products. Consequently,
       it has established an entry mode via pharmaceutical giants GlaxoSmithKline and
       Pfizer. These companies manufacture and distribute Cantab's intellectual property.
       What mode of entry is described in this example?
       a.   international trading company
       b.   franchising
       c.   licensing
       d.   export management company
       e.   joint venture
       (c; difficult; p. 355)

63.   What is compensation referred to under a licensing agreement?
       a.   remuneration
       b.   royalty
       c.   credit
       d.   payment
       e.   fee
       (b; easy; p. 356)

64.   How are royalties determined in licensing agreements?
       a.   flat fee
       b.   fixed amount per unit sold
       c.   percentage of sales
       d.   all of the above
       e.   only b and c
       (d; moderate; p. 356)

65.   In a franchise agreement, what does the franchisor provide to the franchisee?
    a. intellectual property (such as brand name)
    b. operating systems
    c. advertising support service
    d. training
    e. all of the above
    (e; moderate; p. 358)

66.   When is international franchising most likely to succeed?
    a. When the franchisor has unique products.
    b. When the franchisor has an advantageous operating procedure.
    c. When success factors are easily transferable to foreign markets.
    d. When foreign investors are interested in entering into franchise agreements.
    e. All of the above.
    (e; easy; p. 358)

67.   A _____ is used by firms that outsource most or all of their manufacturing needs to other companies.
    a. management contract
    b. turnkey project
    c. contract manufacturing strategy
    d. greenfield strategy
    e. licensing
    (c; moderate; p. 359)

68.   A _____ is an agreement whereby one firm provides managerial assistance, technical expertise, or specialized services to a second firm for some agreed-upon time in return for monetary compensation.
    a. management contract
    b. turnkey project
    c. contract manufacturing strategy
    d. greenfield strategy
    e. licensing
    (a; moderate; p. 359)

69.   A _____ is a contract under which a firm agrees to fully design, construct, and equip a facility and then turn the project over to the purchaser when it is ready for operation.
    a. management contract
    b. turnkey project
    c. contract manufacturing strategy
    d. greenfield strategy
    e. licensing
    (b; moderate; p. 359)

70.   What type of construction project commonly involves the use of an international turnkey contract?
        a. nuclear power plant
        b. airport
        c. oil refinery
        d. all of the above
        e. both a and b
        (d; moderate; p. 359)

71.   A _____ means that the firm builds a facility, operates it, and later transfers ownership of the project to some other party.
        a. management contract
        b. BOT project
        c. contract manufacturing strategy
        d. greenfield strategy
        e. licensing
        (b; moderate; p. 359)

72.   A BOT project is a variant of the _____ type of entry mode.
        a. management contract
        b. turnkey project
        c. contract manufacturing strategy
        d. greenfield strategy
        e. licensing
        (b; moderate; p. 359)

73.   The Hyundai Group is a large construction firm that specializes in designing, constructing, and equipping a facility for a purchaser. What type of entry mode does the Hyundai Group facilitate?
        a. turnkey project
        b. management contract
        c. contract manufacturing strategy
        d. greenfield strategy
        e. licensing
        (a; moderate; p. 359)

74.   Which of the following is a method for foreign direct investment?
        a. building new facilities
        b. buying existing assets in a foreign country
        c. participating in a joint venture
        d. acquisition strategy
        e. all of the above
        (e; easy; p. 361)

75.   The term "greenfield" in the greenfield strategy arose from what origin?
        a.   The old adage, "the grass is greener on the other side."
        b.   An image of building on a virgin green site.
        c.   The notion of the color of money.
        d.   The name of the first company to use this strategy.
        e.   No one knows for sure.
        (b; difficult; p. 361)

True/False

76.   Assessing market potential is the second step in the process of foreign market analysis. (F; easy; p. 337)

77.   Government stability is an important factor in foreign market assessment. (T; easy; p. 340)

78.   Because the textbook labels the Republic of China as the independent nation, Taiwan, sales in the Peoples' Republic of China may be damaged. (T; difficult; p. 340)

79.   Indirect costs are those the firm incurs in entering a new market and include costs associated with setting up a business operation. (F; moderate; p. 341)

80.   Dunning's eclectic theory is useful in understanding which mode of entry to use. (T; moderate; p. 342)

81.   National competitive advantage theory by Michael Porter is useful in understanding which mode of entry to use. (F; difficult; p. 342)

82.   When deciding which mode of entry to use, a firm must consider things like ownership advantages, location advantages, and internalization advantages. (T; easy; p. 342)

83.   The brand image of Dom Perignon champagne is a type of internalization advantage. (F; difficult; p. 343)

84.   Ownership advantages are always tangible resources. (F; moderate; p. 343)

85.   Ownership advantages are also called distinctive competencies. (T; moderate; p. 343)

86.   Pharmaceutical firms routinely use licensing as their entry mode. (T; easy; p. 344)

87.   Exporting is the most complicated mode of internationalizing due to the issue of tariffs and non-tariff barriers. (F; moderate; p. 346)

88.   Foreign direct investment offers both high profit potential and high financial risk. (T; easy; p. 347)

89.   Reactive motivations for exporting are those that pull a firm into foreign markets as a result of opportunities available there. (F; moderate; p. 347)

90.   Intel's computer chips are indirectly exported via Hewlett-Packard computers. (T; moderate; p. 348)

91.   Intracorporate transfers are common in the service sector. (T; moderate; p. 350)

92.   Human resource issues are a primary consideration in which form of exporting to use. (F; easy; p. 351)

93.   Logistical costs are typically lower for exported goods than for those locally produced. (F; easy; p. 353)

94.   Export management companies may be paid on commission. (T; moderate; p. 353)

95.   Export management companies always take title to the goods. (F; moderate; p. 353)

96.   Webb-Pomerene associations play a major role in international business. (F; difficult; p. 353)

97.   The most important trading companies in the global marketplace are Japan's keiretsu. (F; difficult; p. 353)

98.   Royalties are determined most commonly as a percentage of the sales of the licensed products. (T; easy; p. 356)

99.   Licensing agreements generally include a maximum royalty payment to ensure that the foreign licensee will earn a reasonable profit. (F; difficult; p. 356)

100.   Because of the high investment required, the licensees that built Tokyo Disneyland insisted upon a 100-year licensing agreement with The Walt Disney Company. (T; easy; p. 357)

Short Answers

101.   What are the critical factors in assessing new market opportunities? Name at least five of these factors. Answer: There are several factors listed in Table 12.1.

They are product-market dimensions, major product-market differences, structural characteristics of the national product market, competitor analysis, potential target markets, relevant trends, explanation of change, success factors, and strategic options. (moderate; p. 338)

102.   What are the major competitor characteristics one should consider when conducting a competitor analysis? Answer: One should consider the competitor's size, capacity utilization, strengths and weaknesses, technology, supply sources, preferential market arrangements, and relations with the government. It should also include competitor performance in terms of market share, sales growth, and profit margins. (difficult; p. 338)

103.   Where are the three growth markets for beer? Answer: Brazil, Mexico, and China. (difficult; p. 340)

104.   What are direct and opportunity costs? Answer: Direct costs are those the firm incurs in entering a new foreign market and include costs associated with setting up a business operation. Opportunity costs are the costs of missing other opportunities by virtue of entering one market rather than another. (easy; p. 341)

105.   What type of risks are Dole Food Company's international operations frequently subject to? Answer: Weather, insect invasions, changes in tariffs, and changes in import quotas. (difficult; p. 341)

106.   What are the five primary types of entry modes for foreign markets? Answer: Exporting, international licensing, international franchising, specialized modes, and foreign direct investment. (moderate; p. 342)

107.   What are the three types of foreign direct investment? Answer: Greenfield strategy, acquisition strategy, and joint venture. (moderate; p. 342)

108.   What are the three types of specialized modes for entry into foreign markets? Answer: Contract manufacturing, management contracts, and turnkey projects. (moderate; p. 342)

109.   What is the meaning of ownership advantages? Give an example. Answer: Ownership advantages are tangible or intangible resources owned by a firm which grant a competitive advantage over its industry rivals. An example is the brand image and luxurious reputation of Dom Perignon champagne. (moderate; p. 343)

110.   Explain the meaning of internalization advantages. Answer: Internalization advantages are those that make it desirable for a firm to produce a good or service itself rather than contracting with another firm to produce it. (moderate; p. 343)

111. What are the advantages and disadvantages of contract manufacturing? Answer: Its advantages are low financial risk, minimal required resources devoted to manufacturing, and the ability to focus firm's resources on other areas of the value chain. Its disadvantages are reduced control, reduced learning potential, and potential public relations problems. (moderate; p. 347)

112. Explain the meaning of indirect exporting. Provide an example. Answer: Indirect exporting occurs when a firm sells its product to a domestic customer, which in turn exports the product, either in its original form or a modified form. An example is Intel computer chips which are indirectly exported in computers. (moderate; p. 348)

113. What is an intracorporate transfer? Answer: An intracorporate transfer is the sale of goods by a firm in one country to an affiliated firm in another. (moderate; p. 349)

114. Why might exporters market and distribute its goods in international markets using export intermediaries? Answer: Export intermediaries are third parties that specialize in facilitating imports and exports. They offer many services such as transportation and documentation. They may also take on many other broad responsibilities. (easy; p. 353)

115. What service do manufacturers' agents provide? Answer: Manufacturer's agents solicit domestic orders for foreign manufacturers usually on a commission basis. (easy; p. 354)

116. What service is provided by manufacturers' export agents? Answer: They act as foreign sales departments for domestic manufacturers, selling those firms' goods in foreign markets. (easy; p. 354)

117. What service is provided by export and import brokers? Answer: They bring together international buyers and sellers of such standardized commodities as coffee, cocoa, and grains. (easy; p. 354)

118. What service is provided by freight forwarders? Answer: They specialize in the physical transportation of goods, arranging customs documentation, and obtaining transportation services for their clients. (easy; p. 355)

119. What are the advantages and disadvantages of international licensing? Answer: Licensing carries relatively low financial risk. It allows the licensor to learn more about the sales potential of its products in a new market without significant commitment of financial and managerial resources. However, it limits the market opportunities for both parties. It requires interdependence among the parties because they are both involved in maintaining product quality and promoting brand image. (moderate; p. 357)

120.   What are the basic issues addressed in a legal contract for a licensing agreement? Answer: The basic issues covered in the legal contract should include 1) specifying the boundaries of the agreement, 2) determining compensation, 3) establishing rights, privileges, and constraints, and 4) specifying the duration of the contract. (difficult; p. 356)

Essay

121.   What are the advantages of exporting?

Answer: Exporting offers a firm two advantages. First, the firm can control its financial exposure to the host country market as it deems appropriate. Little or no capital investment may be needed. Second, exporting permits a firm to enter a foreign market gradually. Firms can then monitor its success prior to more extensive entry into that market. (moderate; p. 346)

122.   What are soga soshas? What advantages do they offer exporters? Name three examples of prominent soga soshas.

Answer: A soga sosha is an international trading company. Soga soshas are part of Japan's keiretsu system. They have access to information about economic conditions and business opportunities in virtually every corner of the world. Because of their link to a keiretsu, they have ready access financing and a built-in source of customers. They have a low-cost structure and international expertise. The five largest soga sosha are Mitsubishi Corporation, Mitsui and Company, Itochu Corporation, Sumitomo Group, and Marubeni. (difficult; p. 353)

123.   Explain the licensing process.

Answer: The licensing process is depicted in Figure 12.3. The licensor leases the rights to use its intellectual property to the licensee. The licensee uses the intellectual property to create products for local sale. It then pays a royalty back to the licensor. The licensor is able to earn new revenues with relatively low investment. (moderate; p. 355)

124.   What specific issues must be addressed in a detailed legal contract for an international licensing agreement? Discuss the importance of each one.

Answer: Contracts for licensing agreements must include the boundaries of the agreement. The licensor and licensee must determine which rights and privileges are and are not being conveyed in the agreement. This protects both parties. Compensation must also be set out in the agreement. The royalty amount (or method of determination) as well as a minimum royalty payment should be specified. The rights, privileges, and constraints should be addressed in the contract. This protects the image of both companies and ensures the appropriate quality level. Finally, the length of the agreement must be stated. (moderate; p. 356)

125.   What are the three primary methods for foreign direct investment? Describe each one.

Answer: The three methods are building new facilities, buying existing assets, or participating in a joint venture. Building new facilities is also called the greenfield strategy. It allows a firm to select the best possible site and construct the best facility. It does require time and patience, though. The method of buying existing assets in a foreign country is also called the acquisition strategy or the brownfield strategy. Because the firm is acquiring an existing facility, it provides quick control and the ability to continue to generate revenues. Joint ventures are created when two or more firms agree to work together and create a jointly owned separate firm to promote their mutual interests. (easy; p. 361)

Multiple Choice

1.   Which of the following represents a possible form of cooperation between
       international firms?
       a. cross-licensing of proprietary technology
       b. sharing of production facilities
       c. co-funding of research projects
       d. marketing of each other's products
       e. all of the above
       (e; easy; p. 368)

2.   A _____ is a business arrangement whereby two or more firms choose to
       cooperate for their mutual benefit.
       a. competitive advantage
       b. licensing agreement
       c. franchising arrangement
       d. strategic alliance
       e. none of the above
       (d; moderate; p. 368)

3.   One of Kellogg's biggest competitors in the United States is _____.
       a. Nestle
       b. General Mills
       c. Johnson and Johnson
       d. Cereal Partners Worldwide
       e. Proctor and Gamble
       (b; difficult; p. 367)

4.   European consumers generally prefer _____ for breakfast.
       a. cereal
       b. meat
       c. pancakes
       d. doughnuts
       e. instant oatmeal
       (b; moderate; p. 367)

5.   What company created the breakfast cereal market in Europe?
       a. General Mills
       b. Nestle
       c. Kellogg
       d. Quaker Oats Company
       e. none of the above
       (c; moderate; p. 367)

6.   What breakfast food did Kellogg market in Europe?
        a. pop-tarts
        b. cereal
        c. oatmeal
        d. breakfast bars
        e. pancakes
        (b; easy; p. 367)

7.   The growth of the breakfast cereal market in Europe depends largely on _____.
        a. changes in culture
        b. changes in infrastructure
        c. changes in consumer lifestyles
        d. changes in commercial television outlets
        e. all of the above
        (e; moderate; p. 367)

8.   Which of the following tasks was *not* performed by General Mills as a part of its
        efforts for the Cereal Partners Worldwide venture?
        a. Installation of manufacturing systems.
        b. Oversee production of cereals.
        c. Develop advertising campaigns.
        d. Distribute cereals throughout Europe.
        e. Contribute money to CPW.
        (d; moderate; p. 368)

9.   A _____ is a special type of strategic alliance in which two or more firms join
        together to create a new business entity that is legally separate and distinct from
        its parents.
        a. joint venture
        b. licensing agreement
        c. franchising arrangement
        d. strategic alliance
        e. greenfield strategy
        (a; moderate; p. 368)

10.   General Mills and Nestle contributed around $80 million to create a new firm
        called Cereal Partners Worldwide. This is an example of a(n) _____.
        a. franchising arrangement
        b. acquisition strategy
        c. joint venture
        d. licensing agreement
        e. greenfield strategy
        (c; moderate; p. 368)

11.   When a firm discovers that it lacks all the necessary internal resources to effectively compete internationally, it may choose to participate in _____.
       a. exporting
       b. portfolio investments
       c. strategic alliances
       d. franchising
       e. management contracts
       (c; difficult; p. 368)

12.   What is the primary difference between a joint venture and a non-joint venture strategic alliance?
       a. The amount of control awarded to each partner.
       b. The level of risk.
       c. Whether a third, legally separate business entity is formed.
       d. The amount of financial investment required.
       e. The geographic location of the alliance.
       (c; difficult; p. 368)

13.   United Airlines and British Airways entered into an agreement involving their North American and European routes. They agreed to coordinate flights schedules and to market the arrangement. What is this an example of?
       a. franchising arrangement
       b. acquisition strategy
       c. joint venture
       d. licensing agreement
       e. strategic alliance
       (e; difficult; p. 368)

14.   What method did Kellogg initially use to enter the European cereal market?
       a. exporting
       b. licensing
       c. franchising
       d. joint venture
       e. greenfield strategy
       (a; difficult; p. 367)

15.   Which of the following can be used to enter or expand international operations for a firm?
       a. exporting
       b. licensing
       c. joint venture
       d. acquisition strategy
       e. all of the above
       (e; easy; p. 369)

16.   Which characteristic below best describes non-joint–venture alliances?
       a. narrow
       b. risky
       c. expensive
       d. broad
       e. all of the above
       (a; moderate; p. 369)

17.   British Airways and American Airlines codeshare their flights and market
       materials containing both brand names. What type of arrangement is this?
       a. non-joint–venture alliance
       b. joint venture alliance
       c. acquisition strategy
       d. turn key project
       e. licensing
       (a; moderate; p. 369)

18.   When a firm anticipates major obstacles in foreign market entry such as hostile
       government regulations, what benefit of strategic alliances do they primarily
       seek?
       a. ease of market entry
       b. shared risk
       c. shared knowledge
       d. synergy
       e. all of the above
       (a; easy; p. 370)

19.   Which of the following is a benefit of participating in a strategic alliance?
       a. ease of market entry
       b. shared risk
       c. shared knowledge
       d. synergy
       e. all of the above
       (e; easy; p. 370)

20.   Which of the following is *not* a benefit of participating in a strategic alliance?
       a. ease of market entry
       b. shared risk
       c. shared knowledge
       d. reduced profit potential
       e. synergy
       (d; easy; p. 370)

21.   Warner Brothers, a movie distribution subsidiary of Time Warner, recently
        entered into several joint ventures with European movie theater chains. What
        benefit of strategic alliances was Warner Brothers seeking?
        a.   ease of market entry
        b.   shared risk
        c.   shared knowledge
        d.   synergy
        e.   all of the above
        (a; difficult; p. 370)

22.   Boeing collaborated in a strategic alliance with Fuji, Mitsubishi, and Kawasaki in
        the development and production of the Boeing 777 in order to reduce its financial
        risk. What benefit of strategic alliances was Boeing seeking?
        a.   ease of market entry
        b.   shared risk
        c.   shared knowledge
        d.   synergy
        e.   all of the above
        (b; easy; p. 371)

23.   Coca-Cola partnered with a Chinese company to create a noncarbonated line of
        drinks because of _____.
        a.   risk associated with the Chinese market
        b.   governmental pressure
        c.   desire for knowledge of the Chinese company's operations
        d.   desire for synergy
        e.   all of the above
        (b; difficult; p. 371)

24.   Toyota and GM created a joint venture called NUMMI because Toyota wanted to
        learn about how to deal with labor and parts suppliers in the U.S. market while
        GM wanted to observe Japanese management practices. What benefit of strategic
        alliances were Toyota and GM seeking?
        a.   ease of market entry
        b.   shared risk
        c.   shared knowledge
        d.   synergy
        e.   all of the above
        (c; easy; p. 372)

25.   _____ refers to value achieved through the combination of market entry, risk sharing, and learning potential that is greater than what the firm could have done alone.
a.   Shared risk
b.   Shared knowledge
c.   Synergy
d.   Competitive advantage
e.   Both c and d
(e; moderate; p. 372)

26.   Why would Kodak agree to collaborate with Fuji to develop a new film?
a.   ease of market entry
b.   shared risk
c.   shared knowledge
d.   synergy
e.   all of the above
(b; difficult; p. 372)

27.   PepsiCo and Thomas J. Lipton Co. established a joint venture. PepsiCo supplied an extensive distribution network and Lipton provided manufacturing expertise and brand recognition in teas. What benefit of strategic alliances were they seeking?
a.   ease of market entry
b.   shared risk
c.   shared knowledge
d.   synergy
e.   all of the above
(d; moderate; p. 374)

28.   The degree of collaboration in a strategic alliance will depend on the _____ of each partner firm.
a.   history
b.   available resources
c.   basic goals
d.   leadership
e.   all of the above
(c; difficult; p. 374)

29.   A _____ occurs when the participating firms agree to perform together multiple
       stages of the process by which goods or services are brought to the market.
       a. functional alliance
       b. joint venture
       c. production alliance
       d. process alliance
       e. comprehensive alliance
       (e; moderate; p. 375)

30.   Most comprehensive alliances are organized as _____.
       a. non-joint-venture alliance
       b. joint ventures
       c. licensing agreements
       d. management contracts
       e. turnkey projects
       (b; easy; p. 375)

31.   A marketing alliance is a type of _____.
       a. business-level alliance
       b. operational alliance
       c. corporate-level alliance
       d. functional alliance
       e. advertising alliance
       (d; easy; p. 375)

32.   Twentieth Century Fox and Paramount Pictures contributed financial resources to
       the making of Titanic. What type of alliance did they have?
       a. joint venture
       b. marketing alliance
       c. financial alliance
       d. licensing agreement
       e. production alliance
       (c; easy; p. 377)

33.   General Mills and Nestle created a joint venture which fully integrated all the
       efforts necessary to compete against Kellogg in the European cereal market. This
       is an example of a(n) _____ alliance.
       a. functional
       b. comprehensive
       c. production
       d. international
       e. marketing
       (b; moderate; p. 375)

34.   Which of the following is *not* one of the types of functional alliances?
   a.   production
   b.   international
   c.   marketing
   d.   financial
   e.   research and development
   (b; moderate; p. 375)

35.   A(n) _____ alliance occurs when two or more firms each manufacture or provide services in a shared or common facility.
   a.   production
   b.   international
   c.   marketing
   d.   financial
   e.   research and development
   (a; moderate; p. 375)

36.   A production alliance typically does not take the form of a _____.
   a.   non-joint–venture alliance
   b.   joint ventures
   c.   licensing agreements
   d.   management contracts
   e.   turnkey projects
   (b; easy; p. 375)

37.   A(n) _____ alliance occurs when partners share expertise or services related to distribution, pricing, and communications.
   a.   production
   b.   international
   c.   marketing
   d.   financial
   e.   research and development
   (c; moderate; p. 376)

38.   A(n) _____ alliance is a functional alliance of firms that want to reduce financial risks associated with a project.
   a.   production
   b.   international
   c.   marketing
   d.   financial
   e.   research and development
   (d; moderate; p. 375)

39.   BMW and the French automobile manufacturer PSA recently created an alliance to manufacture new engines together. What type of alliance is this an example of?
        a. production
        b. international
        c. marketing
        d. financial
        e. research and development
        (a; moderate; p. 375)

40.   The Japanese company Bandai and the U.S. toymaker Mattel entered into a strategic alliance. Bandai agreed to distribute Mattel products like Barbie dolls in Japan while Mattel agreed to distribute Power Rangers in Latin America. What type of alliance is this an example of?
        a. production
        b. international
        c. marketing
        d. financial
        e. research and development
        (c; moderate; p. 376)

41.   Boeing collaborated in a strategic alliance with Fuji, Mitsubishi, and Kawasaki in the development and production of the Boeing 777 in order to reduce its financial risk. What type of alliance is this an example of?
        a. production
        b. international
        c. marketing
        d. financial
        e. research and development
        (d; moderate; p. 377)

42.   Micron Technology, Intel, Samsung, Hyundai, and Siemens have formed an alliance to develop the next generation of DRAM chips. What type of alliance is this an example of?
        a. production
        b. international
        c. marketing
        d. financial
        e. research and development
        (e; moderate; p. 377)

43.   A _____ is a confederation of organizations that band together to research and
        develop new products and processes for world markets.
        a. research and development alliance
        b. functional alliance
        c. research and development consortium
        d. joint venture
        e. production alliance
        (c; easy; p. 377)

44.   Research suggests that strategic alliances are more likely to be successful if the
        skills and resources of the partners are _____.
        a. identical
        b. complementary
        c. opposites
        d. incompatible
        e. observable
        (b; moderate; p. 378)

45.   Which of the following is *not* one of the four factors a firm should consider prior
        to selecting a partner?
        a. compatibility
        b. potential for competitor to partner
        c. nature of potential partner's products
        d. relative safeness of the alliance
        e. learning potential of the alliance
        (b; difficult; p. 378)

46.   Compatibility is largely based on the extent to which one can_____ the partner.
        a. control
        b. manipulate
        c. trust
        d. take over
        e. imitate
        (c; moderate; p. 378)

47.   Partnerships should be formed between firms whose products _____.
        a. compete directly
        b. complement one another
        c. compete indirectly
        d. are in different product categories
        e. none of the above
        (b; moderate; p. 378)

48.   What form does a joint venture usually take?
        a. limited partnership
        b. partnership
        c. corporation
        d. GmbH
        e. public-private venture
        (c; moderate; p. 379)

49.   Which of the following is a benefit of the corporate form for joint ventures?
        a. beneficial tax structure
        b. unusual ownership arrangements
        c. protection of other assets
        d. new identity
        e. all of the above
        (e; easy; p. 379)

50.   A _____ is a joint venture that involves a partnership between a privately owned
        firm and a government.
        a. limited partnership
        b. partnership
        c. corporation
        d. GmbH
        e. public-private venture
        (e; moderate; p. 379)

51.   The government of the Ivory Coast formed a joint venture with Ranger Oil Ltd.
        What type of joint venture is this an example of?
        a. limited partnership
        b. partnership
        c. corporation
        d. GmbH
        e. public-private venture
        (e; moderate; p. 380)

52.   Strategic alliances may be managed through _____.
        a. shared management agreements
        b. assigned arrangements
        c. delegated arrangements
        d. consensual arrangements
        e. a, b, and c
        (e; moderate; p. 380)

53.   In what type of economy are public-private ventures often necessary?
       a. centrally-planned
       b. capitalist
       c. socialist
       d. Marxist
       e. none of the above
       (a; difficult; p. 380)

54.   Under a(n) _____, each partner in the joint venture fully and actively participates
       in managing the alliance.
       a. shared management agreements
       b. assigned arrangements
       c. delegated arrangements
       d. consensual arrangements
       e. functional alliance
       (a; moderate; p. 381)

55.   Which action below is permissible by the dominant partner in an assigned
       arrangement?
       a. set agendas
       b. make decisions
       c. break ties among decision makers
       d. overrule partner's decisions
       e. all of the above
       (e; easy; p. 381)

56.   Under a(n) _____, one partner assumes primary responsibility for the operations
       of the alliance.
       a. shared management agreements
       b. assigned arrangements
       c. delegated arrangements
       d. consensual arrangements
       e. functional alliance
       (b; moderate; p. 381)

57.   GM, with a 67% stake in a joint venture with Raba, has assumed management
       control over the venture's operations. What management form is this an example
       of?
       a. shared management agreements
       b. assigned arrangements
       c. delegated arrangements
       d. consensual arrangements
       e. functional alliance
       (b; moderate; p. 381)

58.   Under the agreement between Coca-Cola and Danone each company supplies
        three members of the joint venture's board of directors. What management form
        is this an example of?
        a.   shared management agreements
        b.   assigned arrangements
        c.   delegated arrangements
        d.   consensual arrangements
        e.   functional alliance
        (a; moderate; p. 381)

59.   Which management form is most difficult to maintain in joint ventures?
        a.   shared management agreements
        b.   assigned arrangements
        c.   delegated arrangements
        d.   consensual arrangements
        e.   functional alliance
        (a; moderate; p. 381)

60.   Boeing controls the overall operation of its strategic alliance with Fuji, Mitsubishi,
        and Kawasaki. This is an example of a(n) _____.
        a.   shared management agreements
        b.   assigned arrangements
        c.   delegated arrangements
        d.   consensual arrangements
        e.   functional alliance
        (b; moderate; p. 381)

61.   Which of the following could cause a problem in a strategic alliance?
        a.   incompatibility
        b.   information access
        c.   distribution of earnings
        d.   all of the above
        e.   none of the above
        (d; easy; p. 382)

62.   Executives operating a joint venture under a delegated arrangement are in a
        position to _____.
        a.   make day-to-day decisions
        b.   implement strategy
        c.   plan strategically
        d.   make financial obligations
        e.   all of the above
        (e; easy; p. 382)

63.   Of the potential pitfalls of strategic alliances, which one is a primary cause of
        failure?
        a. incompatibility of partners
        b. loss of autonomy
        c. access to information
        d. conflicts over distributing earnings
        e. changing circumstances
        (a; moderate; p. 382)

64.   Which of the following is likely to create incompatibility between partnering
        firms?
        a. corporate culture
        b. national culture
        c. goals
        d. objectives
        e. all of the above
        (e; moderate; p. 382)

65.   Which of the following is *not* a cause of incompatibility between members of an
        alliance?
        a. corporate culture
        b. ambition
        c. national culture
        d. goals
        e. all are causes
        (b; moderate; p. 382)

66.   AT&T and Olivetti announced a strategic alliance. They could not reach an
        agreement on a marketing strategy for the alliance. What type of problem is this
        an example of?
        a. incompatibility
        b. information access
        c. distribution of earnings
        d. loss of autonomy
        e. all of the above
        (a; moderate; p. 383)

67.   When a firm involved in a strategic alliance wants to maintain confidential
        information about its operations, which pitfall of strategic alliances is likely to
        occur?
        a. incompatibility
        b. information access
        c. distribution of earnings
        d. loss of autonomy
        e. all of the above
        (b; moderate; p. 383)

68.   A strategic alliance between Ford and Mazda experienced problems when Mazda
        refused to allow Ford officials to visit the Mazda research laboratory. What was
        the source of this problem?
        a. incompatibility
        b. information access
        c. distribution of earnings
        d. loss of autonomy
        e. all of the above
        (b; moderate; p. 384)

69.   Rubbermaid ended a joint venture in Europe when the partner firm refused to
        reinvest its profits into the development of new products. What was the source of
        this problem?
        a. incompatibility
        b. information access
        c. distribution of earnings
        d. loss of autonomy
        e. all of the above
        (c; moderate; p. 384)

70.   Firms may experience the pitfalls of _____ that limits its decision-making power.
        a. incompatibility
        b. information access
        c. distribution of earnings
        d. loss of autonomy
        e. all of the above
        (d; moderate; p. 384)

71.   Attempts to introduce new products, change the way the alliance does business, or introduce other significant organizational changes without previous discussion and agreement by all members of the alliance represents a(n) _____ by one or more alliance members.
       a. incompatibility
       b. information access
       c. distribution of earnings
       d. loss of autonomy
       e. all of the above
       (d; moderate; p. 384)

72.   _____ affect(s) the viability of strategic alliances when the conditions that first motivated the arrangement no longer exist.
       a. Incompatibility
       b. Information access
       c. Distribution of earnings
       d. Loss of autonomy
       e. Changing circumstances
       (e; easy; p. 384)

73.   A survey of 150 terminated strategic alliances found that more than 75% ended because a Japanese firm has taken over a non-Japanese partner. What was the source of problem?
       a. incompatibility
       b. information access
       c. distribution of earnings
       d. loss of autonomy
       e. all of the above
       (d; moderate; p. 384)

74.   Of the potential pitfalls facing strategic alliances, over which one do the alliance members have the least control?
       a. incompatibility
       b. information access
       c. distribution of earnings
       d. changing circumstances
       e. loss of autonomy
       (d; moderate; p. 385)

75.   Ford wanted to develop a strategic alliance in South America until economic reforms took place in Brazil and trade barriers were reduced. Which pitfall of strategic alliances is this an example of?
       a.   incompatibility
       b.   information access
       c.   distribution of earnings
       d.   loss of autonomy
       e.   changing circumstances
       (e; moderate; p. 385)

True/False

76.   General Mills created the breakfast cereal market in Europe.
       (F; moderate; p. 367)

77.   General Mills created a joint venture with Kellogg called the Cereal Partners Worldwide. (F; moderate; p. 368)

78.   Strategic alliances include cooperation between international firms such as cross-licensing of proprietary technology. (T; easy; p. 368)

79.   A joint venture is a type of strategic alliance. (T; easy; p. 368)

80.   Joint ventures are generally less stable than non-joint–venture strategic alliances. (F; moderate; p. 369)

81.   Warner Brothers partnered with several European movie theater chains in order to gain knowledge and expertise about the European market.
       (F; difficult; p. 370)

82.   Many countries are so concerned about the influence of foreign firms on their economies that they require MNCs to work with a local partner if they want to operate in these countries. (T; moderate; p. 371)

83.   Boeing collaborated with three Japanese partners on the Boeing 777 to share its financial risk and gain access the Japanese market. (T; easy; p. 372)

84.   NUMMI is a joint venture between Toyota and GM. (T; moderate; p. 372)

85.   Strategic alliances involve a 50-50 degree of collaboration from the partners.
       (F; moderate; p. 374)

86.   Comprehensive alliances are usually organized as non-joint–venture strategic alliances. (F; moderate; p. 375)

87.   The Japanese government, Nippon Telephone and Telegraph, Mitsubishi, Matsushita, and three other Japanese firms agreed to work together to create new types of high-capacity memory chips in the form of a R&D consortium. (T; easy; p. 377)

88.   Research suggests that strategic alliances are more likely to be successful if the partners compete but in different geographic markets. (F; difficult; p. 377)

89.   Mutual trust is an important component of compatibility. (T; easy; p. 378)

90.   Puerto Rico is sometimes seen as a favorable tax haven for the incorporation of joint ventures. (F; difficult; p. 379)

91.   Public-private ventures are typical in the oil industry. (T; moderate; p. 380)

92.   Public-private ventures are perhaps most important in market-driven economies. (F; difficult; p. 380)

93.   Share management agreements are the most simple to maintain. (F; moderate; p. 381)

94.   Under an assigned arrangement, management of the alliance is greatly simplified. (T; moderate; p. 381)

95.   In a delegated arrangement, joint venture management has little to no autonomy. (F; easy; p. 382)

96.   Conflict over the distribution of earnings is the number one cause of failure of strategic alliances. (F; difficult; p. 382)

97.   Incompatibility among partners can be anticipated through discussion and analysis prior to forming a strategic alliance. (T; moderate; p. 382)

98.   A strategic alliance may be the first step toward a takeover. (T; moderate; p. 384)

99.   Conflict over distributing earnings can be avoided by negotiating such issues as part of the original contract agreement. (T; easy; p. 384)

100.   Transfer pricing arrangements are not a necessary part of a strategic alliance agreement. (F; moderate; p. 384)

Short Answers

101.   What is the definition of a strategic alliance? Answer: A strategic alliance is a business arrangement whereby two or more firms choose to cooperate for mutual benefit. (easy; p. 368)

102.   What is the relationship between a joint venture and a strategic alliance? Answer: A joint venture is a type of strategic alliance in which two or more firms join together to create a new business entity that is legally separate and distinct from its parents. (easy; p. 368)

103.   Is a strategic alliance the only method a firm can use to enter or expand its international operations? Answer: No. A firm can also use exporting, licensing, franchising, and foreign direct investment. (easy; p. 369)

104.   What are the benefits of strategic alliances? Answer: Benefits of strategic alliances include ease of market entry, shared risk, shared knowledge, and synergy/competitive advantage. (moderate; p. 370)

105.   Why did Warner Brothers enter into joint ventures with several European movie theater chains? Answer: To ease its entry into the European market. (moderate; p. 370)

106.   What influence might governments have on the ease of entry into its market? Answer: Governments may require that an MNC partner with a local firm. (moderate; p. 371)

107.   Toyota wanted an opportunity to learn about U.S. labor practices and GM wanted to learn about Japanese management practices when they created NUMMI. What benefit were both partners seeking? Answer: Shared knowledge and expertise. (easy; p. 372)

108.   What is a comprehensive alliance? Answer: A comprehensive alliance occurs when the participating firms agree to perform together multiple stages of the process by which goods or services are brought to the market. (moderate; p. 375)

109.   What is a functional alliance? Answer: A functional alliance is one that is narrow in scope and involves only one function of the business. (moderate; p. 375)

110.   What types of functional alliances exist? Answer: Production, financial, marketing, research, and development. (moderate; p. 375)

111.   What is an R&D consortium? Answer: It is a confederation of organizations that band together to research and develop new products and processes for the world market. (moderate; p. 377)

112.   What are the four factors that should be considered prior to selecting a partner? Answer: Compatibility, the nature of the potential partner's products, the relative safeness of the alliance, and the learning potential of the alliance. (moderate; p. 378)

113.   What is a public-private venture? Answer: It is a form of joint venture that involves a partnership between a privately owned firm and a government. (moderate; p. 379)

114.   What form is usually taken by a joint venture? Answer: Corporation. (easy; p. 379)

115.   What are the three types of management agreement used for strategic alliances? Answer: Shared management agreements, assigned arrangements, and delegated arrangements. (moderate; p. 380)

116.   How does a shared management agreement work? Answer: Under this agreement, each partner fully and actively participates in managing the alliance. It requires a great deal of coordination and near-perfect agreement among the partners. (moderate; p. 381)

117.   How does an assigned arrangement work? Answer: Under this agreement, one partner assumes primary responsibility for the operations of the strategic alliance. (moderate; p. 381)

118.   How does a delegated arrangement work? Answer: Under a delegated arrangement, the partners agree not to get involved in the ongoing operations, but delegate control to the executives of the joint venture itself. (moderate; p. 382)

119.   What kinds of things might cause incompatibility among partners in a strategic alliance? Answer: Corporate culture, national culture, goals, and objectives. (moderate; p. 382)

120.   Over which pitfall of strategic alliances do managers have the least ability to control and prepare through contract negotiations? Answer: Changing circumstances. (difficult; p. 383)

Essay

121.   What are the critical factors in assessing new market opportunities? Name at least five of these factors.

Answer: There are several factors listed in Table 12.1. They are product-market dimensions, major product-market differences, structural characteristics of the national product market, competitor analysis, potential target markets, relevant trends, explanation of change, success factors, and strategic options. (moderate; p. 338)

122.   What changes have occurred in Europe that have aided in increasing the demand for breakfast cereals like those offered by Kellogg?

Answer: Several changes have affected demand for breakfast cereals. European consumers have become more health conscious and more time-starved. Eggs, meats, and bread have always been popular at breakfasts but now they are considering alternatives. Busy schedules increase demand for prepackaged breakfasts. New large supermarkets have also helped. Smaller stores did not want to take up valuable store space with cereal boxes. (difficult; p. 367)

123.   Explain the three possible methods for managing a joint venture.

Answer: A joint venture may be managed jointly with shared management by the founding firms. It may be primarily managed by one parent. Finally, it may be run by an independent team of managers who are hired by the parent firms. (moderate; p. 369)

124.   What benefits may accrue to firms participating in strategic alliances?

Answer: Firms may benefit from ease of market entry, shared risk, shared knowledge and expertise, and synergy/competitive advantage. Firms may experience entrenched competition, government regulations, or high costs to entering a foreign market. Strategic alliances can ease the costs of entry. Firms may also wish to minimize their risks associated with market entry. Alliances can minimize risks by sharing expenses or by providing non-financial assets such as brand recognition. Firms may also wish to learn about an expertise held by another firm. Finally, firms can achieve synergies and competitive advantages that were not possible working alone. (moderate; p. 370)

125.   What are the five primary pitfalls of strategic alliances? Describe each one.

Answer: The five pitfalls are incompatibility of partners, access to information, distribution of earnings, loss of autonomy, and changing circumstances. Incompatibility of partners can lead to outright conflict. It can stem from corporate culture, national culture, goals and objectives, or any fundamental decision. Limited access to information is another drawback. Partners must be willing to share information that they might otherwise keep secret. Because partners share risks, they must also share rewards. However, the partners must agree on the distribution of joint earnings, the accounting practices used to calculate earnings or profits, and the way transfer pricing will be held. Partners also lose autonomy in that they must share control of the alliance. At the extreme, a strategic alliance may even be the first step toward a takcover. Finally, circumstances may change making the strategic alliance obsolete. (moderate; p. 382)

Multiple Choice

1.   What company is the world's largest packaged consumer goods company?
        a. Unilever
        b. Proctor and Gamble
        c. Johnson and Johnson
        d. Kellogg
        e. Microsoft
        (b; moderate; p. 391)

2.   _____ is the overall pattern of structural components and configurations used to
        manage the total organization.
        a. Organizational design
        b. Functional design
        c. Management
        d. Strategy
        e. None of the above
        (a; easy; p. 392)

3.   Which of the following affects the appropriate organizational design for a firm?
        a. firm size
        b. firm strategy
        c. technology
        d. environment
        e. all of the above
        (e; moderate; p. 392)

4.   Which of the following is *not* one of the characteristics affecting organizational
        design?
        a. firm size
        b. firm strategy
        c. technology
        d. environment
        e. all of these affect organizational design
        (e; moderate; p. 392)

5.   A study of design changes found that most firms make major design changes
        about every _____.
        a. year
        b. two years
        c. five years
        d. ten years
        e. almost never
        (c; moderate; p. 393)

6.   With the _____, the firm delegates responsibility for processing international orders to individuals within an existing department.
      a.   corollary approach
      b.   export department
      c.   international division
      d.   global product design
      e.   none of the above
      (a; easy; p. 393)

7.   The _____ is typical for a firm with only a small level of international activity.
      a.   corollary approach
      b.   export department
      c.   international division
      d.   global product design
      e.   none of the above
      (a; casy; p. 393)

8.   The _____ takes responsibility for overseeing international operations, marketing products, processing orders, working with foreign distributors, and arranging financing when necessary.
      a.   corollary approach
      b.   export department
      c.   international division
      d.   global product design
      e.   none of the above
      (b; easy; p. 393)

9.   Which of the following responsibilities is included as part of an export department's duties?
      a.   overseeing international operations
      b.   marketing products
      c.   processing orders
      d.   working with foreign distributors
      e.   all of the above
      (e; moderate; p. 393)

10.   The _____ allows a firm to concentrate resources and create specialized programs targeted on international business activity while simultaneously keeping that activity segregated from the firm's ongoing domestic activities.
      a.   corollary approach
      b.   export department
      c.   international division
      d.   global product design
      e.   none of the above
      (c; easy; p. 393)

11.   Which of the following types of knowledge is *not* necessary to compete effectively in international business?
        a.   area knowledge
        b.   product knowledge
        c.   functional knowledge
        d.   geocentric knowledge
        e.   all are critical types of knowledge
        (d; moderate; p. 394)

12.   _____ refers to the need for managers to understand cultural, commercial, social, and economic conditions in each host country.
        a.   Area knowledge
        b.   Product knowledge
        c.   Functional knowledge
        d.   Geocentric knowledge
        e.   All are critical types of knowledge
        (a; moderate; p. 394)

13.   _____ refers to the need for managers to comprehend such factors as technological trends, customer needs, and competitive forces affecting the goods the firm produces and sells.
        a.   Area knowledge
        b.   Product knowledge
        c.   Functional knowledge
        d.   Geocentric knowledge
        e.   All are critical types of knowledge
        (b; moderate; p. 394)

14.   _____ refers to the need for managers to have access to co-workers with expertise in basic business functions such as production, marketing, finance, accounting, human resource management, and information technology.
        a.   Area knowledge
        b.   Product knowledge
        c.   Functional knowledge
        d.   Geocentric knowledge
        e.   All are critical types of knowledge
        (c; moderate; p. 394)

15.   Which of the following is not a form of global organization design?
        a.   product
        b.   geocentric
        c.   area
        d.   functional
        e.   customer
        (b; easy; p. 394)

16.   Which of the following is *not* one of the managerial philosophies that guide the approach to functions like organizational design and marketing?
        a. ethnocentric approach
        b. transnational approach
        c. polycentric approach
        d. geocentric approach
        e. all are managerial philosophies useful in design
        (b; moderate; p. 394)

17.   The _____ is used by firms that operate internationally the same way they do domestically.
        a. ethnocentric approach
        b. home replication approach
        c. polycentric approach
        d. geocentric approach
        e. transnational approach
        (a; moderate; p. 394)

18.   The _____ is used by firms that customize their operations for each foreign market they serve.
        a. ethnocentric approach
        b. multidomestic approach
        c. polycentric approach
        d. geocentric approach
        e. transnational approach
        (c; moderate; p. 394)

19.   The _____ is used by firms that analyze the needs of their customers worldwide and then adopt standardized operations for all markets they serve.
        a. ethnocentric approach
        b. global approach
        c. polycentric approach
        d. geocentric approach
        e. transnational approach
        (d; moderate; p. 394)

20.   Which design is the most common form of organizational design adopted by MNCs?
        a. global product design
        b. global area design
        c. global functional design
        d. global matrix design
        e. global hybrid design
        (a; moderate; p. 395)

21.   Which design assigns worldwide responsibility for specific products or product groups to separate operating divisions within a firm?
       a.   global product design
       b.   global area design
       c.   global functional design
       d.   global matrix design
       e.   global hybrid design
       (a; moderate; p. 395)

22.   Which design works best when the firm has diverse product lines or product lines sold in diverse markets?
       a.   global product design
       b.   global area design
       c.   global functional design
       d.   global matrix design
       e.   global hybrid design
       (a; moderate; p. 395)

23.   When products are related, what form does an organization using a global product design utilize?
       a.   C-form
       b.   H-form
       c.   M-form
       d.   X-form
       e.   Z-form
       (c; difficult; p. 394)

24.   The M in M-form stands for _____.
       a.   multinational
       b.   multidivisional
       c.   multicultural
       d.   matrix
       e.   none of the above
       (b; moderate; p. 394)

25.   When products are unrelated in a company using a global product design, what form is used?
       a.   C-form
       b.   H-form
       c.   M-form
       d.   X-form
       e.   Z-form
       (b; difficult; p. 394)

26.   The H in H-form stands for _____.
        a. harmony
        b. holding
        c. hoarding
        d. Hoover
        e. none of the above
        (b; moderate; p. 394)

27.   Shougang is a Chinese firm with a global product design. It has steel businesses,
        financial products, and semiconductor products. What form of global product
        design is it using?
        a. C-form
        b. H-form
        c. M-form
        d. X-form
        e. Z-form
        (b; difficult; p. 395)

28.   What corporate philosophy is facilitated by a global product design?
        a. ethnocentric approach
        b. global approach
        c. polycentric approach
        d. geocentric approach
        e. transnational approach
        (d; moderate; p. 395)

29.   Which type of organizational design organizes the firm's activities around
        specific areas or regions of the world?
        a. global product design
        b. global area design
        c. global functional design
        d. global matrix design
        e. global hybrid design
        (b; moderate; p. 396)

30.   Which organizational design is particularly useful for firms with a polycentric or
        multidomestic corporate philosophy?
        a. global product design
        b. global area design
        c. global functional design
        d. global matrix design
        e. global hybrid design
        (b; moderate; p. 396)

31.   Cadbury Schweppes PLC has five basic divisions, each representing a different area of the world. Which organization design does it use?
       a. global product design
       b. global area design
       c. global functional design
       d. global matrix design
       e. global hybrid design
       (b; moderate; p. 396)

32.   Which organizational design is well suited for companies who are marketing driven rather than driven by manufacturing efficiencies?
       a. global product design
       b. global area design
       c. global functional design
       d. global matrix design
       e. global hybrid design
       (b; moderate; p. 397)

33.   Which of the following is a disadvantage of a global area design?
       a. duplication of functional areas
       b. lack of cost-efficiencies
       c. difficulty in coordination across areas
       d. difficulty in global product planning
       e. all are disadvantages of global area design
       (e; easy; p. 397)

34.   The _____ calls for a firm to create departments or divisions that have worldwide responsibility for common organizational functions.
       a. global product design
       b. global area design
       c. global functional design
       d. global matrix design
       e. global hybrid design
       (c; moderate; p. 398)

35.   The _____ is used by MNCs that have relatively narrow or similar product lines.
       a. global product design
       b. global area design
       c. global functional design
       d. global matrix design
       e. global hybrid design
       (c; moderate; p. 398)

36.   The U in U-form stands for _____.
        a. uniform
        b. unity
        c. universal
        d. Uruguay
        e. none of the above
        (b; moderate; p. 398)

37.   British Airways is a single-business firm with company-wide function operations.
        What type of organizational design does British Airways use?
        a. global product design
        b. global area design
        c. global functional design
        d. global matrix design
        e. global hybrid design
        (c; moderate; p. 398)

38.   Which design is practical only when a firm has relatively few products or
        customers?
        a. global product design
        b. global area design
        c. global functional design
        d. global matrix design
        e. global hybrid design
        (c; moderate; p. 398)

39.   The _____ is used when a firm serves different customers or customer groups,
        each with specific needs calling for special expertise or attention.
        a. global product design
        b. global area design
        c. global functional design
        d. global matrix design
        e. global customer design
        (e; moderate; p. 398)

40.   Kodak has three divisions. One division focuses on selling high-quality film to
        film studios. Another division sells to professional and amateur photographers.
        Finally, its new business division targets emerging markets. What organizational
        design does Kodak utilize?
        a. global product design
        b. global area design
        c. global customer design
        d. global matrix design
        e. global hybrid design
        (c; moderate; p. 398)

41. Which organizational design is appropriate when the various customer groups targeted by a firm are so diverse as to require totally distinct marketing approaches?
     a. global product design
     b. global area design
     c. global functional design
     d. global matrix design
     e. global customer design
     (e; moderate; p. 398)

42. Which organizational design can lead to duplication of resources in the company?
     a. global product design
     b. global area design
     c. global customer design
     d. all of the above
     e. none of the above
     (d; moderate; p. 400)

43. A _____ is the result of superimposing one form of organization design on top of a different, existing form.
     a. global product design
     b. global area design
     c. global functional design
     d. global matrix design
     e. global hybrid design
     (d; moderate; p. 400)

44. Which organizational design promotes flexibility and fluidity in the firm?
     a. global product design
     b. global area design
     c. global functional design
     d. global matrix design
     e. global hybrid design
     (d; moderate; p. 401)

45. Which organization design is not appropriate for firms with few products and relatively stable markets?
     a. global product design
     b. global area design
     c. global functional design
     d. global matrix design
     e. global hybrid design
     (d; moderate; p. 401)

46.   _____ is the process of linking and integrating functions and activities of different groups, units, or divisions.
        a. Communication
        b. Coordination
        c. Control
        d. Commitment
        e. Channeling
        (b; easy; p. 404)

47.   Which of the following can be used to accomplish coordination in a firm?
        a. organizational hierarchy
        b. rules and procedures
        c. liaisons
        d. task forces
        e. all of the above
        (e; moderate; p. 404)

48.   A(n) _____ is a group of managers from different parts of the word who are connected to each other in some way.
        a. liaison
        b. task force
        c. informal management network
        d. formal management network
        e. weak link
        (c; moderate; p. 404)

49.   What occurrence listed below could result in the development of an informal management network?
        a. mutual acquaintances
        b. training programs
        c. interaction during travel
        d. joint meetings
        e. all of the above
        (e; easy; p. 405)

50.   _____ is the process of monitoring ongoing performance and making necessary changes to keep the organization moving toward its performance goals.
        a. Coordination
        b. Commitment
        c. Control
        d. Feedback
        e. Execution
        (c; moderate; p. 405)

51.   Control is conceptually similar to a(n) _____.
        a. prison
        b. thermostat
        c. hall monitor
        d. alarm system
        e. police force
        (b; easy; p. 405)

52.   _____ is intended to monitor both how well an international business formulates
        strategy and how well it goes about implementing that strategy.
        a. Functional control
        b. Strategic control
        c. Organizational control
        d. Operations control
        e. International control
        (b; moderate; p. 406)

53.   Which type of control focuses on how well the firm defines and maintains its
        desired strategic alignment with the firm's environment and how effectively the
        firm is setting and achieving its strategic goals?
        a. functional control
        b. strategic control
        c. organizational control
        d. operations control
        e. international control
        (b; moderate; p. 406)

54.   What is the most critical aspect of strategic control?
        a. control of firm's financial resources
        b. control of a firm's marketing plans
        c. quality control
        d. control of labor issues
        e. all are critical to strategic control
        (a; difficult; p. 406)

55.   The manager who handles financial control in a firm is usually referred to as the
        _____.
        a. chief financial officer
        b. auditor
        c. controller
        d. vice president of financial affairs
        e. any of the above are possible titles
        (c; difficult; p. 406)

56. International controllers are particularly concerned with _____.
    a. local financial control
    b. financial forecasts
    c. budgets
    d. exchange rate risk
    e. all of the above
    (d; difficult; p. 406)

57. What is the most common type of organizational control system?
    a. responsibility center control
    b. generic organizational control
    c. planning process control
    d. operations control
    e. international control
    (a; moderate; p. 407)

58. What is a primary characteristic of the responsibility center control system?
    a. decentralization
    b. centralization
    c. static
    d. duplication
    e. standardization
    (a; difficult; p. 407)

59. Firms using a responsibility center control system develop a _____ system for each responsibility center.
    a. standardized
    b. centralized
    c. unique
    d. generic
    e. similar
    (c; moderate; p. 407)

60. Which control system is the same for each unit or operation with the authority residing at the firm's headquarters?
    a. responsibility center control
    b. generic organizational control
    c. planning process control
    d. operations control
    e. international control
    (b; moderate; p. 407)

61.   _____ is most commonly used by international firms that pursue similar strategies
        in each market that they compete?
        a. Responsibility center control
        b. Generic organizational control
        c. Planning process control
        d. Operations control
        e. International control
        (b; moderate; p. 407)

62.   Firms using a generic organizational control system develop a _____ system.
        a. standardized
        b. centralized
        c. generic
        d. all of the above
        e. none of the above
        (d; easy; p. 409)

63.   A(n) _____ calls for a firm to concentrate its organizational control system on the
        actual mechanics and processes the firm uses to develop strategic plans.
        a. responsibility center control
        b. generic organizational control
        c. planning process control
        d. operations control
        e. international control
        (c; moderate; p. 409)

64.   _____ focuses specifically on operating processes and systems within both the
        firm and its subsidiaries and operating units.
        a. Responsibility center control
        b. Generic organizational control
        c. Planning process control
        d. Operations control
        e. International control
        (d; moderate; p. 409)

65.   How long is the scope of time for operational control typically?
        a. daily or hourly
        b. weekly
        c. monthly
        d. yearly
        e. every few years
        (a; moderate; p. 409)

66.   What is the first step in establishing an international control system?
        a.   set control standards for performance
        b.   measure actual performance
        c.   compare performance against standards
        d.   respond to deviations
        e.   discuss deviations with employees
        (a; easy; p. 410)

67.   Which element of performance is relatively difficult to measure?
        a.   actual output
        b.   worker productivity
        c.   product quality
        d.   advertising effectiveness
        e.   all are difficult to measure
        (d; moderate; p. 411)

68.   Which element of performance is relatively easy to measure?
        a.   worker productivity
        b.   advertising effectiveness
        c.   ethical managerial conduct
        d.   employee attitudes
        e.   employee motivation
        (a; moderate; p. 411)

69.   Why might actual performance exceed the control standard?
        a.   extra effort from employees
        b.   standard was too lo
        c.   competitors may have missed opportunities
        d.   all of the above
        e.   none of the above
        (d; easy; p. 412)

70.   Which of the following is an essential control technique?
        a.   accounting systems
        b.   standard operating procedures
        c.   performance ratios
        d.   regulations
        e.   all of the above
        (e; easy; p. 413)

71.   A(n) _____ is a numerical index of performance that the firm wants to maintain.
        a.   control standard
        b.   performance ratio
        c.   accounting standard
        d.   benchmark
        e.   none of the above
        (b; moderate; p. 415)

72.   Why might individuals resist control in organizations?
        a.   control represents overcontrol
        b.   control is inappropriately focused
        c.   control increases accountability
        d.   all of the above
        e.   none of the above
        (d; easy; p. 416)

73.   When a firm tries to exert more control over individuals than the individuals think
        is appropriate, the result is _____.
        a.   authoritarianism
        b.   overcontrol
        c.   undercontrol
        d.   control resistance
        e.   all of the above
        (b; moderate; p. 416)

74.   How do employees tend to respond to overcontrol by the firm?
        a.   positively
        b.   with resistance
        c.   with anticipation
        d.   happily
        e.   all of the above
        (b; easy; p. 416)

75.   _____ means involving employees who are going to be affected by control in
        planning and implementation, and to enable them to better understand the goal of
        the control system, how and why it works, and how their jobs fit into the system.
        a.   Participation
        b.   Authoritarianism
        c.   Behaviorism
        d.   Competitiveness
        e.   Control
        (a; easy; p. 417)

True/False

76.   Indirect exporting requires no change in an organization's structure.
       (T; moderate; p. 393)

77.   The corollary approach is the final evolution a firm takes in become a global
       organization. (F; moderate; p. 393)

78.   The global design chosen by a firm reflects the relative importance of the three
       types of knowledge in the firm's operations. (T; moderate; p. 394)

79.   The M-form of global product design means the company operates as a type of
       holding company for many unrelated businesses. (F; moderate; p. 394)

80.   The H in the H-form of global product design stands for holding company.
       (T; easy; p. 395)

81.   The global product design discourages duplication of functional-area skills.
       (F; moderate; p. 395)

82.   Global area design is particularly useful for firms with a transnational corporate
       philosophy. (F; moderate; p. 396)

83.   The global matrix design is the result of superimposing one form of
       organizational design on top of a different, existing form. (T; moderate; p. 400)

84.   The global matrix design is most appropriate for firms that operate in stable
       environments. (F; easy; p. 401)

85.   If it were possible to compare the designs used by the world's 500 largest
       MNCs, no two would look exactly the same because they use a hybrid form of
       organizational design. (T; difficult; p. 402)

86.   The level of decentralization or centralization used in a firm is fundamental to a
       firm's organizational design. (T; moderate; p. 402)

87.   Empowering a subsidiary's board promotes centralization. (F; easy; p. 402)

88.   When Mazda and Ford collaborated on the design of the Ford Focus, they
       utilized an existing task force that remains in effect at all times.
       (F; moderate; p. 404)

89.   The higher the level of interdependence among divisions and functions in a firm,
       the more coordination is required. (T; easy; p. 404)

90.   An auditor has the role of handling financial control in an international firm.
        (F; difficult; p. 406)

91.   Responsibility control centers tend to follow a centralized decision making
        system. (F; moderate; p. 407)

92.   Responsibility center control means that the firm creates unique control systems
        for each SBU. (T; moderate; p. 407)

93.   Responsibility center control systems are most commonly used by international
        firms that pursue similar strategies in each market in which they compete.
        (F; moderate; p. 407)

94.   Strategic control often involves time periods of several years. (T; easy; p. 409)

95.   Operations control usually focuses on the lower levels of a firm such as first-
        line managers and operating employees. (T; easy; p. 410)

96.   Holding excessive inventory is beneficial to a firm despite the potential for
        damage and loss because the inventory is recorded as an asset in the firm's
        financial records. (F; difficult; p. 416)

97.   People welcome control in organizations because of the stress associated with
        role ambiguity. (F; difficult; p. 416)

98.   Employees of Disneyland Paris felt the company was exercising overcontrol by
        applying the same grooming standards in Europe as in the United States.
        (T; moderate; p. 416)

99.   Participation is a common technique for overcoming resistance to control.
        (T; easy; p. 417)

100.   Culture is irrelevant in understanding resistance to control because our reactions
        to control represent universal human nature. (F; difficult; p. 417)

Short Answers

101.   What is the meaning of area knowledge? Answer: Area knowledge means that
        managers must understand the cultural, commercial, social, and economic
        conditions in each host country market that the firm does business with.
        (moderate; p. 394)

102.   What types of knowledge are included in the meaning of product knowledge?
        Answer: Product knowledge includes understanding of technological trends,
        customer needs, and competitive forces affecting the goods the firm produces
        and sells. (moderate; p. 394)

103.   What is the meaning of functional knowledge? Answer: Functional knowledge refers to expertise in the basic business functions of production, marketing, finance, accounting, human resource management, and information technology. (easy; p. 394)

104.   What does the H in H-form stand for? Answer: Holding company. (moderate; p. 394)

105.   What does the M in M-form stand for? Answer: Multidivisional. (easy; p. 394)

106.   What are the competitive advantages associated with a global product design Answer: The benefits are 1) expertise in all aspects of the product in a division, 2) facilitation of efficiencies in production, 3) ability to incorporate technology into products, 4) quick response to changes, 5) flexibility in introducing, promoting, and distributing each product, and 6) facilitation of the geocentric corporate philosophy. (moderate; p. 395)

107.   What characteristic does an organization have if it allows a great deal of discretion over strategy, finance, production, and marketing decisions among subsidiaries? Answer: Decentralization. (moderate; p. 402)

108.   If the level of interdependence among a firm's divisions is very low, how much coordination is necessary? Answer: Very little. (easy; p. 404)

109.   What strategies can firms implement to achieve desired coordination? Answer: Firms can use the organizational hierarchy itself. Standard operating procedures aid in coordination. Firms can also use liaisons and task forces or informal management networks to assist in coordination efforts. (moderate; p. 404)

110.   What is the meaning of an informal management network? Answer: An informal management network is simply a group of managers from different parts of the world who are connected to one another in some way. (easy; p. 404)

111.   What are the three levels of international control? Answer: Strategic control, organizational control, and operations control. (moderate; p. 405)

112.   What does strategic control focus on? Answer: Strategic control focuses on how the international business formulates and achieves its strategic goals. (moderate; p. 405)

113.   What does organizational control focus on? Answer: Organizational control focuses on how the international business designs the overall organization in response to changes in the environment or its strategy. (moderate; p. 405)

114.   What does operations control focus on? Answer: Operations control focuses on how the international business utilizes operating systems within the organization,

as well as within individual subsidiaries and operating units, administration, distribution centers, and manufacturing facilities. (moderate; p. 405)

115. What are the different types of organizational control systems? Answer: Responsibility center control, generic organizational control, and planning process control. (moderate; p. 407)

116. What is the primary difference between responsibility center control and generic organizational control? Answer: Responsibility center control is customized for each unit while generic organizational control is the same for all units. (difficult; p. 409)

117. What is the typical time period for operations control? Answer: Hourly or daily. (easy; p. 409)

118. What elements of performance are relatively easy to measure? Answer: Actual output, worker productivity, product quality, unit sales, materials waste, travel expenses, hiring practices, and employee turnover. (moderate; p. 411)

119. What are the possible responses to deviations found during the international control process? Answer: One can change the standard, correct the deviation, or maintain status quo. (moderate; p. 412)

120. What is the most common approach to overcoming resistance to control? Answer: Participation in the process. (moderate; p. 417)

Essay

121.   What are the four functions of organization design?

Answer: Organizational design allocates organizational resources. It assigns tasks to its employees. It informs those employees about the firm's rules, procedures, and expectations. It collects and transmits information necessary for problem solving, decision making, and effective organizational control. (moderate; pp. 392-393)

122. Explain the levels a firm goes through with regard to its organizational design as it moves from domestic to international to global.

Answer: If a firm is participating in indirect exporting, it does not need to change its organizational design. When the firm first begins to export, it can use a corollary approach. This means the firm assigns any tasks related to the international business to some existing department. When the export business grows to an extent that other departments cannot manage sufficiently, the firm will move to an export department approach. In this situation, the department will handle the international business while the other divisions operate as before.

Eventually, more knowledge of foreign markets will be necessary and the firm will develop an international division. As the firm evolves from being domestically oriented with international operations to becoming a true multinational corporation with global aspirations, it will usually create a global organization design. The precise design will depend on the relative importance of area knowledge, product knowledge, and functional knowledge within the firm. (difficult; p. 393)

123.   What are the different types of organizational design? Describe each one briefly.

Answer: The types of organizational designs are global product design, global area design, global functional design, global customer design, global matrix design, and hybrid global designs. The global product design assigns worldwide responsibility for specific products or product groups to separate operating divisions within a firm. The global area design organizes the firm's activities around specific areas or regions of the world. The global functional design calls for a firm to create departments or divisions that have worldwide responsibility for common organizational functions. The global customer design is used when a firm serves different customers or customer groups, each with specific needs calling for special expertise or attention. A global matrix design is the result of superimposing one form of organizational design on top of a different, existing form. A hybrid design is some blending of elements from other designs to meet a firm's specific situation. (moderate; pp. 394-401)

124.   What are the four steps in establishing international control systems?

Answer: The four steps are to set control standards for performance, measure actual performance, compare performance against standards, and respond to deviations. (moderate; p. 410)

125.   Discuss the behavioral aspects of international control and include the reasons for resistance to control and the methods for overcoming that resistance.

Answer: Human behavior plays a fundamental role in how well control works. People may resist control for various reasons. People may feel that the firm is trying to exert more influence than is appropriate. They may resist control because they feel it is inappropriately focused or because the control ultimately increases their accountability. Firms can increase participation in an attempt to overcome employee resistance to control. Firms can also create a control system with reasonable accountability. It can provide a diagnostic mechanism for addressing unacceptable deviations. Ultimately, though, firms must recognize that culture plays an important part in the acceptance of international control. (moderate; pp. 416-417)

Multiple Choice

1.   Which of the following affects individual behavior?
      a. personality
      b. attitudes
      c. perception
      d. stress
      e. all of the above
      (e; easy; p. 424)

2.   _____ is/are the relatively stable set of psychological attributes that distinguishes
      one person from another.
      a. Personality
      b. Attitudes
      c. Perception
      d. Stress
      e. All of the above
      (a; easy; p. 424)

3.   Discussion concerning the extent to which personality attributes are biologically
      inherited is commonly called the _____.
      a. nurture argument
      b. nature argument
      c. DNA approach
      d. biological argument
      e. none of the above
      (b; moderate; p. 424)

4.   Discussion concerning the extent to which personality attributes are shaped by the
      social and cultural environment in which people are raised is commonly called the
      _____.
      a. nurture argument
      b. nature argument
      c. culture factor
      d. biological argument
      e. none of the above
      (a; moderate; p. 424)

5.   What personality trait refers to a person's ability to get along with others?
      a. agreeableness
      b. extroversion
      c. openness
      d. conscientiousness
      e. emotional stability
      (a; easy; p. 425)

6. Which of the following personality traits describes a person whose behavior is gentle, cooperative, understanding, and good-natured?
    a. agreeableness
    b. extroversion
    c. openness
    d. conscientiousness
    e. emotional stability
    (a; moderate; p. 425)

7. Jeff is irritable, short-tempered, and uncooperative with others. He is lacking in _____.
    a. agreeableness
    b. extroversion
    c. openness
    d. conscientiousness
    e. emotional stability
    (a; easy; p. 425)

8. What personality trait refers to the order and precision a person imposes on activities?
    a. agreeableness
    b. extroversion
    c. openness
    d. conscientiousness
    e. emotional stability
    (d; easy; p. 425)

9. Which of the following personality traits describes a person who is organized, systematic, and responsible?
    a. agreeableness
    b. extroversion
    c. openness
    d. conscientiousness
    e. emotional stability
    (d; moderate; p. 425)

10. Andrea is disorganized, careless, and irresponsible. She is lacking in _____.
    a. agreeableness
    b. extroversion
    c. openness
    d. conscientiousness
    e. emotional stability
    (d; moderate; p. 425)

11. What personality trait refers to one's inclination to maintain a balanced emotional state?
     a. agreeableness
     b. extroversion
     c. openness
     d. conscientiousness
     e. emotional stability
     (e; easy; p. 425)

12. Which of the following personality traits describes a person who is poised, calm, and secure?
     a. agreeableness
     b. extroversion
     c. openness
     d. conscientiousness
     e. emotional stability
     (e; moderate; p. 425)

13. Jackie is insecure, reactive, and subject to extreme mood swings. She is lacking in _____.
     a. agreeableness
     b. extroversion
     c. openness
     d. conscientiousness
     e. emotional stability
     (e; moderate; p. 425)

14. What personality trait refers to one's comfort level with relationships?
     a. agreeableness
     b. extroversion
     c. openness
     d. conscientiousness
     e. emotional stability
     (b; easy; p. 425)

15. Mike is talkative, sociable, and assertive. He could be described using the personality trait of _____.
     a. agreeableness
     b. extroversion
     c. openness
     d. conscientiousness
     e. emotional stability
     (b; easy; p. 425)

16.   What personality trait refers to one's rigidity of beliefs and range of interests?
        a. agreeableness
        b. extroversion
        c. openness
        d. conscientiousness
        e. emotional stability
        (c; moderate; p. 425)

17.   People who are high in _____ are willing to listen to new ideas and to change their own beliefs as a result of new information.
        a. agreeableness
        b. extroversion
        c. openness
        d. conscientiousness
        e. emotional stability
        (c; moderate; p. 425)

18.   _____ is the extent to which people believe that their behavior has a real effect on what happens to them.
        a. Self-efficacy
        b. Locus of control
        c. Authoritarianism
        d. Extroversion
        e. Optimism
        (b; moderate; p. 426)

19.   John just found out that he did not get the promotion he wanted. He isn't upset because he believes fate just wasn't on his side. What personality trait best explains John's views on his promotion?
        a. pessimism
        b. internal locus of control
        c. external locus of control
        d. self-efficacy
        e. conscientiousness
        (c; moderate; p. 426)

20.   Jason spends every weekend studying for his advanced degree and regularly attends seminars designed to improve his skills. He believes this effort will pay off in career success. What personality trait best explains Jason's belief?
        a. pessimism
        b. internal locus of control
        c. external locus of control
        d. self-efficacy
        e. conscientiousness
        (b; moderate; p. 426)

21.   _____ indicates a person's beliefs about his or her capabilities to perform a task.
a. Pessimism
b. Internal locus of control
c. External locus of control
d. Self-efficacy
e. Conscientiousness
(d; moderate; p. 426)

22.   Colin has a big meeting with the managers of a company in Germany that he
hopes to develop a strategic alliance. Colin seriously doubts his ability to
negotiate the deal. What personality trait best describes Colin's situation?
a. pessimism
b. internal locus of control
c. external locus of control
d. self-efficacy
e. conscientiousness
(d; moderate; p. 426)

23.   Lisa is busy studying for the GMAT. She realizes how important a good GMAT
score is in her graduate school applications, but she is confident she will perform
well. What personality trait best describes Lisa's confidence?
a. optimism
b. internal locus of control
c. external locus of control
d. self-efficacy
e. conscientiousness
(d; moderate; p. 426)

24.   _____ is the extent to which an individual believes that power and status
differences are appropriate within hierarchical social systems like business
organizations.
a. Locus of control
b. Self-efficacy
c. Authoritarianism
d. Extraversion
e. Conscientiousness
(c; moderate; p. 426)

25.   Which of the following behaviors might *not* be seen in a person who is low in
        authoritarianism?
        a.   Agree with the boss no matter what.
        b.   Express disagreement with the boss.
        c.   Allow subordinates a bigger role in making decisions.
        d.   Encourage participation in decisions.
        e.   All of the above.
        (a; difficult; p. 426)

26.   _____ is the extent to which a person believes that he or she is a worthwhile and
        deserving individual.
        a.   Locus of control
        b.   Self-esteem
        c.   Self-efficacy
        d.   Extraversion
        e.   Openness
        (b; easy; p. 427)

27.   Courteney seeks good jobs, is confident in her abilities, and gets a lot of intrinsic
        satisfaction from her accomplishments. She could be described as someone with
        _____.
        a.   internal locus of control
        b.   external locus of control
        c.   high self-esteem
        d.   high self-efficacy
        e.   low self-esteem
        (c; moderate; p. 427)

28.   _____ are complexes of beliefs and feelings that people have about specific ideas,
        situations, or other people.
        a.   Job satisfaction
        b.   Commitment
        c.   Attitudes
        d.   Beliefs
        e.   Thoughts
        (c; easy; p. 427)

29.   Which attitude reflects the extent to which an individual is gratified by or fulfilled
        in his or her work?
        a.   job satisfaction
        b.   commitment
        c.   liking
        d.   awareness
        e.   motivation
        (a; easy; p. 427)

30.   Which behavior is associated with a satisfied employee?
    a. low absenteeism
    b. positive contributor at work
    c. commitment to the organization
    d. low intent to turnover
    e. all of the above
    (e; easy; p. 427)

31.   Which attitude reflects an individual's identification with and loyalty to an organization?
    a. job satisfaction
    b. organizational commitment
    c. liking
    d. awareness
    e. motivation
    (b; easy; p. 427)

32.   _____ is the set of processes by which an individual becomes aware of and interprets information about the environment.
    a. Environmental scanning
    b. Perception
    c. Attitude development
    d. Job satisfaction
    e. Commitment
    (b; moderate; p. 428)

33.   Which perceptual process occurs when we make inferences about someone because of one or more characteristics they possess?
    a. attitudes
    b. commitment
    c. liking
    d. stereotyping
    e. all of the above
    (d; moderate; p. 428)

34.   When individuals experience a strong stimulus, the natural response is _____.
    a. happiness
    b. pressure
    c. stress
    d. exhaustion
    e. frustration
    (c; easy; p. 430)

35. In a study of stress among executives from 10 countries, executives from _____ experienced the least stress.
    a. United States
    b. United Kingdom
    c. Japan
    d. Sweden
    e. Germany
    (d; difficult; p. 430)

36. In a study of stress among executives from 10 countries, executives from _____ experienced difficulties managing their stress.
    a. Japan
    b. United States
    c. Germany
    d. Sweden
    e. United Kingdom
    (a; difficult; p. 430)

37. _____ is the overall set of forces that causes people to choose certain behaviors from a set of available behaviors.
    a. Perception
    b. Commitment
    c. Consideration
    d. Leadership
    e. Motivation
    (e; moderate; p. 431)

38. Which of the following refers to what an individual must have or wants to have?
    a. desires
    b. beliefs
    c. goals
    d. needs
    e. values
    (d; easy; p. 432)

39. Things that people require in order to survive, such as food, are called _____.
    a. secondary needs
    b. primary needs
    c. survival goals
    d. sufficiency items
    e. all of the above
    (b; easy; p. 432)

40. Which of the following is *not* an example of a primary need?
     a. food
     b. affiliation
     c. shelter
     d. water
     e. all are primary needs
     (b; moderate; p. 432)

41. Which of the following is an example of a secondary need?
     a. food
     b. affiliation
     c. shelter
     d. water
     e. all are primary needs
     (b; moderate; p. 432)

42. Which of the following is *not* an example of a secondary need?
     a. affiliation
     b. power
     c. shelter
     d. achievement
     e. security
     (c; moderate; p. 432)

43. What are values influenced by?
     a. family
     b. peers
     c. experiences
     d. culture
     e. all of the above
     (e; easy; p. 432)

44. Which models of motivation attempt to identify the specific need or set of needs
     that result in motivated behavior?
     a. need-based models
     b. process-based models
     c. reinforcement models
     d. perceptual models
     e. all of the above
     (a; moderate; p. 432)

45.   Which models of motivation focus more on the conscious thought processes
       people use to select one behavior from among several?
       a.   need-based models
       b.   process-based models
       c.   reinforcement models
       d.   perceptual models
       e.   all of the above
       (b; moderate; p. 432)

46.   Which model of motivation deals with how people assess the consequences of
       their behavioral choices and how that assessment goes into their future choice of
       behaviors?
       a.   need-based model
       b.   process-based model
       c.   reinforcement model
       d.   perceptual model
       e.   all of the above
       (c; moderate; p. 432)

47.   Which model of motivation incorporates the roles of rewards and punishment in
       maintaining or altering existing behavioral patterns?
       a.   need-based model
       b.   process-based model
       c.   reinforcement model
       d.   perceptual model
       e.   all of the above
       (c; moderate; p. 432)

48.   Which model listed below is *not* a need based model of motivation?
       a.   Hofstede's cultural dimensions
       b.   Maslow's hierarchy of needs
       c.   Vroom's expectancy theory
       d.   McClelland's learned needs framework
       e.   Herzberg's two-factor theory
       (c; difficult; p. 433)

49.   Which of the following is not specified as part of Maslow's hierarchy of needs?
       a.   physiological needs
       b.   achievement needs
       c.   security needs
       d.   social needs
       e.   need for self-actualization
       (b; difficult; p. 433)

50.   In McClelland's learned needs framework, the need to grow, learn, and accomplish important things is called the need for _____.
        a. affiliation
        b. power
        c. achievement
        d. accomplishment
        e. actualization
        (c; moderate; p. 433)

51.   What type of culture is most likely to foster and promote a high need for affiliation?
        a. collectivistic
        b. passive goal behavior
        c. uncertainty-accepting
        d. both a and b
        e. both b and c
        (d; difficult; p. 433)

52.   Which type of culture is least likely to foster and promote a high need for achievement?
        a. individualistic
        b. uncertainty-avoiding
        c. power-respecting
        d. both a and c
        e. both b and c
        (e; difficult; p. 433)

53.   Which theory suggests that motivational needs can be taught to people in different cultures?
        a. Hofstede's cultural dimensions
        b. Maslow's hierarchy of needs
        c. Vroom's expectancy theory
        d. McClelland's learned needs framework
        e. Herzberg's two-factor theory
        (d; moderate; p. 433)

54.   Which theory suggests that one set of factors affects dissatisfaction and another set affects satisfaction?
        a. Hofstede's cultural dimensions
        b. Maslow's hierarchy of needs
        c. Vroom's expectancy theory
        d. McClelland's learned needs framework
        e. Herzberg's two-factor theory
        (e; moderate; p. 433)

55.   Which theory suggests that people are motivated to behave in certain ways to the extent that they perceive such behaviors will lead to outcomes they find personally attractive.
        a. Hofstede's cultural dimensions
        b. Maslow's hierarchy of needs
        c. Vroom's expectancy theory
        d. McClelland's learned needs framework
        e. Herzberg's two-factor theory
        (c; moderate; p. 434)

56.   Which theory is essentially a model of individual decisions regarding individual behavioral choices targeted at individual outcomes?
        a. Hofstede's cultural dimensions
        b. Maslow's hierarchy of needs
        c. Vroom's expectancy theory
        d. McClelland's learned needs framework
        e. Herzberg's two-factor theory
        (c; difficult; p. 433)

57.   Which theory says that behavior resulting in a positive outcome will likely be repeated under the same circumstances in the future?
        a. reinforcement model
        b. hierarchy of needs
        c. expectancy theory
        d. learned needs framework
        e. two-factor theory
        (a; moderate; p. 433)

58.   _____ is the use of noncoercive influence to shape the goals of a group or organization, to motivate behavior toward reaching those goals, and to help determine the group or organizational culture.
        a. Motivation
        b. Commitment
        c. Trust
        d. Leadership
        e. Management
        (d; easy; p. 434)

59.   _____ tends to rely on formal power and authority and to focus on administration and decision making.
        a. Motivation
        b. Administration
        c. Management
        d. Leadership
        e. Supervision
        (c; moderate; p. 435)

60.   _____ relies on personal power and focuses on motivation and communication.
       a. Motivation
       b. Administration
       c. Management
       d. Leadership
       e. Supervision
       (d; moderate; p. 435)

61.   Which situational factor commonly affects leader behavior?
       a. group characteristics
       b. individual differences among subordinates
       c. organizational characteristics
       d. all of the above
       e. none of the above
       (d; easy; p. 435)

62.   _____ is the process of choosing one alternative from among a set of alternatives in order to promote the decision maker's objectives.
       a. Decision making
       b. Perception
       c. Motivation
       d. Prioritizing
       e. Leadership
       (a; easy; p. 437)

63.   Which model of decision making suggests that managers apply logic and rationality in making the best decisions?
       a. need-based
       b. process-based
       c. normative
       d. descriptive
       e. central
       (c; moderate; p. 438)

64.   Which model of decision making argues that behavioral processes limit a manager's ability to always be logical and rational?
       a. need-based
       b. process-based
       c. normative
       d. descriptive
       e. central
       (d; moderate; p. 438)

65.   Which model of decision making recognizes that managers are influenced by bounded rationality?
        a.   need-based
        b.   process-based
        c.   normative
        d.   descriptive
        e.   central
        (d; moderate; p. 438)

66.   _____ suggests that decision makers are constrained in their ability to be objective and rational by limitations of the human mind?
        a.   Satisficing
        b.   Objectivism
        c.   Rational thought
        d.   Bounded rationality
        e.   All of the above
        (d; moderate; p. 439)

67.   What behavioral process suggests that managers sometimes adopt the first minimally acceptable alternative they identify, when a further search might suggest an even better alternative?
        a.   satisficing
        b.   objectivism
        c.   maximizing
        d.   bounded rationality
        e.   sufficiency
        (a; moderate; p. 439)

68.   What is the first step in the normative model of decision making?
        a.   identifying alternatives
        b.   problem recognition
        c.   selecting the best alternative
        d.   evaluating alternatives
        e.   implementation
        (b; easy; p. 439)

69.   What is the third step in the normative model of decision making?
        a.   identifying alternatives
        b.   problem recognition
        c.   selecting the best alternative
        d.   evaluating alternatives
        e.   implementation
        (d; easy; p. 439)

70.   XXM Inc has been researching the potential for a new manufacturing plant in China. Despite the research, there is still much the managers do not know about the potential risks of pursuing the venture. In this case, the decision is affected by _____.
a.   fear
b.   bounded rationality
c.   risk
d.   decision making delays
e.   all of the above
(b; moderate; p. 438)

71.   What system is used in Japan for identifying alternatives?
a.   soga sosha
b.   keiretsu
c.   ringi
d.   guanxi
e.   none of the above
(c; moderate; p. 439)

72.   Which task characteristic is more appropriate for problem-solving by homogeneous teams?
a.   complex
b.   non-routine
c.   routine
d.   ambiguous
e.   all are appropriate for homogeneous teams
(c; moderate; p. 442)

73.   Which of the following is *not* a characteristic of mature teams?
a.   well-defined role structure
b.   established norms for members
c.   cohesiveness
d.   inefficient role structure
e.   informal leadership
(d; easy; p. 442)

74.   What benefit is common among homogeneous teams?
a.   low levels of conflict
b.   good communication
c.   high cohesiveness
d.   informal leadership
e.   all of the above
(e; easy; p. 442)

75.   Which of the following is a benefit of heterogeneous teams?
        a. low levels of conflict
        b. high creativity
        c. low levels of cohesiveness
        d. more ambiguous leadership
        e. few norms for behavior
        (b; moderate; p. 442)

True/False

76.   Psychologists agree that personality is set primarily by nurture.
        (F; moderate; p. 424)

77.   The Big Five personality traits include the trait of locus of control.
        (F; moderate; p. 425)

78.   Agreeableness refers to a person's ability to get along with others.
        (T; easy; p. 425)

79.   Extroversion describes the level of order and precision a person imposes on
        activities. (F; easy; p. 425)

80.   People with an internal locus of control believe that fate, chance, and luck
        determine what happens to them. (F; moderate; p. 426)

81.   Self-efficacy indicates a person's abilities to perform a task.
        (F; difficult; p. 426)

82.   Research shows that high levels of employee satisfaction will result in high
        levels of employee productivity. (F; difficult; p. 427)

83.   A study of organizational commitment among U.S. expatriates found that those
        who had received extensive pretransfer training had high levels of
        organizational commitment while those with less pretransfer training were less
        committed. (T; moderate; p. 428)

84.   The perceptions that Germans are precise and that Japanese are workaholics are
        stereotypes. (T; easy; p. 429)

85.   Stress can be caused by good things in our lives. (T; moderate; p. 430)

86.   Because stress is a physiological response, all humans experience the same
        forms of stress and handle that stress in the same ways. (F; moderate; p. 430)

87.   Process-based models of motivation are those that attempt to identify the specific need or set of needs that result in motivated behavior. (F; moderate; p. 432)

88.   Contemporary leadership theories recognize that leaders can always succeed by using the same set of behaviors in all circumstances. (F; easy; p. 435)

89.   Hofstede's cultural dimensions can be classified as a need-based model of motivation. (T; easy; p. 432)

90.   Herzberg's two-factor theory suggests that different factors affect satisfaction and dissatisfaction. (T; easy; p. 433)

91.   Maslow's hierarchy of needs is relevant in all cultures. (T; moderate; p. 433)

92.   McClelland's learned needs framework includes the need for affiliation, the need for power, and the need for accomplishment. (F; moderate; p. 433)

93.   Herzberg's Two-Factor theory provides value as a heuristic but has failed to yield consistent results in any culture. (T; moderate; p. 434)

94.   The reinforcement model is based on the idea that people will memorize through repetition. (F; easy; p. 434)

95.   Expectancy theory applies more to people with an external locus of control. (F; easy; p. 434)

96.   Leaders have the primary responsibility of planning, budgeting, and organizing. (F; difficult; p. 435)

97.   Management relies on formal power and authority rather than on motivation. (T; moderate; p. 435)

98.   In power-respecting cultures, employees expect leaders to take charge, make decisions, and direct their efforts. (T; easy; p. 436)

99.   People in passive goal behavior cultures tend to value money and other material rewards. (F; moderate; p. 437)

100.   The normative model of decision making illustrates what managers actually do. (F; difficult; p. 438)

Short Answers

101.   What is personality? Answer: Personality is the relatively stable set of psychological attributes that distinguishes one person from another.

(easy; p. 424)

102.   What traits are included in the Big Five Personality Traits? Answer: Agreeableness, conscientiousness, emotional stability, extroversion, and openness. (moderate; p. 425)

103.   What is the meaning of agreeableness? Answer: Agreeableness refers to a person's ability to get along with others. (easy; p. 425)

104.   Explain the difference between an internal and external locus of control. Answer: Locus of control is the extent to which people believe that their behavior has a real effect on what happens to them. People who maintain that individuals are in control of their lives are said to have an internal locus of control. People who think that forces beyond their control dictate what happens to them are said to have an external locus of control. (moderate; p. 426)

105.   What is self-efficacy? Answer: Self-efficacy indicates a person's beliefs about his or her capabilities to perform a task. (easy; p. 426)

106.   What is job satisfaction? What factors influence an individual's level of job satisfaction? Answer: Job satisfaction or dissatisfaction is an attitude that reflects the extent to which an individual is gratified by or fulfilled in his or her work. Research conducted on job satisfaction has indicated that personal factors such as an individual's needs and aspirations determine this attitude along with group and organizational factors such as relationships with co-workers and supervisors ad working conditions, work policies, and compensation. (moderate; p. 427)

107.   Explain the meaning of stereotyping. Why is stereotyping common among international business people? Answer: Stereotyping occurs when we make inferences about someone because of one or more characteristics they possess. Sometimes stereotypes are useful as cultural generalizations. However, we must be aware of our tendency to use stereotypes to understand different environments and situations and recognize that everyone will not fit our preconceived impressions. (moderate; pp. 428-429)

108.   What is the term for a stress stimulus? Answer: Stressor. (moderate; p. 430)

109.   Explain what happens when we experience too little stress, the right amount of stress, and too much stress. Answer: In the absence of stress, we may experience lethargy and stagnation. At the optimal level of stress, we may feel motivated and excited. Too much stress however can have negative consequences and ultimately result in burnout. (moderate; p. 430)

110.   What is the meaning of motivation? Answer: Motivation is the overall set of forces that causes people to choose certain behaviors from a set of available behaviors. (easy; p. 431)

111.   Explain the difference between needs and values. Answer: Needs are what an individual must have or wants to have. Values are what people believe to be important. (moderate; p. 432)

112.   What are need-based models of motivation? Answer: Need-based models of motivation are those that attempt to identify the specific need or set of needs that result in motivated behavior. (moderate; p. 432)

113.   What are the need levels in Maslow's hierarchy of needs? Answer: Physiological, security, social, self-esteem, and self-actualization. (easy; p. 433)

114.   What changes should managers consider when applying Maslow's hierarchy of needs in other countries? Answer: While the needs are relevant, the relative importance of each need and their ordering should be adjusted depending on the culture of the country under consideration. (difficult; p. 433)

115.   What is the basic theory behind the reinforcement model? Answer: This model says that behavior resulting in a positive outcome (reinforcement) will likely be repeated under the same circumstances in the future. (easy; p. 434)

116.   How might work outcomes vary based on management versus leadership? Answer: Managers will produce a degree of predictability and order while leaders will produce change. (difficult; p. 435)

117.   Explain how decisions are made under the normative model of decision making. Answer: The normative model suggests that managers apply logic and rationality in making the best decisions. It begins when a problem is recognized and continues through until the best alternative is identified and implemented. (moderate; p. 438)

118.   Explain how decisions are made under the descriptive model of decision making. Answer: The descriptive model argues that behavioral processes limit a manager's ability to always be logical and rational. It recognizes that managers make decisions with a lack of information and may choose the first acceptable alternative rather than the best possible alternative. (moderate; p. 438)

119.   What is a group? Is it different from a team? Answer: A group is any collection of people working together to accomplish a common purpose, while a team is a specific type of group that assumes responsibility for is own work. (easy; p. 441)

120.   Considering tasks a team might complete, when should a team be homogeneous rather than heterogeneous? Answer: If the task is relatively routine and straightforward, a homogeneous team may be more effective. If the task is nonroutine or complex, a heterogeneous team may be better because of their diverse backgrounds, experience, and knowledge. (difficult; p. 442)

Essay

121.   What is personality? Why are the Big Five Personality Traits useful in understanding personality? What are the Big Five traits? Explain the meaning of each trait.

Answer: Personality is the relatively stable set of psychological attributes that distinguishes one person from another. While psychologists have identified thousands of personality traits and dimensions that differentiate one person from another. Five traits were found to be particularly useful to organizations. The Big Five traits include agreeableness, conscientiousness, emotional stability, extroversion, and openness. Agreeableness is the ability to get along with others. Conscientiousness is the drive to impose order and precision. Emotional stability is the inclination to maintain a balanced emotional state. Extroversion is one's comfort level with relationships. Openness is one's rigidity of beliefs and range of interest. (moderate; p. 425)

122.   After the Big Five personality traits, what three other personality traits are relevant to employees?

Answer: The other three relevant traits are locus of control, self-efficacy, and authoritarianism. Locus of control is the extent to which people believe that their behavior has a real effect on what happens to them. If an individual has an internal locus of control, he or she believes that behavior determines what happens to them. Those with an external locus of control believe that fate or luck determines what happens. (moderate; p. 426)

123.   What is the difference between leadership and management?

Answer: Management tends to rely on formal power and authority and to focus on administration and decision making. Leadership relies more on personal power and focuses on motivation and communication. Management focuses on planning, budgeting, and establishing detailed steps and timetables for achieving needed results. Management organizes, staffs, controls, and conducts problem solving. Leadership establishes direction and develops a vision. Leaders align people and communicate and motivate. (moderate; p. 435)

124.   What is the difference between the normative model of decision making and the descriptive model? Which is the most reflective of what managers actually do? Explain.

Answer: The normative model suggests that managers apply logic and rationality in making the best decisions, while the descriptive model argues that there are limits to a manager's ability to make a logical and rational decision. The normative model is what managers should do while the descriptive model is what managers actually do. The descriptive model recognizes that we suffer from bounded rationality and consequently might satisfice in decision making rather than optimize. (moderate; p. 438)

125.   What are the characteristics found in mature teams?

Answer: Mature teams develop a well-defined role structure. Each member has a part to play on the team. The team establishes norms for its members. The team is cohesive. The team members identify strongly with the team and each member respects and values the others. Some teams identify informal leaders among their members. (moderate; p. 442)

Multiple Choice

1.   _____ is the process of planning and executing the conception, pricing, promotion, and distribution of ideas, goods, and services to create exchanges that satisfy individual and organizational objectives.
a. Distribution
b. Marketing
c. Production
d. Organizational design
e. Management
(b; easy; p. 456)

2.   When marketing managers develop products, pricing strategies, promotional strategies, and distribution tactics that differentiate the firm's products or services from those of its competitors in the eyes of customers, what is the firm's overall business strategy?
a. differentiation
b. cost leadership
c. focus
d. niche
e. related diversification
(a; moderate; p. 457)

3.   Which of the following can be the basis of a differentiation strategy?
a. fashion
b. quality
c. reliability
d. all of the above
e. both b and c
(d; moderate; p. 457)

4.   Which of the following companies follows a differentiation strategy?
a. Wal-Mart
b. Hyundai
c. Rolex
d. Hanes
e. All of the above
(c; moderate; p. 457)

5.   When marketing managers concentrate their promotional efforts on advertising the low price of the product, what business strategy is the firm supporting?
a. differentiation
b. cost leadership
c. focus
d. niche
e. related diversification
(b; moderate; p. 457)

6.   Which of the following companies appears to follow a cost leadership business strategy?
a. Wal-Mart
b. Rolex
c. Target
d. BMW
e. All of the above
(a; easy; p. 457)

7.   When marketing managers concentrate their efforts on particular segments of the consumer market or on particular areas or regions within a market, what business strategy is the company pursuing?
a. differentiation
b. cost leadership
c. focus
d. niche
e. related diversification
(c; moderate; p. 458)

8.   Which of the four Ps of the marketing mix includes the development of the tangible and intangible features that meet customer needs in diverse markets?
a. product
b. pricing
c. promotion
d. place
e. all of the above
(a; easy; p. 459)

9.   Which of the four Ps of the marketing mix includes the development of policies that bring in revenue and strategically shape the competitive environment?
a. product
b. pricing
c. promotion
d. place
e. all of the above
(b; easy; p. 459)

10.   Which of the four Ps of the marketing mix includes devising ways to enhance the desirability of the product or service to potential buyers?
        a. product
        b. pricing
        c. promotion
        d. place
        e. all of the above
        (c; easy; p. 459)

11.   Which of the four Ps of the marketing mix focuses on getting products and services into customers' hands via transportation and merchandising?
        a. product
        b. pricing
        c. promotion
        d. place
        e. all of the above
        (d; easy; p. 459)

12.   Which of the following is *not* a key decision-making factor that influences the international marketing mix?
        a. legal forces
        b. cultural influences
        c. competition
        d. economic factors
        e. all of the above are key decision-making factors
        (e; easy; p. 459)

13.   Timex is working to adapt its advertising campaign for a market in Europe. What element of the marketing mix is being addressed in this example?
        a. product
        b. pricing
        c. promotion
        d. place
        e. all of the above
        (c; easy; p. 459)

14.   Which approach to international marketing is the easiest for a firm to adopt?
        a. ethnocentric approach
        b. polycentric approach
        c. geocentric approach
        d. multidomestic approach
        e. transnational approach
        (a; moderate; p. 460)

15. When adopting a(n) _____ approach, a firm applies the domestic marketing mix abroad.
     a. ethnocentric
     b. polycentric
     c. geocentric
     d. multidomestic
     e. transnational
     (a; moderate; p. 460)

16. Which approach to international marketing is the most expensive to adopt?
     a. ethnocentric approach
     b. polycentric approach
     c. geocentric approach
     d. multidomestic approach
     e. transnational approach
     (b; moderate; p. 460)

17. When adopting a(n) _____ approach, a firm customizes the firm's marketing mix in each market the firm enters.
     a. ethnocentric
     b. polycentric
     c. geocentric
     d. multidomestic
     e. transnational
     (b; moderate; p. 460)

18. Proponents of _____ point out that customers in the Triad are becoming increasingly alike.
     a. customization
     b. standardization
     c. adaptation
     d. differentiation
     e. all of the above
     (b; moderate; p. 460)

19. Of those characteristics listed below, which customer characteristic is increasingly similar worldwide?
     a. incomes
     b. educational achievements
     c. lifestyles
     d. aspirations
     e. all of the above
     (e; moderate; p. 461)

20.   What advantage does a firm that standardizes its international marketing mix achieve?
        a. market share
        b. revenues
        c. economies of scale
        d. economies of scope
        e. all of the above
        (c; difficult; p. 461)

21.   What is the greatest challenge for firms that standardize their international marketing mix?
        a. achieving streamlined operations
        b. meeting customer needs
        c. developing promotional efficiencies
        d. achieving manufacturing efficiencies
        e. all of the above
        (b; moderate; p. 461)

22.   Which approach to international marketing advocates standardization of the international marketing mix?
        a. ethnocentric approach
        b. polycentric approach
        c. geocentric approach
        d. both a and c
        e. both b and c
        (d; moderate; p. 460)

23.   Which approach to international marketing is related to the saying, "think globally, act locally"?
        a. ethnocentric approach
        b. polycentric approach
        c. geocentric approach
        d. both a and c
        e. both b and c
        (b; moderate; p. 460)

24.   Which of the following factors determines the degree of standardization or customization a firm adopts?
        a. product type
        b. cultural differences between home and host countries
        c. host countries' legal systems
        d. all of the above
        e. both a and b
        (d; moderate; p. 461)

25.	What organizational characteristic is suggested by the standardization approach to international marketing?
	a.	tall hierarchy
	b.	centralized
	c.	decentralized
	d.	global product design
	e.	global area design
	(b; moderate; p. 461)

26.	Which of the following components is a part of the product portion of the marketing mix?
	a.	image
	b.	packaging
	c.	installation
	d.	warranty
	e.	all of the above
	(e; easy; p. 462)

27.	What aspect of product is likely to be affected by consumer protection regulations in different host countries?
	a.	technical specifications
	b.	packaging
	c.	labeling requirements
	d.	all of the above
	e.	both b and c
	(d; easy; p. 463)

28.	What product component is most likely to be standardized even when other aspects are adapted for different country markets?
	a.	packaging
	b.	size
	c.	features
	d.	brand name
	e.	warranty
	(d; moderate; p. 465)

29.	International firms generally select the _____ pricing policy.
	a.	standard
	b.	two-tiered
	c.	market
	d.	all of the above
	e.	none of the above
	(d; moderate; p. 467)

30.   Which pricing policy do firms generally adopt with a geocentric approach to
        international marketing?
        a. standard
        b. two-tiered
        c. market
        d. both a and b
        e. both b and c
        (a; moderate; p. 467)

31.   Which product category listed below lends itself to a standard price policy?
        a. commodities
        b. luxury goods
        c. consumer packaged goods
        d. services
        e. all of the above
        (a; difficult; p. 467)

32.   What pricing policy do firms with an ethnocentric marketing approach generally
        adopt?
        a. standard
        b. two-tiered
        c. market
        d. both a and b
        e. both b and c
        (b; moderate; p. 467)

33.   Under a _____ price policy, the firm sets one price for all its domestic sales and a
        second price for all its international sales.
        a. standard
        b. two-tiered
        c. market
        d. both a and b
        e. both b and c
        (b; moderate; p. 467)

34.   Under a _____ price policy, the firm charges the same price for its products and
        services regardless of where they are sold or the nationality of the customer.
        a. standard
        b. two-tiered
        c. market
        d. both a and b
        e. both b and c
        (a; moderate; p. 467)

35. Under a _____ price policy, the firm customizes its prices on a market-by-market basis to maximize its profits in each market.
   a. standard
   b. two-tiered
   c. market
   d. both a and b
   e. both b and c
   (c; moderate; p. 467)

36. What pricing policy do firms using a polycentric marketing approach generally adopt?
   a. standard
   b. two-tiered
   c. market
   d. both a and b
   e. none of the above
   (c; moderate; p. 467)

37. Which is the most complex of the pricing policies commonly used by MNCs?
   a. standard
   b. two-tiered
   c. market
   d. all are complex
   e. none are complex
   (c; moderate; p. 467)

38. Under the _____ price policy, firms can set higher prices where markets will tolerate them and lower prices where necessary to remain competitive.
   a. standard
   b. two-tiered
   c. market
   d. both a and b
   e. both b and c
   (c; moderate; p. 467)

39. What risk is a firm using when a market pricing policy is exposed?
   a. complaints about dumping
   b. damage to its brand name
   c. development of a gray market
   d. consumer resentment against discriminatory prices
   e. all of the above
   (e; easy; p. 469)

40.   Which of the following is not a risk for firms using a market pricing policy?
        a.   complaints about dumping
        b.   damage to its brand name
        c.   loss of revenue due to underpricing
        d.   development of a gray market
        e.   consumer resentment against discriminatory prices
        (c; moderate; p. 469)

41.   A _____ is a market that results when products are imported into a country legally,
        but outside the normal channels of distribution authorized by the manufacturer.
        a.   gray market
        b.   parallel importing
        c.   black market
        d.   both a and b
        e.   both b and c
        (d; moderate; p. 469)

42.   When might a gray market develop?
        a.   When the price in one market is sufficiently lower than the price the firm
             charges in another market.
        b.   When the price in all markets is roughly equal excluding transportation costs.
        c.   When products are illegal in one market but legal in another.
        d.   All of the above.
        e.   None of the above.
        (a; easy; p. 469)

43.   Japanese discounters were able to purchase and import Coke made in the United
        States for 27% less than the price of Coke made in Japan. This is a example of a

        a.   black market
        b.   gray market
        c.   white market
        d.   all of the above
        e.   none of the above
        (b; moderate; p. 469)

44.   Which of the following is *not* a product commonly influenced by gray markets?
        a.   automobiles
        b.   DVDs
        c.   cameras
        d.   computers
        e.   watches
        (b; difficult; p. 469)

45.   Which component of the marketing mix encompasses all efforts by an
        international firm to enhance the desirability of its products among potential
        buyers?
        a. product
        b. price
        c. place
        d. promotion
        e. all of the above
        (d; easy; p. 470)

46.   To whom are international promotional activities targeted?
        a. buyers
        b. distributors
        c. general public
        d. potential investors
        e. all of the above
        (e; easy; p. 470)

47.   What do marketing managers call the elements used to promote and communicate
        information about a brand?
        a. marketing mix
        b. promotion mix
        c. advertising
        d. communications mix
        e. none of the above
        (b; easy; p. 470)

48.   Which of the following is not one of the elements of the promotion mix?
        a. advertising
        b. personal selling
        c. internet marketing
        d. sales promotion
        e. public relations
        (c; easy; p. 470)

49.   The _____ of an advertisement is the facts or impressions the advertiser wants to
        convey to potential customers.
        a. medium
        b. message
        c. copy
        d. graphic
        e. signature line
        (b; moderate; p. 471)

50.   Honda's advertising stresses its reliability and functionality. Reliability is the
        _____.
        a. medium
        b. message
        c. copy
        d. graphic
        e. signature line
        (b; moderate; p. 471)

51.   The _____ is the communication channel used by the advertiser to convey a
        message.
        a. medium
        b. message
        c. copy
        d. graphic
        e. signature line
        (a; moderate; p. 471)

52.   Rolex is placing ads in several international magazines including *Town and
        Country* and *Harper's Bazaar*. The magazines are a communication _____.
        a. medium
        b. message
        c. copy
        d. graphic
        e. signature line
        (a; moderate; p. 471)

53.   Which country below bans cigarette advertising on television?
        a. South Korea
        b. Malaysia
        c. Hong Kong
        d. China
        e. All of the above
        (e; moderate; p. 471)

54.   Which of the following products lends itself to standardized advertising due to its
        universal appeal?
        a. Coca-Cola soft drinks
        b. Levi's jeans
        c. McDonald's hamburgers
        d. Bic pens
        e. All of the above
        (e; moderate; p. 472)

55.   What element of the promotion mix promotes a close, personal contact with customers?
a.   advertising
b.   public relations
c.   personal selling
d.   sales promotions
e.   brand placements
(c; easy; p. 473)

56.   _____ comprise(s) specialized marketing efforts such as coupons.
a.   Advertising
b.   Public relations
c.   Personal selling
d.   Sales promotions
e.   Brand placements
(d; easy; p. 473)

57.   Which of the following is *not* a tactic used in sales promotions?
a.   in-store promotions
b.   sampling
c.   print ads
d.   cooperative advertising
e.   all are sales promotion techniques
(c; moderate; p. 474)

58.   Pizza Hut is offering free pizza slices in Beijing. This is an example of _____.
a.   advertising
b.   sales promotion
c.   personal selling
d.   public relations
e.   brand placement
(b; moderate; p. 474)

59.   Philip Morris competed in Taiwan by handing out free cigarettes. This is an example of _____.
a.   advertising
b.   sales promotion
c.   personal selling
d.   public relations
e.   brand placement
(b; moderate; p. 474)

60.   Which element of the promotion mix consists of efforts aimed at enhancing a firm's reputation and image with the general public?
        a. advertising
        b. sales promotion
        c. personal selling
        d. public relations
        e. brand placement
        (d; easy; p. 474)

61.   Toyota operates a manufacturing facility in Georgetown, Kentucky. To build goodwill, Toyota provides grants to local charities, funds college scholarships to graduating high school students, and sponsors local youth sports teams. This is an example of _____.
        a. advertising
        b. sales promotion
        c. personal selling
        d. public relations
        e. brand placement
        (d; easy; p. 474)

62.   The benefit of a good public relations program is _____.
        a. good will
        b. positive image
        c. reputation
        d. all of the above
        e. none of the above
        (d; moderate; p. 474)

63.   _____ is the process of getting products and services from the firm into the hands of customers.
        a. Product development
        b. Distribution
        c. Marketing
        d. Pricing
        e. Promoting
        (b; moderate; p. 475)

64.   Which of the following factors are affected by the transportation mode selected for a product's distribution?
        a. inventory costs
        b. customer service levels
        c. product's useful shelf life
        d. exposure to damage
        e. all of the above
        (e; moderate; p. 475)

65.   DeBeers plans to transport its unset diamonds to the United States from Africa via airplane. What advantage will DeBeers gain by using this transportation mode?
       a. safety
       b. expensive
       c. limited access
       d. slow
       e. indirect route
       (a; difficult; p. 475)

66.   Sony plans to transport DVD players from its warehouse in Ohio to distribution facilities throughout the country. The players will be transported by truck. What disadvantage will Sony face?
       a. versatility
       b. inexpensive
       c. fast
       d. small size
       e. limited access
       (d; difficult; p. 475)

67.   Toyota is shipping Camrys from its plant in Kentucky via train to distribution centers throughout the United States. Which of the following is *not* an advantage of trains as a mode of transportation?
       a. safety
       b. reliable
       c. speed
       d. inexpensive
       e. versatility
       (c; moderate; p. 475)

68.   Distribution channels consist of all of the following *except* _____.
       a. manufacturer
       b. wholesaler
       c. retailer
       d. customer
       e. all are parts of a distribution channel
       (e; easy; p. 476)

69.   What term refers to the number of stages in the distribution channel?
       a. direct sales
       b. channel members
       c. stage hierarchy
       d. channel length
       e. channel width
       (d; easy; p. 476)

70.   Dell Computer takes customer orders toll-free via 24-hour telephone lines. This is
        _____.
        a. indirect sales
        b. direct sales
        c. retailer-based sales
        d. wholesaler-based sales
        e. none of the above
        (b; easy; p. 476)

71.   A _____ buys products and services from the manufacturer and then resells them
        to retailers.
        a. manufacturer
        b. wholesaler
        c. retailer
        d. customer
        c. gray marketer
        (b; moderate; p. 476)

72.   A _____ buys from wholesalers and then sells to customers.
        a. manufacturer
        b. wholesaler
        c. retailer
        d. customer
        e. gray marketer
        (c; moderate; p. 476)

73.   A _____ buys a product or service for final consumption.
        a. manufacturer
        b. wholesaler
        c. retailer
        d. customer
        e. gray marketer
        (d; moderate; p. 476)

74.   Marks and Spencer buys apparel from international wholesalers for sale in its
        stores in the United Kingdom. Marks and Spencer is a _____.
        a. manufacturer
        b. wholesaler
        c. retailer
        d. customer
        e. gray marketer
        (c; moderate; p. 476)

75.   A direct channel includes what channel members?
        a. manufacturer, import agent, customer
        b. manufacturer, import agent, retailer, customer
        c. manufacturer, import agent, wholesaler, retailer, customer
        d. manufacturer, retailer
        e. retailer, customer
        (a; moderate; p. 476)

True/False

76.   Wal-Mart bought the Wertkauf chain in Germany as well as Spar Handels AG.
        Wal-Mart adopted a greenfield strategy in Germany. (F; difficult; p. 455)

77.   International marketing activities should not integrate with the firm's functional
        strategies. (F; easy; p. 457)

78.   Advertising regulations vary by country. (T; easy; p. 457)

79.   Swatch watches and Rolex both follow a differentiation strategy.
        (F; moderate; p. 458)

80.   The marketing mix involves a firm's product, price, promotion, and place.
        (T; easy; p. 459)

81.   International marketing strategies will vary based on the firm's business
        strategy. (T; easy; p. 459)

82.   The ethnographic approach to international marketing is the easiest to adopt.
        (T; moderate; p. 460)

83.   The geocentric approach calls for customization of the international marketing
        mix. (F; moderate; p. 460)

84.   Customization focuses on the cost-side of the profit equation.
        (F; difficult; p. 461)

85.   Standardization allows the firm to develop cost efficiencies in manufacturing,
        distribution, and promotion while customization allows a firm to tailor the
        marketing mix to meet customer needs. (T; moderate; p. 461)

86.   Standardization implies that power and control should be centralized.
        (T; moderate; p. 461)

87.   Customized international marketing creates efficiencies in research and development and production. (F; moderate; p. 462)

88.   Product comprises only tangible factors that the consumer can see or touch (physical product and packaging). (F; moderate; p. 462)

89.   Brand image is a component of promotion, not product. (F; moderate; p. 462)

90.   Many international firms adopt a blend of customization and standardization. (T; easy; p. 463)

91.   An example of a cultural influence on product is the introduction of shrimp-flavored potato chips in the Korean market. (T; easy; p. 464)

92.   For Japanese consumers, an automobile is more of a status symbol than a mode of transportation. (T; easy; p. 464)

93.   Brand names of products are usually customized to reflect language differences and culture. (F; moderate; p. 465)

94.   Firms that use two-tiered pricing are vulnerable to charges of dumping. (T; moderate; p. 465)

95.   If an exporter's home currency rises in value, the exporter must choose between maintaining its prices in the home currency (which cuts its profit margins) and maintaining prices in the host currency (which makes its goods more expensive). (F; difficult; p. 466)

96.   Intense competition among distributors in the United States minimizes the margin between retail prices and manufacturers' prices. (T; moderate; p. 466)

97.   Exchange rate fluctuations contribute to challenges in pricing. (T; easy; p. 466)

98.   A firm following a geocentric approach will use a two-tiered pricing policy. (F; moderate; p. 467)

99.   Domestic firms that are just beginning to internationalize use two-tiered pricing often. (T; moderate; p. 467)

100.   China has a ban on cigarette advertising on television. (T; moderate; p. 471)

Short Answers

101.   What is the definition of marketing? Answer: Marketing is the process of planning and executing the conception, pricing, promotion, and distribution of

ideas, goods, and services to create exchanges that satisfy individual and organizational objectives. (easy; p. 456)

102.   Why are synergies and coordination important in international marketing? Answer: Synergies are important because they provide opportunities for additional revenues, growth, and cross-fertilization. Coordination is important because it can help lower marketing costs and create a unified marketing effort. (moderate; p. 457)

103.   What are the three forms of business strategy that affect international marketing? Answer: Differentiation, cost leadership, or focus. (easy; p. 457)

104.   How does a differentiation strategy affect international marketing decisions? Answer: A differentiation strategy requires marketing managers to develop products as well as pricing, promotional, and distribution tactics that differentiate the firm's products or services from those of its competitors (in the eyes of the customers). (moderate; p. 457)

105.   How can international marketing managers achieve cost leadership? Answer: Cost leadership can be pursued and achieved through systematic reductions in production and manufacturing costs, reductions in sales cots, the acceptance of lower profit margins, the use of less expensive materials and component parts, or other means. (moderate; p. 457)

106.   What are the three basic approaches marketers choose from when deciding whether to customize or standardize their firm's marketing mix? Answer: Ethnocentric, polycentric, and geocentric. (moderate; p. 460)

107.   Why is the polycentric approach more costly for the firm? Answer: The polycentric approach is more costly because it requires the firm to customize the marketing mix in each market the firm enters in order to meet the idiosyncratic needs of customers in that market. (moderate; p. 460)

108.   Compare and contract the ethnocentric approach and the geocentric approach. Answer: Both approaches support the use of standardization of the marketing mix. However, the ethnographic approach supports the use of what is done in the domestic market while the geocentric approach supports the use of a standardized solution that is not based on any particular market. (moderate; p. 460)

109.   What factors affect the degree of standardization or customization a firm adopts? Answer: Product type, cultural differences between home country and host country, and the host countries' legal systems. (moderate; p. 461)

110.   By what two-step process do international firms address organizational issues? Answer: The decision to standardize some elements of the marketing mix (eg,

product design, brand name, packaging, and product positioning) is made centrally. Then local managers are called on to critique the global marketing program and to develop plans to implement customized elements of the marketing mix (eg, promotion and distribution). (difficult; p. 462)

111.   What factors comprise product? Answer: Product comprises both the set of tangible factors that the consumer can see or touch and numerous intangible factors (eg, image, installation, warranties, and credit terms). (easy; p. 464)

112.   What are the three pricing policies used by international firms? Answer: Standard price policy, two-tiered pricing, and market pricing. (easy; p. 467)

113.   What is two-tiered pricing? Answer: The firm sets one price for all its domestic sales and a second price for all its international sales. (moderate; p. 467)

114.   Why is it logical that an international firm following a geocentric approach will tend to use a standard price policy? Answer: A standard pricing policy states that the firm will use a standard price in each country in which it sells products. A geocentric approach suggests a standardized international marketing mix. Therefore, a geocentric approach is consistent with a standard price policy. (moderate; p. 467)

115.   What is a gray market? Answer: A gray market is a market that results when products are imported into a country legally, but outside the normal channels of distribution authorized by the manufacturer. This is also known as parallel importing. (moderate; p. 469)

116.   What products are commonly influenced by gray markets? Answer: Automobiles, cameras, computers, ski equipment, and watches. (difficult; p. 469)

117.   What are the three factors firms must consider as they develop an advertising strategy? Answer: Firms must consider the message it wants to convey, the media available for conveying the message, and the extent to which the firm wants to globalize its advertising effort. (moderate; p. 470)

118.   What is the most common approach to personal selling? Answer: The use of sales representatives who call on potential customers and attempt to sell them a firm's products or services is the most common approach to personal selling. (easy; p. 473)

119.   What are the two important sets of distribution issues faced by international firms? Answer: The firm must address how it wants to physically transport its goods and services from where they are created, to the various markets in which

they are to be sold and select the means by which to merchandise its goods in the markets it wants to serve. (moderate; p. 475)

120.   What modes of transportation are used in international distribution? Answer: Train, airplane, truck, ship, and electronic media. (moderate; p. 475)

Essay

121.   What four issues must international marketing managers address?

Answer: The four issues are 1) How to develop the firm's products; 2) how to price those products; 3) how to sell those products; and 4) how to distribute those products to the firm's customers. (moderate; p. 459)

122.   What are the advantages and disadvantages of standardized international marketing?

Answer: The advantages of standardized international marketing are 1) reduced marketing costs, 2) facilitates centralized control of marketing, 3) promotes efficiency in R&D, 4) results in economies of scale in production, and 5) reflects the trend toward a single global marketplace. The disadvantages are that it 1) ignores different conditions of product use, 2) ignores local legal differences, 3) ignores differences in buyer behavior patterns, 4) inhibits local marketing initiatives, and 5) ignores other differences in individual markets. (moderate; p. 462)

123.   What are the advantages and disadvantages of customized international marketing?

Answer: The advantages of customized international marketing are that it 1) reflects different conditions of product use, 2) acknowledges local legal differences, 3) accounts for differences in buyer behavior patterns, 4) promotes local marketing initiatives, and 5) accounts for other differences in individual markets. The disadvantages are that it 1) increases marketing costs, 2) inhibits centralized control of marketing, 3) creates inefficiency in R&D, 4) reduces economies of scale in production, and 5) ignores the trend toward a single global marketplace. (moderate; p. 462)

124.   Explain why pricing strategies are especially difficult for MNCs. Include the potential influence of exchange rates, tariffs, and distribution.

Answer: A firm's costs of doing business vary widely by country. Differences in transportation charges and tariffs cause the landed price of goods to vary by country. Differences in distribution practices also affect the final price the end customer pays. (difficult; p. 466)

125.   What are the advantages of personal selling for international firms?

Answer: Firms that hire local sales representatives can be reasonably confident that those individuals understand the local culture, norms, and customs. Personal selling promotes close, personal contact with customers. Personal selling makes it easier for the firm to obtain valuable market information. Knowledgeable sales representatives are an excellent source of information that can be used to develop new products and/or improve existing products for the local market. (moderate; p. 473)

Multiple Choice

1.   What are the keys to Benetton's success in the international marketplace?
       a. fashionable styling
       b. reasonable prices
       c. expertise in operations management
       d. commitment to quality
       e. all of the above
       (e; easy; p. 485)

2.   _____ is the set of activities an organization uses to transform different kinds of inputs into final goods and services.
       a. Distribution
       b. Marketing
       c. Operations management
       d. Organizational design
       e. None of the above
       (c; easy; p. 486)

3.   What is the central role of operations management within an international firm?
       a. To minimize expenses.
       b. To create value.
       c. To manage the flow of goods.
       d. To manage inventory.
       e. To support vertical integration.
       (b; moderate; p. 487)

4.   What business strategy is associated with an operations management focus on creating goods that are clearly different from those of the company's competitors?
       a. differentiation
       b. cost leadership
       c. focus
       d. niche
       e. all of the above
       (a; moderate; p. 487)

5.   Porsche competes on the basis of product performance and status. Its production facilities may need to be located where there is a skilled labor force despite the higher costs of that labor. What business strategy is affecting operations management decisions in this case?
       a. differentiation
       b. cost leadership
       c. focus
       d. niche
       e. all of the above
       (a; moderate; p. 487)

6.   Which business strategy is associated with an operations management focus on reducing the costs of creating goods or services to the absolute minimum so the firm can lower prices while still earning an acceptable level of profits?
a. differentiation
b. cost leadership
c. focus
d. niche
e. all of the above
(b; moderate; p. 488)

7.   Hong Kong's Roly International Holdings locates its factories in China where it can produce inexpensive Christmas decorations due to low labor costs. These goods are then shipped via slow, low-cost cargo ships to discounters like Wal-Mart. Roly International Holdings follows a _____ strategy in its operations management.
a. differentiation
b. cost leadership
c. focus
d. niche
e. all of the above
(b; moderate; p. 488)

8.   Which of the following is *not* one of the areas of focus for operations managers?
a. resources
b. location
c. accounting
d. logistics
e. all are areas of focus
(c; moderate; p. 488)

9.   When managers decide where and how to obtain resources the firm needs to produce its products, what area of international operations management is involved?
a. resources
b. location
c. accounting
d. logistics
e. all are areas of focus
(a; moderate; p. 488)

10.   When managers decide where to build administrative facilities, sales offices, and plants, what area of international operations management is involved?
        a. resources
        b. location
        c. accounting
        d. logistics
        e. all are areas of focus
        (b; moderate; p. 488)

11.   When managers decide on modes of transportation and methods of inventory control, what area of international operations management is involved?
        a. resources
        b. location
        c. accounting
        d. logistics
        e. all are areas of focus
        (d; moderate; p. 488)

12.   What are operations management decisions, processes, and issues that involve the creation of tangible goods called?
        a. service operations management
        b. production management
        c. management of goods
        d. manufacturing
        e. none of the above
        (b; moderate; p. 489)

13.   What are operations management decisions, processes and issues that involve the creation of intangible services called?
        a. service operations management
        b. production management
        c. management of goods
        d. manufacturing
        e. none of the above
        (a; moderate; p. 489)

14.   _____ is the creation of goods by transforming raw materials and component parts in combination with capital, labor, and technology.
        a. Service operations management
        b. Production management
        c. Management of goods
        d. Manufacturing
        e. None of the above
        (d; moderate; p. 489)

15.   BMW takes thousands of component parts including sheet metal, engine parts, and upholstery and combines them to make automobiles. This is an example of _____ activities.
        a.   manufacturing
        b.   marketing
        c.   distribution
        d.   planning
        e.   operations
        (a; easy; p. 489)

16.   What is the term for the set of processes and steps a firm uses to acquire the various resources it needs to create it products?
        a.   supply chain management
        b.   sourcing
        c.   procuring
        d.   all of the above
        e.   none of the above
        (d; moderate; p. 489)

17.   Supply chain management affects _____.
        a.   product cost
        b.   product quality
        c.   internal capital demands
        d.   all of the above
        e.   none of the above
        (d; easy; p. 489)

18.   As Rolex plans for the manufacturing of raw materials into finished goods, what is the first step it must take in operations management?
        a.   Decide how to acquire raw materials.
        b.   Determine appropriate degree of vertical integration.
        c.   Decide whether to make inputs itself.
        d.   Decide how to transport finished goods to buyers.
        e.   None of the above.
        (a; difficult; p. 489)

19.   _____ is the extent to which a firm either provides its own resources or obtains them from other sources.
        a.   Supply chain management
        b.   Horizontal integration
        c.   Vertical integration
        d.   Operations management
        e.   Cross-ownership
        (c; moderate; p. 489)

20.   When various units within the firm can be seen as suppliers to other units within the firm, this is called _____.
       a.   supply chain management
       b.   horizontal integration
       c.   vertical integration
       d.   operations management
       e.   cross-ownership
       (c; moderate; p. 489)

21.   Determining the appropriate degree of _____ is the first step in developing a supply chain management strategy.
       a.   standardization
       b.   horizontal integration
       c.   vertical integration
       d.   operations management
       e.   customization
       (c; moderate; p. 489)

22.   Firms that have little _____ are involved in only one step or just a few steps in the production chain.
       a.   standardization
       b.   horizontal integration
       c.   vertical integration
       d.   operations management
       e.   customization
       (c; moderate; p. 489)

23.   BP has several units responsible for its business. One unit explores the world for natural gas and crude oil. Another unit extracts the oil and gas. Another unit transports the oil and gas, and its refineries transform the crude oil into gasoline and other products. Its trucks transport the refined products to company-owned service stations where it is sold to the final consumer. BP's operations management system is based on _____.
       a.   horizontal integration
       b.   vertical integration
       c.   intracompany transfers
       d.   cross-ownership
       e.   all of the above
       (b; moderate; p. 490)

24.   Heineken NV buys grains, labels, bottles, and cartons from other suppliers prior
        to brewing and bottling its beer. This suggests that Heineken has little _____.
        a.   supply chain management
        b.   horizontal integration
        c.   intracompany transfers
        d.   vertical integration
        e.   cross-ownership
        (d; moderate; p. 490)

25.   What factor might influence the decision to make-or-buy inputs for
        manufacturing?
        a.   firm's size
        b.   scope of operations
        c.   technological expertise
        d.   nature of product
        e.   all of the above
        (e; easy; p. 490)

26.   When a firm chooses to make its own inputs, it increases control over _____.
        a.   product quality
        b.   delivery schedules
        c.   design changes
        d.   costs
        e.   all of the above
        (e; moderate; p. 491)

27.   What threat exists for firms who rely upon suppliers for inputs?
        a.   supplier could go out of business
        b.   supplier could raise prices
        c.   supplier could product poor-quality materials
        d.   all of the above
        c.   b and c only
        (d; easy; p. 491)

28.   The choice to make inputs or buy inputs from suppliers results in trade-offs
        between costs and _____.
        a.   control
        b.   risk
        c.   investment
        d.   flexibility
        e.   all of the above
        (e; moderate; p. 491)

29.   Which factor influences the decision of where to locate production facilities?
      a.   country-related issues
      b.   product-related issues
      c.   government policies
      d.   organizational issues
      e.   all of the above
      (e; moderate; p. 493)

30.   Which of the following is a country-related issue affecting the location decision
      for production facilities?
      a.   country-of-origin marketing effects
      b.   value to weight ratio
      c.   required production technology
      d.   inventory management policies
      e.   all of the above
      (a; moderate; p. 493)

31.   Christopher Radko, a premium holiday ornament manufacturer, is considering
      locating manufacturing facilities in China in order to lower costs. However, the
      firm fears a backlash from ornament collectors who prefer ornaments made in
      Eastern Europe. What location issue is Christopher Radko dealing with?
      a.   resource availability
      b.   infrastructure
      c.   country-of-origin effects
      d.   product-related issues
      e.   inventory management policies
      (c; moderate; p. 493)

32.   Which theory suggested that countries that enjoy large, low-cost endowments of a
      factor of production would attract firms needing that factor of production?
      a.   national competitive advantage
      b.   Heckscher-Ohlin theory
      c.   mercantilism
      d.   relative factor endowments
      e.   absolute advantage
      (b; difficult; p. 493)

33.   Which theory explains why China has been capable of attracting toy, footwear, and textile manufacturers to develop manufacturing facilities in China due to its low labor costs?
       a. national competitive advantage
       b. Heckscher-Ohlin theory
       c. mercantilism
       d. relative factor endowments
       e. absolute advantage
       (b; difficult; p. 493)

34.   Which of the following is *not* a country-related issue affecting the location decision for manufacturing facilities?
       a. resource availability
       b. cost
       c. required production technology
       d. infrastructure
       e. country-of-origin effects
       (c; moderate; p. 493)

35.   Firms require construction materials, equipment, materials suppliers, construction contractors, and transportation to operate a foreign-based facility. What consideration in the location decision do these issues relate to?
       a. resource availability
       b. cost
       c. infrastructure
       d. both a and b
       e. both a and c
       (e; moderate; p. 493)

36.   What is the primary determinant of whether an individual country is a suitable location?
       a. resource availability
       b. cost
       c. infrastructure
       d. country-of-origin effects
       e. both a and b
       (e; moderate; p. 493)

37.   _____ refer(s) to the reputation a country has for products it produces.
       a. Country brand image
       b. National reputation
       c. Country-of-origin effects
       d. Ethnocentric effects
       e. None of the above
       (c; moderate; p. 494)

38.   An experiment found that consumer preference for Tempomax watches fell by
      74% when the consumers were told that Tempomax watches were produced in
      Pakistan instead of Germany refers to _____.
      a.   national competitive advantage
      b.   country-of-origin effects
      c.   ethnocentric effects
      d.   national reputation
      e.   all of the above
      (b; moderate; p. 494)

39.   Which of the following is *not* an example of country-of-origin effects?
      a.   Japan's reputation for high-quality products.
      b.   Italy's reputation for style and fashion, particularly in apparel and leather
           goods.
      c.   Switzerland's reputation for quality chocolate.
      d.   Germany's reputation for engineering.
      e.   All are examples of country-of-origin effects.
      (d; difficult; p. 494)

40.   A product's value-to-weight ratio affects the importance of _____.
      a.   inventory management
      b.   the make-or-buy decision
      c.   transportation costs
      d.   customer feedback
      e.   all of the above
      (c; moderate; p. 496)

41.   When a firm's sales are large relative to an efficient-sized facility, the firm is
      likely to operate _____ facilities in _____ location(s).
      a.   many, many
      b.   few, few
      c.   many, few
      d.   few, many
      (a; difficult; p. 496)

42.   Which of the following is *not* an issue related to government policy that can affect
      the location decision for manufacturing facilities?
      a.   stability of political process
      b.   national trade policies
      c.   economic development incentives
      d.   foreign trade zones
      e.   all of the above
      (e; easy; p. 497)

43.   When Nissan chose to locate a new manufacturing facility in Jackson, Mississippi,
       it received $295 million in incentives. What factor was likely the most critical in
       the location decision?
       a. infrastructure
       b. government policies
       c. country-of-origin effects
       d. resource availability
       e. product-related issues
       (b; moderate; p. 497)

44.   A(n) _____ is a specially designated and controlled geographical area in which
       imported or exported goods receive preferential tariff treatment.
       a. economic union
       b. customs union
       c. free trade zone
       d. free trade area
       e. all of the above
       (c; easy; p. 497)

45.   What is the advantage to locating a facility near an FTZ?
       a. lower costs
       b. flexibility
       c. ability to import products duty free
       d. all of the above
       e. none of the above
       (d; easy; p. 497)

46.   _____ refers to an emerging logistical trend where a customer contracts with one
       transportation company to handle all of its shipments from door to door.
       a   One-stop shipping
       b. Door-to-door transportation
       c. Materials management
       d. International logistics
       e. Customized logistics
       (a; easy; p. 499)

47.   _____ is the management of the flow of materials, parts, supplies, and other
       resources from suppliers to the firm; the flow of materials, parts, supplies, and
       other resources within and between units of the firm itself; and the flow of
       finished products, services, and goods from the firm to customers.
       a. International logistics
       b. International distribution
       c. Transportation
       d. International operations management
       e. Organizational design
       (a; moderate; p. 499)

48.   The portion of international logistics dealing with the flow of finished products, services, and goods from the firm to customers is called _____.
        a. materials management
        b. physical distribution
        c. distribution
        d. both a and b
        e. both b and c
        (e; easy; p. 499)

49.   Which of the following is *not* a factor that differentiates domestic and international materials management functions?
        a. distance involved in shipping
        b. number of transport modes
        c. type of transport modes
        d. complexity of regulatory context
        e. all are relevant factors
        (c; difficult; p. 499)

50.   What is the term for a firm that transforms resources into an intangible output that creates utility for its customers?
        a. international service business
        b. international operations business
        c. logistics management
        d. utility business
        e. none of the above
        (a; easy; p. 501)

51.   Which of the following is *not* a characteristic of services?
        a. intangible
        b. not storable
        c. require customer participation
        d. bundled with other products
        e. all are characteristics of services
        (e; easy; p. 501)

52.   _____ is deciding how many customers a firm will be able to serve at a given time.
        a. Operations management
        b. Services production planning
        c. Capacity planning
        d. Service operations management
        e. Services design
        (c; moderate; p. 501)

53.   What characteristic of services this scenario describes: a customer goes to an
       accountant to obtain financial advice?
       a.   intangible
       b.   not storable
       c.   require customer participation
       d.   bundled with other products
       e.   all of the above
       (a; moderate; p. 501)

54.   What characteristic of services is described by this scenario: a service call to
       repair a broken washing machine can occur only when the technician is physically
       transported to the site of the broken appliance and is wasted if no one is home to
       unlock the door?
       a.   intangible
       b.   not storable
       c.   require customer participation
       d.   bundled with other products
       e.   all of the above
       (b; difficult; p. 501)

55.   What characteristic of services this scenario describes: travel agents book tours
       for client vacations?
       a.   intangible
       b.   not storable
       c.   require customer participation
       d.   bundled with other products
       e.   all of the above
       (c; moderate; p. 501)

56.   What are the potential consequences of poor capacity planning?
       a.   lost sales
       b.   increased costs
       c.   lower profits
       d.   all of the above
       e.   both a and b
       (d; moderate; p. 501)

57.   The Swedish appliance maker AB Electrolux manufactures vacuum cleaners and
        has service operations set up to repair those products for consumers who buy
        them. What characteristic of services does this represent?
        a. intangible
        b. not storable
        c. require customer participation
        d. bundled with other products
        e. all of the above
        (d; moderate; p. 502)

58.   What change has been brought about due to deregulation and reduced trade
        barriers?
        a. cross-border investments
        b. strategic alliances
        c. start-up companies
        d. all of the above
        e. none of the above
        (d; easy; p. 502)

59.   What function is performed in the management of international services
        operations?
        a. capacity planning
        b. location planning
        c. facilities design and layout
        d. operations scheduling
        e. all of the above
        (e; moderate; p. 502)

60.   _____ is an economic measure of efficiency that summarizes the value of outputs
        relative to the value of the inputs used to create the outputs.
        a. GNP
        b. GDP
        c. Productivity
        d. Turnover ratio
        e. Return on investment
        (c; moderate; p. 503)

61.   Productivity is important because it _____.
        a. helps to determine a firm's overall success
        b. contributes to firm's long-term survival
        c. contributes to the overall standard of living within a particular country
        d. all of the above
        e. both a and b
        (d; moderate; p. 503)

62.   Which of the following strategies can enhance a firm's productivity?
       a.   invest more heavily in research and development
       b.   improve operations
       c.   increase employee involvement
       d.   all of the above
       e.   both b and c
       (d; moderate; p. 504)

63.   How do firms typically increase employee involvement to enhance productivity?
       a.   decrease work hours
       b.   provide salary increases
       c.   improve benefits
       d.   implement self-managed teams
       e.   improve participation
       (d; moderate; p. 504)

64.   _____ is the totality of features and characteristics of a product or service that
       bear on its ability to satisfy stated or implied needs.
       a.   Production
       b.   Quality
       c.   Benefit
       d.   Marketing
       e.   Operations management
       (b; easy; p. 504)

65.   Which of the following areas is *not* covered by ISO 9000 standards?
       a.   product testing
       b.   employee training
       c.   logistics
       d.   repair policies and procedures
       e.   record keeping
       (c; difficult; p. 505)

66.   _____ is an integrated effort to systematically and continuously improve the
       quality of an organization's products and/or services.
       a.   ISO 9000
       b.   Standard
       c.   Quality
       d.   Total quality management
       e.   Just-in-time management
       (d; moderate; p. 505)

67.   What are the guidelines that provide the basis for quality certification called?
       a. WTO standards
       b. ISO 1000
       c. ISO 9000: 2000
       d. Total quality management
       e. The Deming system
       (c; easy; p. 504)

68.   What organization has developed and refined an international set of quality
       guidelines?
       a. American Society for Quality Control
       b. World Trade Organization
       c. International Standards Organization
       d. International Organization for Standardization
       e. None of the above
       (d; moderate; p. 504)

69.   Which of the following operational components is important for quality
       improvement?
       a. employee involvement
       b. high quality materials
       c. up-to-date technology
       d. effective methods
       e. all of the above
       (e; easy; p. 505)

70.   _____ is a family of mathematically based tools for monitoring and controlling
       quality.
       a. Total quality management
       b. Statistical process control
       c. Benchmarking
       d. Operations management
       e. Just-in-time management
       (b; moderate; p. 506)

71.   _____ is the process of legally and ethically studying how other firms do
       something in a high-quality way and then either imitating or improving on their
       methods.
       a. Total quality management
       b. Statistical process control
       c. Benchmarking
       d. Espionage
       e. Competitive parity
       (c; easy; p. 506)

72.   Xerox sent a team of managers to Japan to study Canon copiers there. They found the copier was of higher quality than Xerox's copiers. Xerox then attempted to imitate Canon's methods. This is an example of _____.
        a. total quality management
        b. statistical process control
        c. benchmarking
        d. espionage
        e. competitive parity
        (c; moderate; p. 506)

73.   Perrier takes samples of finished products and measures their actual content to assess if the contents measure within the appropriate range. This is an example of _____.
        a. total quality management
        b. statistical process control
        c. benchmarking
        d. espionage
        e. competitive parity
        (b; easy; p. 506)

74.   When data is in a form that is valuable to a manager in making decisions and performing related tasks, it is called _____.
        a. reports
        b. information
        c. vital
        d. analysis
        e. all of the above
        (b; easy; p. 506)

75.   A(n) _____ is a methodology created by a firm to gather, assemble, and provide data in a form or forms useful to managers.
        a. TQM program
        b. information system
        c. benchmarking plan
        d. process
        e. statistical process control
        (b; moderate; p. 507)

True/False

76.   The business strategy followed by the firm sets the stage for the role of operations management within an international firm. (T; easy; p. 487)

77.   For firms following a cost leadership approach, the operations management function must be able to create goods or services that are clearly different from

those of the company's competitors. (F; moderate; p. 487)

78.   If the firm uses a customized approach to each market, its operations management should be globally integrated. (F; difficult; p. 488)

79.   Operations managers must deal with complex issues regarding resources, location, and logistics. (T; easy; p. 488)

80.   Supply chain management is the process of selecting whether to make or buy the resources necessary for the manufacturing process. (F; moderate; p. 489)

81.   The decision to buy rather than make dictates the need to choose between long-term and short-term supplier relationships. (T; moderate; p. 490)

82.   Firms that have little vertical integration typically make the inputs necessary for manufacturing. (F; difficult; p. 490)

83.   Because Saab is a relatively small automobile manufacturer, it is more likely to buy its component parts from other suppliers. (T; moderate; p. 490)

84.   Resource dependence is a risk for firms that choose to buy rather than make their inputs. (T; moderate; p. 491)

85.   A weakness of the Japanese keiretsu system is its inability to reduce the problem of enforcing contracts between a firm and its suppliers.
(F; moderate; p. 491)

86.   All else being equal, a firm will choose to make or buy simply on the basis of whether it can obtain the resource cheaper by making it internally or by buying it from an external supplier. (T; easy; p. 491)

87.   Supplier relationships can range from partnerships to antagonistic business dealings. (T; easy; p. 492)

88.   Buying inputs for manufacturing increases the firm's level of investment.
(F; moderate; p. 492)

89.   Infrastructure and country-of-origins effects constitute the primary determinants of whether an individual country is a suitable location for a facility.
(F; moderate; p. 493)

90.   A firm that buys rather than makes lacks the flexibility to change suppliers as circumstances dictate. (F; easy; p. 493)

91.   Products manufactured in Italy are subject to a country-of-origin effect due to its reputation for manufacturing high-quality products. (F; moderate; p. 494)

92.   Often the only comparative advantage that developing countries have in the international marketplace is low wage rates. (T; moderate; p. 495)

93.   If foreign MNCs were required to pay above-market wages or to provide working conditions equal to those in developed countries, the economic development of poorer countries would be improved significantly.
(F; difficult; p. 495)

94.   A product's value-to-weight ratio affects the importance of transportation costs in the product's delivered price. (T; easy; p. 496)

95.   Adoption of a global area structure centralizes authority at headquarters.
(F; difficult; p. 498)

96.   The management of the flow of finished products, services, and goods from the firm to customers is called materials management. (F; easy; p. 499)

97.   Most countries regulate aspects of their internal transportation systems including price, safety, and packaging. (T; easy; p. 500)

98.   The American Society for Quality Control developed and refined an international set of quality guidelines which are now called ISO 9000: 2000.
(F; moderate; p. 504)

99.   Many firms report that just preparing for an ISO 9000 audit has been helpful.
(T; moderate; p. 505)

100.   The importance of information management depends on the type of strategy and organization design the firm uses. (T; easy; p. 507)

Short Answers

101.   What is the definition of operations management? Answer: Operations management is the set of activities an organization uses to transform different kinds of inputs into final goods and services. (easy; p. 486)

102.   What types of decisions are part of the acquisition of resources component of the international operations management process? Answer: Supply chain management, vertical integration, and make-or-buy decisions. (moderate; p. 487)

103.   What types of decisions are part of the location decisions made in the international operations management process? Answer: Country-related issues,

product-related issues, government policies, and organizational issues. (moderate; p. 487)

104.   What types of decisions are part of the logistics and materials management components of the international operations management process? Answer: Flow of materials, transportation options, inventory levels, and packaging. (moderate; p. 487)

105.   What three general areas must operations managers address? Answer: Resources, location, and logistics. (moderate; p. 488)

106.   What are the three important dimensions of international production management? Answer: International supply chain management, international facilities location, and international logistics. (moderate; p. 489)

107.   What is the definition of supply chain management? What other terms can be used for supply chain management? Answer: Supply chain management is the set of processes and steps a firm uses to acquire the various resources it needs to create its products. Sourcing and procuring both refer to supply chain management. (moderate; p. 489)

108.   Explain the meaning of the make-or-buy decision. Answer: The make-or-buy decision refers to the firm's choice to make its necessary inputs itself or buy them from outside suppliers. (easy; p. 490)

109.   What factors influence the make-or-buy decision? Answer: The make-or-buy decision can be influenced by a firm's size, scope of operations, technological expertise, and nature of product. (moderate; p. 490)

110.   What features of countries can influence the decision about where to locate an international facility? Answer: Resource availability, cost, infrastructure, and country-of-origin marketing effects. (moderate; p. 493)

111.   What product-related characteristics may influence the decision about where to locate an international facility? Answer: Product's value-to-weight ratio and the required production technology. (moderate; p. 495)

112.   Which government policies are especially important in the decision about where to locate an international facility? Answer: Stability of the political process, national trade policies, economic development incentives, and existence of foreign trade zones. (moderate; p. 497)

113.   How does a JIT inventory management system work? Answer: With a JIT system, a firm's suppliers deliver their products directly to the firm's manufacturing center, usually in frequent small shipments, just as they are needed for production. (easy; p. 498)

114.   What is the definition of international logistics? Answer: International logistics is the management of the flow of materials, parts, supplies, and other resources from suppliers to the firm; the flow of materials, parts, supplies, and other resources within and between units of the firm itself; and the flow of finished products, services, and goods from the firm to customers. (moderate; p. 499)

115.   What factors differentiate the domestic and materials management functions? Answer: Distance involved in shipping, number of transport modes involved, and the complexity of the regulatory context.
(moderate; p. 499)

116.   What is an international service business? Answer: An international service business is a firm that transforms resources into an intangible output that creates utility for its customers. (moderate; p. 501)

117.   Provide two examples of international services. Answer: British Airway's transporting of passengers from London to New Delhi and PricewaterhouseCooper's assistance with the accounting and auditing functions of firms such as BP and IBM. (easy; p. 501)

118.   What is TQM? Answer: Total quality management is an integrated effort to systematically and continuously improve the quality of an organization's products and/or services. (easy; p. 505)

119.   Explain benchmarking and statistical process control. Answer: Statistical process control is a family of mathematically based tools for monitoring and controlling quality. Benchmarking is the process of legally and ethically studying how other firms do something in a high-quality way and then either imitating or improving their methods. (moderate; p 506)

120.   What is an information system? Answer: An information system is a methodology created by a firm to gather, assemble, and provide data in a form or forms useful to managers. (easy; p. 507)

Essay

121.   When making the make-or-buy decision, international firms must make tradeoffs between costs and three other variables. What are they? Explain the nature of the trade-off international firms must make.

        Answer: International firms must make trade-offs between costs and control, risk, investment, and flexibility. Control: Making a component has the advantages of increasing the firm's control over product quality, delivery schedules, design changes, and costs. A firm that buys from external suppliers may become overly dependent on those suppliers. It can also be expensive to enforce contracts with suppliers. Risk: Buying a component rather than making it has the advantage of reducing the firm's financial and operating risks. Investment: Buying from others lowers the firm's level of investment. By not having to build a new factory or learn a technology, a firm can free up capital for other productive uses. Flexibility: A firm that buys rather than makes retains the flexibility to change suppliers as circumstances dictate. (moderate; p. 491)

122.

What are the advantages of choosing a location based on the existence of a foreign trade zone?

Answer: The FTZ allows international firms to import products duty free into those zones for specified purposes. The FTZ gives the firm greater flexibility regarding importing or exporting and creates avenues for lowering costs. A firm may be able to import component parts, supplement them with other component parts obtained locally, and assemble them all into finished goods. (moderate; p. 497)

123.   What are the four characteristics of services? Explain.

Answer: Services are often intangible, not storable, require customer participation, and may be linked with tangible goods. Because of this intangibility, assessing the value or quality of a service is often more difficult than assessing the value or quality of a good. Services often cannot be created ahead of time and inventoried or saved for future usage. International services such as tourism cannot occur without the physical presence of the customer. Many firms offer product-support services. These services may be critical to the sale of the related product. (moderate; p. 501)

124.   Why is quality important to international firms?

Answer: Firms today compete on the basis of quality. Firms with poor quality are unlikely to be successful. Quality is also important because it is directly linked with productivity. Higher quality means increased productivity because of fewer defects, fewer resources devoted to reworking defective products, and fewer resources devoted to quality control itself. Higher quality also helps firms develop and maintain customer loyalty. (moderate; p. 505)

125.   Explain the four essential components of total quality management.

Answer: The four components are employee involvement, high quality materials, up-to-date technology, and effective methods. All employees must participate in helping to accomplish the firm's quality-related objectives.

Requiring higher-quality parts and materials from suppliers can improve quality. The firm must be willing to invest in new technology to become more efficient and to achieve higher quality manufacturing processes. The firm must be willing to adopt new and improved methods of getting work done. (moderate; p. 505)

Multiple Choice

1.   Where is the international air carrier, KLM, based?
      a. The United States
      b. Germany
      c. The Netherlands
      d. The United Kingdom
      e. Hong Kong
      (c; easy; p. 515)

2.   Which task listed below is managed by KLM's financial managers as a part of
      doing business in more than 150 cities on six continents?
      a. maintain local currency cash balances in each country
      b. find low-cost capital
      c. protect against exchange rate fluctuations
      d. monitor foreign-exchange market
      e. all of the above
      (e; easy; p. 515)

3.   When a transaction involves a buyer and a seller from two countries, what issue
      arises?
      a. Which currency to use for the transaction?
      b. When and how to check credit?
      c. Which form of payment to use?
      d. How to arrange financing?
      e. All of the above.
      (e; moderate; p. 516)

4.   Which currency does an exporter typically prefer to use in a transaction?
      a. U.S. dollars
      b. Euro
      c. Japanese yen
      d. Home country currency
      e. Host country currency
      (d; moderate; p. 516)

5.   Which currency does an importer typically prefer to use in a transaction?
      a. U.S. dollars
      b. Euro
      c. Japanese yen
      d. Home country currency
      e. Host country currency
      (d; moderate; p. 516)

6.   Which currency is used the most in international invoices?
        a. U.S. dollars
        b. Euro
        c. Japanese yen
        d. Home country currency
        e. Host country currency
        (a; easy; p. 516)

7.   Which method of payment listed below is the safest method?
        a. payment in advance
        b. open account
        c. letter of credit
        d. countertrade
        e. all are equally safe
        (a; moderate; p. 517)

8.   What delivery method is preferred for payment in advance to exporters?
        a. check
        b. wire transfer
        c. credit card
        d. cash
        e. all of the above are acceptable
        (b; easy; p. 517)

9.   When paying via _____, the goods are shipped by the exporter and received by
        the importer prior to payment, and the exporter then bills the importer for the
        goods, stipulating the amount, form, and time at which payment is expected.
        a. payment in advance
        b. open account
        c. documentary collection
        d. letters of credit
        e. countertrade
        (b; moderate; p 518)

10.   In specialized international lending activity, firms may engage in _____ ,where
        they buy foreign accounts receivable at a discount from face value.
        a. factoring
        b. open account
        c. lading
        d. documentary collecting
        e. drafting
        (a; moderate; p. 518)

11.   Importers asked to pay using the _____ method may seek out other suppliers
      rather than experience its disadvantages.
      a.   payment in advance
      b.   open account
      c.   documentary collection
      d.   letter of credit
      e.   credit card
      (a; moderate; p. 518)

12.   Which payment method requires the least amount of paperwork?
      a.   payment in advance
      b.   open account
      c.   documentary collection
      d.   letter of credit
      e.   none of the above
      (b; difficult; p. 518)

13.   Using the _____ payment method, commercial banks serve as agents to facilitate
      the payment process.
      a.   payment in advance
      b.   open account
      c.   documentary collection
      d.   letter of credit
      e.   credit card
      (c; moderate; p. 518)

14.   What document serves as a title to the goods in question under the document
      collection payment method?
      a.   sight draft
      b.   time draft
      c.   bill of lading
      d.   bill of exchange
      e.   trade acceptance
      (c; moderate; p. 519)

15.   What document serves as a contract for transportation between the exporter and
      the carrier?
      a.   sight draft
      b.   time draft
      c.   bill of lading
      d.   bill of exchange
      e.   trade acceptance
      (c; moderate; p. 519)

16.   A _____ requires payment upon the transfer of title to the goods from the exporter to the importer.
       a. sight draft
       b. time draft
       c. bill of lading
       d. bill of exchange
       e. trade acceptance
       (a; moderate; p. 519)

17.   Under the payment method of document collection, the term draft is referred to as _____ outside of the United States.
       a. bill of exchange
       b. bill of lading
       c. time draft
       d. sight draft
       e. trade acceptance
       (a; easy; p. 518)

18.   Under the document collection payment method, who draws up the draft?
       a. importer
       b. exporter
       c. importer's bank
       d. exporter's bank
       e. none of the above
       (b; moderate; p. 518)

19.   A _____ extends credit to the importer by requiring payment at some specified time after the importer receives the goods.
       a. sight draft
       b. time draft
       c. bill of lading
       d. bill of exchange
       e. trade acceptance
       (b; moderate; p. 519)

20.   An accepted time draft is called a _____.
       a. sight draft
       b. time draft
       c. bill of lading
       d. bill of exchange
       e. trade acceptance
       (e; moderate; p. 519)

21.   When acceptances are sold _____, it means that the buyer of the acceptance is
        stuck with the loss if the importer does not pay.
        a.   without recourse
        b.   with recourse
        c.   with pay
        d.   without pay
        e.   none of the above
        (a; moderate; p. 519)

22.   When acceptances are sold _____, it means that the exporter will have to
        reimburse the buyer of the acceptance in the case of nonpayment by the importer.
        a.   without recourse
        b.   with recourse
        c.   with pay
        d.   without pay
        e.   none of the above
        (b; moderate; p. 519)

23.   Storage fees at foreign loading docks are known as _____.
        a.   rent
        b.   lease
        c.   demurrage
        d.   remuneration
        e.   penalty
        (c; moderate; p. 520)

24.   What is the term for a document that is issued by a bank and contains its promise
        to pay the exporter on receiving proof that the exporter has fulfilled all
        requirements specified in the document?
        a.   bill of lading
        b.   bill of exchange
        c.   letter of credit
        d.   open account
        e.   trade acceptance
        (c; moderate; p. 520)

25.   Under most letters of credit, what item must exporters supply as documentation?
        a.   invoice
        b.   bill of lading
        c.   packing list
        d.   proof of insurance
        e.   all of the above
        (e; easy; p. 520)

26.   A(n) _____ confirms that the goods being shipped were produced in the exporting
        country.
        a. export license
        b. certificate of product origin
        c. inspection certificate
        d. trade acceptance
        e. bill of lading
        (b; moderate; p. 520)

27.   A(n) _____ provides assurance that the products have been inspected and that
        they conform to relevant standards.
        a. export license
        b. certificate of product origin
        c. inspection certificate
        d. trade acceptance
        e. bill of lading
        (c; moderate; p. 520)

28.   Which of the following is not a type of letter of credit?
        a. advised letter of credit
        b. confirmed letter of credit
        c. irrevocable letter of credit
        d. unconfirmed letter of credit
        e. revocable letter of credit
        (d; easy; p. 521)

29.   After issuing the letter of credit, the importer's bank sends it and the
        accompanying documents to the exporter's bank, which advises the exporter of
        the terms of the instrument, thereby creating a(n) _____.
        a. advised letter of credit
        b. confirmed letter of credit
        c. irrevocable letter of credit
        d. unconfirmed letter of credit
        e. revocable letter of credit
        (a; moderate; p. 521)

30.   When the exporter requests its bank to add its own guarantee of payment to a
        letter of credit, this creates a(n) _____.
        a. advised letter of credit
        b. confirmed letter of credit
        c. irrevocable letter of credit
        d. unconfirmed letter of credit
        e. revocable letter of credit
        (b; moderate; p. 521)

31.   The _____ is a letter of credit that cannot be altered without the written consent of
       both the importer and the exporter.
       a. advised letter of credit
       b. confirmed letter of credit
       c. irrevocable letter of credit
       d. unconfirmed letter of credit
       e. revocable letter of credit
       (c; easy; p. 521)

32.   The _____ is a letter of credit that the bank may alter at any time and for any
       reason.
       a. advised letter of credit
       b. confirmed letter of credit
       c. irrevocable letter of credit
       d. unconfirmed letter of credit
       e. revocable letter of credit
       (e; easy; p. 521)

33.   What services are provided when a bank issues a letter of credit for an exporter?
       a. authentication of credit or amendments
       b. protection from fraud
       c. review of amendments for boycott status
       d. check of the SDN list
       e. all of the above
       (e; easy; p. 521)

34.   The U.S. government list of names of businesses and individuals around the world
       who have forfeited their rights to import from or export to the United States is
       called the _____ list.
       a. specially designated nationals
       b. export embargo
       c. black
       d. patriot act of nationalism
       e. U.S. list of sanctions and embargos
       (a; moderate; p. 521)

35.   Under the _____, it is the responsibility of the advising bank to report boycott
       provisions in a letter of credit to the U.S. Department of Commerce or Treasury.
       a. Helms-Burton Act
       b. Export Administration Act
       c. Exports and Imports Boycott Act
       d. General Agreement for Tariffs and Trade
       e. WTO
       (b; difficult; p. 521)

36.   What is a common workability issue for letters of credit?
       a. conflicting stipulations
       b. incorrect terms
       c. expired availability dates
       d. all of the above
       e. both a and b
       (d; easy; p. 521)

37.   Which form of letter of credit is most appropriate when the exporter is concerned
       about political risk?
       a. advised letter of credit
       b. confirmed letter of credit
       c. irrevocable letter of credit
       d. revocable letter of credit
       e. none of the above
       (b; difficult; p. 521)

38.   Which of the following credit cards is *not* commonly accepted for small
       international transactions?
       a. VISA
       b. MasterCard
       c. American Express
       d. Discover
       e. All are accepted for international business transactions
       (d; easy; p. 522)

39.   Credit card companies collect _____ from the merchant for assuming the costs of
       collecting the funds from the customer and any risks of nonpayment.
       a. commissions
       b. flat fees
       c. transaction fees
       d. translation fees
       e. [au: include "e" to keep consistent]
       (c; easy; p. 522)

40.   _____ occurs when a firm accepts something other than money as payment for its
       goods or services.
       a. Countertrade
       b. Payment via credit cards
       c. In-kind payment
       d. Open account payment
       e. Documentary collection
       (a; easy; p. 522)

41.   Which of the forms listed below is the simplest form of countertrade?
       a.   counterpurchase
       b.   barter
       c.   parallel barter
       d.   offset purchase
       e.   clearinghouse accounts
       (b; moderate; p. 523)

42.   The State Trading Corporation of India agreed to exchange wheat and other grains
       to Turkmenistan in return for cotton. What form of countertrade is this?
       a.   counterpurchase
       b.   barter
       c.   parallel barter
       d.   offset purchase
       e.   clearinghouse accounts
       (b; moderate; p. 523)

43.   What is the most common form of countertrade?
       a.   counterpurchase
       b.   barter
       c.   parallel barter
       d.   offset purchase
       e.   clearinghouse accounts
       (a; moderate; p. 523)

44.   Which form of countertrade is used when each party simultaneously swaps its
       products for the products of the other?
       a.   counterpurchase
       b.   barter
       c.   parallel barter
       d.   offset purchase
       e.   clearinghouse accounts
       (b; moderate; p. 523)

45.   Japan's Fukusuke Corporation sold 10 knitting machines and raw materials to
       Chinatex, a Shanghai-based clothing manufacturer in exchange for one million
       pairs of underwear to be produced on the knitting machines. What form of
       countertrade is this?
       a.   buy-back
       b.   barter
       c.   parallel barter
       d.   offset purchase
       e.   clearinghouse accounts
       (a; moderate; p. 523)

46.   Which form of countertrade is used when one firm sells its products to another at one point in time and is compensated in the form of the other's products at some future time?
        a. counterpurchase
        b. barter
        c. parallel barter
        d. offset purchase
        e. clearinghouse accounts
        (a; moderate; p. 523)

47.   A soga sosha might assist in the sale of Mitsubishi trucks in Ghana, taking payment in cocoa, which then can be sold to keiretsu-linked food processors back in Japan or to independent candy makers anywhere. This is an example of _____.
        a. counterpurchase
        b. switching arrangements
        c. parallel barter
        d. offset purchase
        e. clearinghouse accounts
        (b; moderate; p. 523)

48.   Which countries find countertrade the most important?
        a. those in the Triad
        b. those in the Quad
        c. those without convertible currency
        d. less developed nations
        e. most favorable nations
        (c; moderate; p. 524)

49.   Which form of countertrade involves compensation arrangements whereby one firm sells capital goods to a second firm, and is compensated in the form of output generated as a result of their use?
        a. counterpurchase
        b. buy-back
        c. parallel barter
        d. offset purchase
        e. clearinghouse accounts
        (b; moderate; p. 523)

50.   Which form of countertrade is used when part of an exported good is produced in the importing country?
        a. counterpurchase
        b. barter
        c. parallel barter
        d. offset purchase
        e. clearinghouse accounts
        (d; moderate; p. 523)

51.   _____ occur when the exporting firm incurs a counterpurchase obligation of an equivalent value, which is then recorded in an account. When the exporter firm eventually buys goods from its partner, the obligation is reduced.
a. Open accounts
b. Barter accounts
c. Parallel barters
d. Offset purchases
e. Clearinghouse accounts
(e; moderate; p. 523)

52.   Which of the following is a component of payment terms for international transactions?
a. down payments
b. penalty payments for cancellation
c. inflation clauses
d. concessionary interest rates for long-term financing
e. all of the above
(e; moderate; p. 524)

53.   Which of the following payment methods holds a risk for the importer?
a. payment in advance
b. open account
c. documentary collection
d. letter of credit
e. countertrade
(a; difficult; p. 525)

54.   Which of the following payment methods exposes the exporter to no risk whatsoever?
a. payment in advance
b. open account
c. documentary collection
d. letter of credit
e. countertrade
(a; easy; p. 525)

55.   Which of the following payment methods is available for exporters by discounting draft from its face value?
a. payment in advance
b. open account
c. documentary collection
d. letter of credit
e. countertrade
(c; difficult; p. 525)

56.   Which of the following payment methods is appropriate when the exporter has complete trust in the importer?
        a. payment in advance
        b. open account
        c. letter of credit
        d. countertrade
        e. all of the above
        (b; difficult; p. 525)

57.   Which of the following payment methods does *not* time the delivery of goods when the goods arrive in the importer's country?
        a. countertrade
        b. credit card
        c. letter of credit
        d. open account
        e. payment in advance
        (c; difficult; p. 525)

58.   Which of the following is *not* one of the types of foreign-exchange exposure?
        a. transaction exposure
        b. currency conversion
        c. translation exposure
        d. economic exposure
        e. all are types of foreign-exchange exposure
        (b; moderate; p. 531)

59.   ___ occurs when exchange rate movements that occur after the firm is legally obligated to complete the transaction can affect the financial benefits and costs of an international transaction.
        a. Exchange rate risk
        b. Transaction exposure
        c. Translation exposure
        d. Currency conversion risk
        e. All of the above
        (b; moderate; p. 526)

60.   The purchase of goods, services, or assets denominated in a foreign currency can lead to _____.
        a. exchange rate risk
        b. translation exposure
        c. transaction exposure
        d. currency conversion risk
        e. all of the above
        (c; easy; p. 526)

61.   Which of the following is *not* an option for responding to transaction exposure?
       a. go naked
       b. buy currency options
       c. buy forward currency
       d. acquire an offsetting asset
       e. all of the above
       (e; moderate; p. 528)

62.   _____ is the impact on the firm's consolidated financial statements of fluctuations
       in exchange rates that change the value of foreign subsidiaries as measured in the
       parent's currency.
       a. Exchange rate risk
       b. Transaction exposure
       c. Translation exposure
       d. Currency conversion risk
       e. All of the above
       (c; moderate; p. 530)

63.   How can firms reduce their translation exposure?
       a. go naked
       b. use a balance sheet hedge
       c. buy forward currency
       d. acquire an offsetting asset
       e. all of the above
       (b; moderate; p. 530)

64.   A(n) _____ is created when an international firm matches its assets denominated
       in a given currency with its liabilities denominated in that same currency.
       a. forward currency
       b. offsetting asset
       c. income statement hedge
       d. balance sheet hedge
       e. cash account
       (d; moderate; p. 530)

65.   Which of the following long-term investments are particularly vulnerable to
       economic exposure?
       a. property
       b. plant
       c. equipment
       d. all of the above
       e. none of the above
       (d; difficult; p. 531)

66.   Which of the following is not one of the commonly used methods for evaluating investment projects among international financial officers?
        a. net present value
        b. internal rate of return
        c. pay-back period
        d. return on equity
        e. all are commonly used methods
        (d; difficult; p. 536)

67.   KLM Royal Dutch Airlines is considering an investment in new routes that should bring in significant revenues in the future. It will evaluate _____ as it assesses the value of the investment.
        a. risk adjustment
        b. internal rate of return
        c. net present value
        d. return on equity
        e. pay-back period
        (c; easy; p. 537)

68.   _____ is the current value of future revenues.
        a. Risk adjustment
        b. Internal rate of return
        c. Net present value
        d. Return on equity
        e. Pay-back period
        (c; easy; p. 537)

69.   The amount of risk adjustment applied when calculating net present value should reflect the _____.
        a. risk of operating in the country in question
        b. translation exposure
        c. transaction exposure
        d. economic exposure
        e. exchange rate risk
        (a; moderate; p. 537)

70. Ford Motor Company is considering a cash investment in a joint venture with Hyundai in South Korea. Ford considers the number of years it will take the firm to recover the original cash investment from the project's earnings, which is called the _____.
    a. internal rate of return
    b. net present value
    c. hurdle rate
    d. payback period
    e. return on equity
    (d; moderate; p. 538)

71. The _____ is the number of years it will take the firm to recover the original cash investment from the project's earnings.
    a. internal rate of return
    b. net present value
    c. payback period
    d. return on investment
    e. return on equity
    (c; easy; p. 538)

72. KLM Royal Dutch Airlines is considering an investment in new routes that should bring in significant revenues in the future. It will evaluate the _____, which is the number of years it will take to recover the original cash investment from the project's earnings.
    a. internal rate of return
    b. net present value
    c. payback period
    d. return on investment
    e. return on equity
    (c; easy; p. 538)

73. The minimum rate of return the firm finds acceptable for its capital investments is called _____.
    a. payback period
    b. hurdle rate
    c. internal rate of return
    d. return on investment
    e. saturation rate
    (b; moderate; p. 538)

74.   Rubbermaid has set a minimum rate of return of 15% on all its capital investments.
        Fifteen percent is Rubbermaid's _____.
        a. payback period
        b. hurdle rate
        c. internal rate of return
        d. return on investment
        e. saturation rate
        (b; moderate; p. 538)

75.   DaimlerChrysler is considering a Greenfield investment in China. As it evaluates
        the potential value of the project, what measure will DaimlerChrysler take into
        consideration?
        a. hurdle rate
        b. net present value
        c. payback period
        d. internal rate of return
        e. all of the above
        (e; moderate; p. 538)

True/False

76.   International commercial transactions are so common now that credit checks are
        unnecessary. (F; easy; p. 517)

77.   Parties to international commercial transactions normally negotiate a method of
        payment based on the exporter's assessment of the importer's creditworthiness
        and the norms of their industry. (T; moderate; p. 517)

78.   Payment in advance is the riskiest method from the exporter's perspective.
        (F; easy; p. 517)

79.   Exporters prefer that payments in advance be made by check.
        (F; moderate; p. 517)

80.   Open account is the safest form of payment from the importer's perspective.
        (T; moderate; p. 518)

81.   Exporters tend to prefer the open account method of payment while importers
        prefer payment in advance. (F; moderate; p. 518)

82.   Both payment in advance and open account share the characteristic of shifting
        the cash flow burden and risk of default to one party in a transaction.
        (T; moderate; p. 518)

83.	Payment in advance places the cash flow burden and risk of default on the seller while an open account places the cash flow burden and risk of default on the buyer. (F; difficult; p. 518)

84.	Export licenses are issued by agency of the exporter's home country.
(T; easy; p. 520)

85.	Inspection certificates may be needed to provide assurance that the products have been inspected and that they conform to relevant standards.
(T; moderate; p. 520)

86.	When goods are sold under a letter of credit, payment depends on meeting the terms of the sales contract. (F; difficult; p. 521)

87.	Advising banks have a responsibility to use reasonable care to check that any credit or amendment they advise to a beneficiary is authentic.
(T; moderate; p. 521)

88.	The most difficult form of countertrade is barter. (F; easy; p. 523)

89.	Compensation arrangements whereby one firm sells capital goods to a second firm and is compensated in the form of output generated as a result of their use is called counterpurchase. (F; moderate; p. 523)

90.	Countertrade agreements forbid the use of switching arrangements, whereby countertrade obligations are transferred from one firm to another.
(F; difficult; p. 523)

91.	The open account payment method is one of the most used because it holds no risk for both importer and exporter. (F; easy; p. 525)

92.	A firm faces translation exposure when exchange rate movements that occur after the firm is legally obligated to complete the transaction can affect the financial benefits and costs of an international transaction.
(F; moderate; p. 526)

93.	In most international transactions, one of the parties has to bear transaction exposure. (T; easy; p. 528)

94.	The term, go naked, means for a firm to fully accept exchange rate risk while hoping that the exchange rates will move in its favor. (T; moderate; p. 528)

95.	Translation exposure occurs when exchange rate movements that occur after the firm is legally obligated to complete the transaction can affect the financial benefits and costs of an international transaction.

(F; moderate; p. 528)

96.   If exchange rates were fixed, translation exposure would not exist.
        (T; difficult; p. 530)

97.   Economic exposure is the impact on the value of a firm's operations of
        unanticipated exchange rate changes. (T; moderate; p. 531)

98.   The rate of return on working capital is high, therefore financial officers prefer
        to invest funds in working capital. (F; moderate; p. 533)

99.   Bilateral netting occurs when two subsidiaries net out their mutual invoices.
        (T; easy; p. 535)

100.   The net present value approach is based on a basic precept of finance theory that
        a dollar today is worth less than a dollar in the future. (F; moderate; p. 537)

Short Answers

101.   What is the advantage of payment in advance for exporters? Answer: The
        exporter receives the importer's money prior to shipping the goods. Using this
        method, the exporter reduces its risk and receives payment quickly. (easy; p.
        517)

102.   Why do importers consider payment in advance undesirable? Answer: The
        importer must give up the use of its cash prior to its receipt of the goods and
        bears the risk that the exporter will fail to deliver the goods in accordance with
        the sales contract. (moderate; p. 518)

103.   What two roles are played by the bill of lading? Answer: It serves both as a
        contract for transportation between the exporter and the carrier and as a title to
        the goods in question. (moderate; p. 518)

104.   What are the two major forms of drafts? Answer: Sight draft and time draft.
        (easy; p. 519)

105.   How does a time draft become a banker's acceptance? Answer: A time draft
        becomes a banker's acceptance when the importer's bank also accepts the time
        draft, for a fee, and thereby adds its own obligation to pay the draft to the
        importer's obligation. (moderate; p. 519)

106.   What kinds of products generally require an export license? Answer: Politically
        sensitive goods such as nuclear fuels or high-technology goods that may have
        military uses. (moderate; p. 520)

107.   What are the four variations that can occur with letters of credit? Answer: Advised letter of credit, confirmed letter of credit, irrevocable letter of credit, and revocable letter of credit. (difficult; p. 521)

108.   When does countertrade occur? Answer: Countertrade occurs when a firm accepts something other than money as payment for its goods or services. (easy; p. 522)

109.   What is meant by the term switching arrangements? Answer: Switching arrangements are a type of countertrade whereby the countertrade obligations are transferred from one firm to another. (easy; p. 523)

110.   When does a firm face transaction exposure? Answer: A firm faces transaction exposure when the financial benefits and costs of an international transaction can be affected by exchange rate movements that occur after the firm is legally obligated to complete the transaction. (moderate; p. 526)

111.   What types of transactions denominated in a foreign currency can lead to transaction exposure? Answer: Purchase of goods, services, or assets; sales of goods, services, or assets; extension of credit; and borrowing of money. (easy; p. 526)

112.   Suppose that Saks Fifth Avenue agrees on April 10th to buy 5 million Swiss francs' worth of Rolex watches from Rolex's Swiss manufacturer, payable upon delivery on October 10th. Given the potential that the Swiss franc rises in value against the dollar, which partner experiences this transaction exposure? Answer: Saks Fifth Avenue. (moderate; p. 526)

113.   Suppose that Saks Fifth Avenue agrees on April 10th to buy 5 million Swiss francs' worth of Rolex watches from Rolex's Swiss manufacturer, payable upon delivery on October 10th. Given the potential that the Swiss franc falls in value against the dollar, which partner experiences this transaction exposure? Answer: Rolex. (moderate; p. 526)

114.   What options are available to a firm to protect against transaction exposure? Answer: Go naked, buy Swiss francs forward, buy Swiss franc currency options, acquire an offsetting asset. (moderate; p. 528)

115.   What is translation exposure? Answer: Translation exposure is the impact on the firm's consolidated financial statements on fluctuations in exchange rates that change the value of foreign subsidiaries as measured in the parent's currency. (easy; p. 530)

116.   While managing foreign-exchange exposure, what corporate financial goals must be managed by international financial officers? Answer: Minimizing

working-capital balances, minimizing currency conversion costs, and minimizing foreign-exchange risk. (moderate; p. 533)

117.   Why must financial officers hold working capital? Answer: To facilitate day-to-day transaction and to cover the firm against unexpected demands for cash. (moderate; p. 533)

118.   What is the role of a centralized cash manager? Answer: A centralized cash manager coordinates the MNC's worldwide cash. (easy; p. 533)

119.   How does a leads and lags strategy work? Answer: A leads and lags strategy attempts to increase a firm's net holdings of currencies that are expected to rise in value and decrease in net holdings of currencies that are expected to fall in value. (moderate; p. 536)

120.   How is net present value calculated? Answer: To calculate the net present value of a project, a firm's financial officers estimate the cash flows the project will generate in each time period and then discount them back to the present. (moderate; p. 537)

Essay

121.   What are the possible forms of payment for international commercial transactions? Describe three of these forms.

        Answer: The possible forms of payment are highlighted in Table 18.1 on page 525 and are described in the text on pages 517-525. The possible forms include payment in advance, open account, documentary collection, letters of credit, credit cards, and countertrade. Payment in advance means that the exporter receives the importer's money prior to shipping the goods. Open account means that goods are shipped by the exporter and received by the importer prior to payment. Under documentary collection, commercial banks serve as agents to facilitate the payment process. A letter of credit is a document that is issued by a bank and contains its promise to pay the exporter upon receiving proof that the exporter has fulfilled all requirements specified in the document. Countertrade occurs when a firm accepts something other than money as payment for its goods and services. (moderate; pp. 517-525)

122.   How does the process of documentary collection as an international payment method work?

        Answer: The exporter draws up a document called a draft (or bill of exchange) in which payment is demanded from the buyer at a specified time. After the exporter ships its goods, it submits to its local banker the draft and appropriate shipping documents (eg, the packing list and the bill of lading). Acting on the exporter's instructions, the exporter's bank then contacts its correspondent bank in the importer's country. The latter bank is authorized to release the bill of lading, thereby transferring title of the goods, when the importer honors the terms of the exporter's draft. (difficult; p. 518)

123.   Explain the conditions that favor the use of each form of payment.

Answer: Payment in advance is favored when the exporter has strong bargaining power and the importer is unknown to the exporter. An open account is favored when the exporter has complete trust in the importer and/or the exporter and importer are part of the same corporate family. Documentary collection is favored when the exporter trusts importer to pay as specified and/or when the risk of default is low. A letter of credit is favored when the exporter lacks knowledge of the importer and/or when the importer has good credit with a local bank. Credit cards are favored when the transaction size is small. Countertrade is favored when the importer lacks convertible currency and/or the importer or exporter wants access to foreign distribution network. (moderate; p. 525)

124.   What are the three types of foreign-exchange exposure confronting international firms? Explain each one.

Answer: The three types of foreign-exchange exposure are transaction exposure, translation exposure, and economic exposure. A firm faces transaction exposure when exchange rate movements that occur after the firm is legally obligated to complete the transaction can affect the financial benefits and costs of an international transaction. Translation exposure is the impact on the firm's consolidated financial statements of fluctuations in exchange rates that change the value of foreign subsidiaries as measured in the parent's currency. Economic exposure is the impact on the value of a firm's operations of unanticipated exchange rate changes. (moderate; p. 526)

125.   What three corporate financial goals international financial officers must balance? Explain.

Answer: The three corporate financial goals that must be balanced are minimizing working-capital balances, minimizing currency conversion costs, and minimizing foreign-exchange risk. Firms need enough working capital to facilitate day-to-day transactions and to cover the firm against unexpected demands for cash. At the same time, though, the rate of return on working capital is low so financial offers prefer to invest surplus funds in some other form than cash. Currency conversion fees and expenses may average 0.3 percent of the value of the transaction. It is best for financial officers to minimize these expenses. Financial officers also typically adjust the mix of currencies that make up the firm's working capital to minimize foreign-exchange risk. (moderate; p. 533)

Multiple Choice

1.   In the corporate world, the "Big Five" refers to _____.
        a. personality traits
        b. the world's largest corporations
        c. the world's largest accounting firms
        d. the five main types of risk in international business
        e. none of the above
        (c; easy; p. 549)

2.   How many major corporate accounting firms exist worldwide today?
        a. 4
        b. 5
        c. 8
        d. 12
        e. 15
        (a; moderate; p. 549)

3.   Which major accounting firm was associated with Enron's creative accounting
        and subsequent bankruptcy?
        a. Ernst and Young
        b. PriceWaterhouseCoopers
        c. KPMG
        d. Arthur Anderson
        e. None of the above
        (d; easy; p. 549)

4.   Who uses information from a company's accounting system?
        a. line managers
        b. government
        c. marketing executives
        d. investors
        e. all of the above
        (e; moderate; p. 550)

5.   Which of the following phrases refers to the discipline of accounting?
        a. language of business
        b. language of numbers
        c. soul of business
        d. numbers are the heart of a company
        e. none of the above
        (a; easy; p. 550)

6.   What environmental factor influences a country's accounting standards?
        a. legal
        b. cultural
        c. political
        d. economic
        e. all of the above
        (e; moderate; p. 551)

7.   Countries with a legal system based on _____ develop accounting procedures via
        decisions of independent, standard-setting boards.
        a. common law
        b. bureaucratic law
        c. religious law
        d. code law
        e. theocratic law
        (a; moderate; p. 551)

8.   Accountants in common law countries typically follow the _____ in providing a
        true and fair view of a firm's performance.
        a. statutory law
        b. procedures set by the ruling party
        c. religious policies on which law is based
        d. generally accepted accounting principles
        e. none of the above
        (d; easy; p. 551)

9.   The _____ provide the basic standards by which accountants provide a true and
        fair view of a firm's performance.
        a. GAAP
        b. GATT
        c. PAAG
        d. ISO 9000
        e. FASB
        (a; moderate; p. 551)

10.   In countries using common law, who or what determines accounting practices?
        a. law
        b. central government
        c. collective wisdom of professional accounting groups
        d. court decisions
        e. ruling party
        (c; easy; p. 551)

11.   What does GAAP stand for in the world of international accounting?
        a.   General Agreement on Accounting Practices
        b.   Generally Accepted Accounting Principles
        c.   General Act on Accounting and Procedures
        d.   German Accord on Public Accountants
        e.   None of the above
        (b; easy; p. 551)

12.   In countries using code law, who or what determines accounting practices?
        a.   law
        b.   central government
        c.   collective wisdom of professional accounting groups
        d.   court decisions
        e.   ruling party
        (a; easy; p. 551)

13.   What decision in a firm is affected by differences among countries' accounting
        practices?
        a.   reported income and profits
        b.   valuation of assets and inventories
        c.   tax reporting
        d.   use of accounting reserves
        e.   all of the above
        (e; moderate; p. 551)

14.   Which of the following countries adheres to accounting practices as required by
        law or court decisions?
        a.   The United States
        b.   The United Kingdom
        c.   Germany
        d.   Australia
        e.   India
        (c; moderate; p. 552)

15.   The U.S. system primarily relies upon _____ to enforce the accuracy and honesty
        of firm's accounting practices.
        a.   accountants
        b.   certified public accountants
        c.   private litigation
        d.   government enforcement
        e.   auditors
        (c; moderate; p. 552)

16.   The French system, based on code law, primarily relies upon _____ to enforce the accuracy and honesty of firm's accounting practices.
        a. accountants
        b. certified public accountants
        c. private litigation
        d. government enforcement
        e. auditors
        (d; moderate; p. 552)

17.   A(n) _____ details the treatment and compensation of their workforces in French firms.
        a. code of ethical treatment
        b. social balance sheet
        c. ethical statement
        d. code of social balances
        e. none of the above
        (b; moderate; p. 552)

18.   Michelin prepares a(n) _____ each year to report its treatment and compensation of its workforce in France.
        a. code of ethical treatment
        b. social balance sheet
        c. ethical statement
        d. code of social balances
        e. none of the above
        (b; moderate; p. 552)

19.   Publicly-owned firms must satisfy all the disclosure regulations of the _____.
        a. FDA
        b. SEC
        c. SCC
        d. WTO
        e. CIA
        (b; easy; p. 553)

20.   Which of the following countries focuses more on the information needs of individual investors than on the information required by lending banks?
        a. Japan
        b. Germany
        c. France
        d. The United States
        e. South Korea
        (d; moderate; p. 553)

21.   Which of the following is *not* a source of national accounting differences affecting international business?
       a.   valuation and revaluation of assets
       b.   disclosure regulations
       c.   valuation of inventories
       d.   dealing with tax authorities
       e.   use of accounting reserves
       (b; difficult; p. 554)

22.   An asset is carried on a firm's books according to the _____ in most countries.
       a.   asset's current market value
       b.   asset's original cost less depreciation
       c.   asset's original market value less depreciation
       d.   asset's future market value
       e.   asset's net present value
       (b; moderate; p. 553)

23.   When a firm's assets are carried on the firm's books at a level lower than the market value of an asset, the firm may wish to conduct a(n)_____.
       a.   asset revaluation
       b.   audit
       c.   review of accounting reserves
       d.   formal disclosure
       e.   none of the above
       (a; easy; p. 553)

24.   In which country, is the upward revaluation of assets illegal?
       a.   The United States
       b.   Japan
       c.   The United Kingdom
       d.   The Netherlands
       e.   Both a and b
       (e; moderate; p. 553)

25.   Asset revaluation procedures in a country affect investors in that the balance sheet may appear _____ in countries allowing upward asset revaluations.
       a.   stronger
       b.   weaker
       c.   about the same
       d.   asset revaluation does not affect the balance sheet
       (a; moderate; p. 553)

26.   What is the principle method for valuing inventories?
       a. LIFO
       b. FIFO
       c. LILO
       d. Both a and b
       e. Both b and c
       (d; moderate; p. 554)

27.   Philip Morris wishes to lower its taxes by reducing its reported profits. Which
       inventory valuation method is Philip Morris most likely to use?
       a. LIFO
       b. FIFO
       c. Actual cost
       d. Weighted cost
       e. FILO
       (a; difficult; p. 554)

28.   Which principle method for valuing inventories provides the clearest estimate of
       the value of firm's existing inventories?
       a. Inventory audit
       b. LIFO
       c. FIFO
       d. LILO
       e. FILO
       (c; moderate; p. 554)

29.   Which country below does *not* allow firms to choose either inventory valuation
       approaches?
       a. The United States
       b. Japan
       c. Canada
       d. Australia
       e. All allow firms to choose
       (d; moderate; p. 554)

30.   Which country only allows the use of the FIFO valuation of inventories?
       a. The United States
       b. Japan
       c. The United Kingdom
       d. New Zealand
       e. Canada
       (c; moderate; p. 554)

31.   In the United States, how many different sets of financial statements are reported?
        a. 1
        b. 2
        c. 3
        d. 4
        e. 5
        (b; moderate; p. 554)

32.   Siemens is based in Germany. How many sets of financial statements will it report?
        a. 1
        b. 2
        c. 3
        d. 4
        e. 5
        (a; moderate; p. 554)

33.   In Germany, how many different sets of financial statements are reported?
        a. 1
        b. 2
        c. 3
        d. 4
        e. 5
        (a; moderate; p. 554)

34.   In the United States, shareholders and _____receive a firm's financial statements.
        a. employees
        b. bankers
        c. the IRS
        d. the SEC
        e. all of the above
        (c; moderate; p. 554)

35.   The acronym, SEC, stands for _____.
        a. Standard Exchange-rate Corporation
        b. Securities Exchange Commission
        c. Stocks, Exchange rates, and Corporations
        d. Social Equity Conduct
        e. None of the above
        (b; easy; p. 554)

36.   _____ are accounts created in a firm's financial reports to record foreseeable future expenses that might affect its operations.
        a. Social balance sheets
        b. Working capitals
        c. Accounting reserves
        d. Cash reserves
        e. Operational funds
        (c; easy; p. 554)

37.   German firms use accounting reserves for _____.
        a. deferred maintenance
        b. future repairs
        c. exposure to international risks
        d. both a and b
        e. all of the above
        (e; easy; p. 554)

38.   _____ reduce reported income on which taxes are based.
        a. Social balance sheets
        b. Working capitals
        c. Accounting reserves
        d. Cash reserves
        e. Operational funds
        (c; easy; p. 554)

39.   When a firm pays more than the book value of an acquired firm's stock, the excess payment is called _____.
        a. capitalization
        b. goodwill
        c. reserves
        d. negative equity
        e. none of the above
        (b; moderate; p. 555)

40.   Which of the following countries was *not* a founding member of the International Accounting Standards Committee?
        a. The United States
        b. Canada
        c. South Korea
        d. Ireland
        e. The United Kingdom
        (c; difficult; p. 557)

41.   The _____ has issued a series of International Accounting Standards designed to
       harmonize national treatment of various accounting issues within its member
       countries.
       a. WTO
       b. IASB
       c. IASC
       d. OECD
       e. ISO
       (b; moderate; p. 558)

42.   The International Accounting Standards Board seeks to establish standards for
       _____.
       a. inventory valuation
       b. depreciation
       c. deferred income taxes
       d. both a and b
       e. all of the above
       (e; easy; p. 558)

43.   Under European Union guidelines, inventories are valued using the _____
       valuation approach.
       a. LIFO
       b. FIFO
       c. Actual cost
       d. Weighted cost
       e. All of the above
       (e; moderate; p. 558)

44.   Which of the following is a routine accounting problem for international
       businesses?
       a. Accounting for transactions denominated in foreign currencies.
       b. Reporting operation results of foreign subsidiaries in the firm's consolidated
           financial statements.
       c. Differences in national accounting systems.
       d. Both b and c.
       e. All of the above.
       (e; easy; p. 558)

45.   Because it is likely that the exchange rate will change between the time a firm
        enters into an international transaction and the time it receives payment or pays
        for the products, U.S. firms must use a(n) _____ to account for such international
        transactions in their financial statements.
        a. two-transaction approach
        b. exchange-rate transaction approach
        c. transaction risk minimization approach
        d. cost method
        e. equity method
        (a; moderate; p. 559)

46.   Target has purchased Christmas ornaments from China to stock its stores for the
        holiday season. Because the exchange rate between U.S. dollars and Chinese yuan
        will likely change before Target pays for the shipment, Target will use a(n) _____
        in its financial statements.
        a. two-transaction approach
        b. exchange-rate transaction approach
        c. transaction risk minimization approach
        d. cost method
        e. equity method
        (a; moderate; p. 559)

47.   _____ is the process of transforming a subsidiary's reported operations
        denominated in a foreign currency into the parent's home currency.
        a. Transaction
        b. Translation
        c. Revaluation
        d. Exchange
        e. None of the above
        (b; easy; p. 560)

48.   DaimlerChrysler must convert its subsidiaries' reported operations into Euros.
        What is this process called?
        a. transaction
        b. translation
        c. revaluation
        d. exchange
        e. none of the above
        (b; moderate; p. 560)

49.   _____ report the combined operations of a parent and its subsidiaries in a single
       set of an accounting statement denominated in a single currency.
       a. Income statements
       b. Balance sheets
       c. Consolidated financial statements
       d. Parent financial statements
       e. All of the above
       (c; easy; p. 560)

50.   Firms using the _____ translate the financial reports using the exchange rate at the
       time the foreign shares were acquired.
       a. cost method
       b. equity method
       c. consolidation method
       d. current rate method
       e. temporal method
       (a; moderate; p. 560)

51.   Ford Motor Company accounts for its 9.4% ownership of Kia Motors by
       recording the investment in the accounting records at cost using the exchange rate
       at the time the foreign shares were acquired. Ford uses the _____.
       a. cost method
       b. equity method
       c. consolidation method
       d. current rate method
       e. temporal method
       (a; moderate; p. 560)

52.   According to the FASB Statement 52, the treatment of foreign investments in a
       firm's consolidated financial statements is based on the _____.
       a. time of acquisition
       b. ownership stake
       c. country of the foreign investment
       d. historical exchange rate
       e. all of the above
       (b; moderate; p. 560)

53.   Ford Motor Company has a 9.4% ownership stake in South Korea's Kia Motors.
        According to the FASB Statement 52, what method must Ford use to account for
        this foreign investment?
        a. current rate method
        b. equity method
        c. consolidation method
        d. cost method
        e. temporal method
        (d; moderate; p. 560)

54.   Ford Motor Company has a 33% ownership stake in Japan's Mazda. According to
        the FASB Statement 52, what method must Ford use to enter this ownership stake
        into Ford's consolidated financial statements?
        a. cost method
        b. equity method
        c. consolidation method
        d. current rate method
        e. temporal method
        (b; moderate; p. 560)

55.   Ford purchased all of the stock in Volvo. According to the FASB Statement 52,
        what method must Ford use to account for its ownership in Volvo in Ford's
        consolidated financial statements?
        a. cost method
        b. equity method
        c. consolidation method
        d. current rate method
        e. temporal method
        (c; moderate; p. 560)

56.   A consolidation method is used when the parent's ownership stake in the foreign
        firm is _____.
        a. less than 10%
        b. between 10% and 25%
        c. between 26% and 50%
        d. more than 50%
        e. 100%
        (d; easy; p. 560)

57.   An equity method is used for the treatment of foreign investments in consolidated financial statements when the parent's ownership stake in the foreign firm is
_____.
a.   less than 10%
b.   between 10% and 50%
c.   between 50% and 75 %
d.   more than 75%
e.   100%
(b; easy; p. 560)

58.   A cost method is used for the treatment of foreign investments in consolidated financial statements when the parent's ownership stake in the foreign firm is
_____.
a.   less than 10%
b.   between 10% and 50%
c.   between 50% and 75 %
d.   more than 75%
e.   100%
(a; easy; p. 560)

59.   The _____ calls for the U.S. to first record its initial investment in the foreign firm at cost using the historical exchange rate. However, when the foreign firm earns profits or suffers losses, the value of the investment carried on the U.S. firm's consolidated financial statements is adjusted to reflect those profits or losses using the exchange rate prevailing when they were reported.
a.   cost method
b.   equity method
c.   consolidation method
d.   current rate method
e.   temporal method
(b; moderate; p. 560)

60.   The _____ calls for the accounting records of both the parent and foreign firm to be consolidated when the U.S. firm reports its operating results to its shareholders and the SEC is used when the U.S. firm has more than a 50% ownership stake in the foreign firm.
a.   cost method
b.   equity method
c.   consolidation method
d.   current rate method
e.   temporal method
(c; moderate; p. 560)

61.   What method will a U.S. firm use to translate a subsidiary's financial statements into the U.S. dollar?
       a.   cost method
       b.   current rate method
       c.   temporal method
       d.   both a and b
       e.   both b and c
       (e; moderate; p. 561)

62.   The _____ for translating a subsidiary's financial statements into the parent's currency is used if the subsidiary's functional currency is the host country's currency.
       a.   cost method
       b.   current rate method
       c.   temporal method
       d.   both a and b
       e.   both b and c
       (b; moderate; p. 561)

63.   The _____ for translating a subsidiary's financial statements into the parent's currency is used if the subsidiary's functional currency is the U.S. dollar.
       a.   cost method
       b.   current rate method
       c.   temporal method
       d.   both a and b
       e.   both b and c
       (c; moderate; p. 561)

64.   A(n) _____ is an accounting entry that makes a firm's assets equal the sum of its liabilities and shareholders' equity in order to make a balance sheet balance despite different exchange rates.
       a.   cumulative translation adjustment
       b.   credit
       c.   translation entry
       d.   exchange rate debit
       e.   none of the above
       (a; easy; p. 562)

65. What term refers to the prices one branch or subsidiary of a parent charges a second branch or subsidiary for goods or services?
    a. intradivisional pricing
    b. interdivisional pricing
    c. transfer pricing
    d. translation pricing
    e. cumulative adjustment pricing
    (c; easy; p. 563)

66. Samsung plans to export memory chips from South Korea for use in assembling personal computers at one of its U.S. subsidiaries. The price Samsung Korea charges the U.S. Samsung refers to _____.
    a. intradivisional pricing
    b. interdivisional pricing
    c. transfer pricing
    d. translation pricing
    e. cumulative adjustment pricing
    (c; easy; p. 563)

67. The _____ method of transfer pricing utilizes prices determined in the open market to transfer goods between units of the same corporate parent.
    a. non-market based
    b. market-based
    c. cost-based
    d. both a and b
    e. both b and c
    (b; moderate; p. 563)

68. What term refers to countries that impose little or no corporate income taxes?
    a. tax heaven
    b. tax evasion
    c. tax haven
    d. little Switzerland
    e. none of the above
    (c; easy; p. 565)

69. The _____ in the U.S. tax code states that earnings of its foreign subsidiaries will be taxed only when they are remitted to the parent in the form of dividends.
    a. dividend rule
    b. remittal rule
    c. deferral rule
    d. foreign sales corporation rule
    e. active income rule
    (c; moderate; p. 568)

70.   A foreign corporation in which U.S. shareholders, each of which holds at least 10% of the firm's shares, together own a majority of its stock is called a _____.
       a. foreign branch
       b. controlled foreign corporation
       c. foreign sales corporation
       d. tax haven
       e. none of the above
       (b; moderate; p. 568)

71.   What type of income is income of controlled foreign corporations?
       a. active income
       b. passive income
       c. subpart F income
       d. both b and c
       e. all of the above
       (e; moderate; p. 568)

72.   Which type of income of controlled foreign corporations is income generated by traditional business operations (eg, production, marketing, and distribution)?
       a. active income
       b. passive income
       c. subpart F income
       d. both b and c
       e. all of the above
       (a; moderate; p. 568)

73.   Which type of income of controlled foreign corporations is generated by activities (eg, the collection of dividends, interest, royalties, and licensing fees)?
       a. active income
       b. passive income
       c. subpart F income
       d. both b and c
       e. all of the above
       (d; moderate; p. 568)

74.   Home countries can reduce the burden of potential dual taxation from the host country and home country by granting a(n) _____ to the parent corporation for income taxes paid to the host country.
       a. deferral
       b. tax credit
       c. asset revaluation
       d. tax haven
       e. all of the above
       (b; moderate; p. 568)

75.   Ford Motor Company paid taxes on behalf of Volvo's earnings in Sweden.
       Consequently, it may receive a(n) _____ for that amount to reduce its tax burden
       in the U.S.
       a. deferral
       b. tax credit
       c. asset revaluation
       d. tax haven
       e. all of the above
       (b; moderate; p. 568)

True/False

76.   The accounting tasks of international businesses are very similar to those of
       domestic firms. (F; easy; p. 550)

77.   International businesses must develop an accounting system that provides both
       the internal information required by its managers to run the firm and the
       external information needed by shareholders, lenders, and government officials
       in the countries in which the firm operates. (T; moderate; p. 551)

78.   The underlying goals and philosophies of national accounting systems are very
       similar from country to country. (F; moderate; p. 551)

79.   Countries whose accounting systems rely upon generally accepted accounting
       principles have determined these principles by law. (F; moderate; p. 551)

80.   In countries relying on code law, accounting practices are determined by the
       collective wisdom of professional accounting groups. (F; moderate; p. 551)

81.   The accounting system in France creates accounting records designed to serve
       as proof in legal procedures. Consequently, all corporate accounting records
       must officially be registered with the government. (T; moderate; p. 552)

82.   Strong anti-inflation biases are embedded in German accounting procedures to
       prevent hyperinflation. (T; easy; p. 552)

83.   Because of the level of transparency in accounting standards, firms in less
       developed countries generally find it easy to obtain capital.
       (F; moderate; p. 553)

84.   Most publicly traded Japanese firms are members of a keiretsu. (T; easy; p. 553)

85.   Most Japanese firms have large debt-to-equity ratios by Western standards.
       (T; moderate; p. 553)

86.   In times of inflation, FIFO tends to raise the firm's reported costs of goods sold, lower the book value of its inventories, and reduce its reported profits more than LIFO does. (F; difficult; p. 554)

87.   FIFO produces a clearer estimate of the value of the firm's existing inventories than does LIFO. (T; difficult; p. 554)

88.   To compare the performance of two firms, one must know whether the firm uses LIFO or FIFO to value its inventories. (T; moderate; p. 554)

89.   Because German firms must develop only one set of financial statements, investors must recognize that the reported profits of German firms are biased upward. (F; difficult; p. 554)

90.   The IRS likes accounting reserves because charges to them increase a firm's taxable income. (F; moderate; p. 554)

91.   National governments often ignore the IASB accounting standards because the IASB has no enforcement power. (T; moderate; p. 558)

92.   Under the Bretton Woods system, international business activities denominated in foreign currencies tended to be more difficult than under today's fluctuating system. (F; moderate; p. 558)

93.   German firms must account for international transactions by using the three-transaction approach, which allows for the transaction to be recorded in U.S. dollars, Euros, and the German Deutschmark. (F; difficult; p. 559)

94.   Exchange rates often fluctuate between the time a firm signs an exporting contract and when it receives its money. (T; easy; p. 559)

95.   The process of transforming a subsidiary's reported operations denominated in a foreign currency into the parent's home currency is called transformation. (F; easy; p. 560)

96.   When a parent's ownership stake is less than 10% in a foreign investment, the firm must use the equity method to translate the foreign investment. (F; moderate; p. 560)

97.   According to the FASB Statement 52, a firm adopting the current rate method to translate a subsidiary's income statement must use either the exchange rate on the day a transaction occurred or a weighted average of exchange rates during the period covered by the income statement. (T; difficult; p. 561)

98.   Cumulative translation adjustments are used to make the firm's assets equal the sum of its liabilities and shareholders' equity despite currency translations. (T; easy; p. 562)

99.   Non-market–based transfer prices can decrease tariffs paid on components imported from a subsidiary and a corporation's overall income tax. (T; moderate; p. 564)

100.   Countries operating as tax havens earn revenues via corporate income taxes but at a reduced rate from what corporations would have paid in other non-tax haven countries. (F; moderate; p. 567)

Short Answers

101.   What is the goal of an accounting system? Answer: The goal of an accounting system is to identify, measure, and communicate "economic information to permit informed judgments and decisions by users of the information." (easy; p. 550)

102.   What environmental influences affect a country's accounting standards? Answer: Legal, cultural, political, and economic factors. (easy; p. 551)

103.   What corporate decisions are affected by differences among countries' accounting practices? Answer: Differences among countries' accounting practices effect a firm's decisions on reported income and profit, valuations of assets and liabilities, tax reporting, desire to operate in a given country, and use of accounting reserves. (moderate; p. 551)

104.   What standards are following for accounting in the United States? Answer: Generally accepted accounting principles or GAAP. (easy; p. 551)

105.   How might accounting systems vary based on whether the country is a centrally-planned economy or a market economy? Answer: In a centrally-planned economy, the accounting systems focus on documenting how state funds are used and whether state-mandated production quotas are being met. In market-oriented economies, managers and investors require profit-and cost-oriented information. (moderate; p. 553)

106.   Why might a firm wish to revaluate its assets? Answer: In most countries, an asset is carried on the firm's books according to the asset's original cost, less depreciation. Because of inflation, however, the market value of an asset is often higher than its historical cost. Raising the value would allow a firm to better reflect the true replacement cost of the asset. (moderate; p. 553)

107.   What are the two principle methods for valuing inventories? Answer: LIFO and FIFO. (easy; p. 554)

108.   What are accounting reserves? Answer: Accounting reserves are accounts created in a firm's financial reports to record foreseeable future expenses that might affect its operations. (easy; p. 554)

109.   Why is the use of accounting reserves disliked by both the IRS and the SEC? Answer: The IRS dislikes accounting reserves because charges to them reduce a firm's taxable income. The SEC fears that a firm may manipulate its accounting reserves to provide misleading pictures of its financial performance. (moderate; p. 554)

110.   What is goodwill? Answer: Goodwill refers to the excess payment firms may pay when acquiring a second firm. (easy; p. 555)

111.   What organization was formed to attempt to harmonize the various national accounting practices? Answer: International Accounting Standards Committee. (easy; p. 557)

112.   What is the primary goal of the International Accounting Standards Board? Answer: The most important goal of the IASB is the promotion of comparability of financial statements across countries by establishing standards for inventory valuation, depreciation, deferred income taxes, and other matters. (moderate; p. 557)

113.   What two types of specific accounting problems are routinely encountered when business is conducted internationally? Answer: Accounting for transactions denominated in foreign currencies and reporting the operating results of foreign subsidiaries in the firm's consolidated financial statements. (moderate; p. 558)

114.   Explain why a two-transaction approach is necessary for the reporting of international transactions. Answer: Under the existing flexible exchange rate system it is very likely that the exchange rate will change between the time a firm enters into an international transaction and the time it receives payment or pays for the goods, services, or assets in question. In accordance with FASB Statement 52, issued in 1981, U.S. firms must account for such international transactions by using the two-transaction approach in their financial statements. (moderate; p. 559)

115.   What is the function of a consolidated financial statement? Answer: A consolidated financial statement reports the combined operations of a parent and its subsidiaries in a single set of accounting statements denominated in a single currency. (easy; p. 560)

116.   What different methods can be used to translate financial reports from one
         currency into another based on a parent company's ownership stake? Answer:
         Cost method, equity method, and consolidation method. (moderate; p. 560)

117.   What are the two ways in which transfer prices can be calculated? Answer:
         Market-based method and non-market based method. (easy; p. 563)

118.   Why is the income of a foreign branch taxed as though it were the earnings of
         the U.S. parent company? Answer: A foreign branch is an unincorporated unit
         of a corporation. It operates in a foreign country but because it is legally
         identical to the parent, the branch's income is treated as if it were the parent's.
         (moderate; p. 567)

119.   What must tax havens provide to attract MNCs? Answer: It must refrain from
         imposing income taxes and also provide a stable political and business climate
         an efficient court system, as well as sophisticated banking and communication
         industries. (moderate; p. 566)

120.   How does a tax haven earn income? Answer: A tax haven earns income by
         capturing franchising and incorporation fees and generating numerous lucrative
         professional jobs far beyond what an economy of its size could do normally.
         (moderate; p. 567)

Essay

121.   In what ways is accounting for international firms more complex than
         accounting for domestic firms?

         Answer: The accounting system of a purely domestic firm must meet the
         professional and regulatory standards of its home country. An MNC and its
         subsidiaries, however, must meet the sometimes contradictory standards of all
         the countries in which they operate The firm will also have to pay taxes to the
         countries in which it does business based on the accounting statements it
         develops in these countries. Further, the subsidiary's accounting records must
         be translated into the parent's home currency using accounting procedures
         dictated by the parent company. Additionally, the parent corporation must
         integrate the accounting records of its subsidiaries to create consolidated
         financial statements.
         (moderate; p. 550)

122.   What are the eight significant national differences possible in accounting
         practices?

         Answer: Valuation and revaluation of assets, valuation of inventories, dealing
         with tax authorities, use of accounting reserves, capitalization of financial leases,

preparation of consolidated financial statements, capitalization of research and development expenses, and treatment of goodwill.
(difficult; pp. 553-555)

123.   How do German firms use accounting reserves? How is this different from the U.S. use of accounting reserves?

Answer: The U.S. system is quite restrictive and is carefully monitored by the IRS and SEC. However, the German Commercial Code liberally permits German firms to establish accounting reserves for various potential future expenses (eg, deferred maintenance, future repairs, or exposure to international risks). Because these reserves reduce reported income on which taxes are based, most German firms use them aggressively. (moderate; p. 554)

124.   What are the advantages to the information-laden accounting practices used by U.S. firms?

Answer: Many foreign bankers believe that the United States is the easiest foreign locale in which to lend because of U.S. public disclosure policies. Those policies result in reliable numbers for assessing the riskiness of potential loans. Transparent accounting approaches encourage investment. (moderate; pp. 555-557)

125.   What strategic goals can be accomplished by the use of non-market–based transfer prices? What technique is used to accomplish each goal?

Answer: If a firm wants to decrease the tariffs paid on components imported from a subsidiary, it can lower the transfer price charged by the subsidiary. If a firm wants to decrease its overall corporate income tax, it can raise transfer prices paid by subsidiaries in high-tax countries and/or lower transfer prices charged by those subsidiaries, and/or lower transfer prices paid by subsidiaries in low-tax countries, and/or raise transfer prices charged by those subsidiaries. If the firm wants to repatriate profits from a subsidiary located in a host country that blocks repatriation, it can raise transfer prices paid by the subsidiary and/or lower transfer prices charged by the subsidiary. (difficult; p. 564)

Multiple Choice

1.   What decision must be made when staffing a new international facility?
       a. How many employees the firm needs?
       b. What skills employees must have?
       c. Where employees will be hired?
       d. How much to pay new employees?
       e. All of the above.
       (e; easy; p. 575)

2.   _____ is the set of activities directed at attracting, developing, and maintaining
       the effective workforce necessary to achieve a firm's objectives.
       a. Staffing
       b. Development
       c. Human resource management
       d. Operations design
       e. Training
       (c; easy; p. 576)

3.   Which of the following is the goal of human resource management?
       a. attracting effective employees
       b. developing employees
       c. retaining good employees
       d. both a and b
       e. all of the above
       (e; moderate; p. 576)

4.   Which human resource management activity may need to be adjusted on a
       country-by-country basis to account for national differences?
       a. hiring
       b. firing
       c. training
       d. compensation
       e. all of the above
       (e; easy; p. 576)

5.   Which of the following environmental factors tends to influence human resource
       management procedures in a host country?
       a. culture
       b. legal systems
       c. economic development
       d. both a and b
       e. all of the above
       (e; moderate; p. 576)

6.   Where might employees for an international position come from?
        a. home country
        b. host country
        c. third country
        d. both a and b
        e. all of the above
        (e; easy; p. 576)

7.   What is the primary task of an international HR manager when dealing with
        managerial and executive positions?
        a. recruiting
        b. training
        c. retaining
        d. both a and b
        e. all of the above
        (e; moderate; p. 578)

8.   What is the first step in the international human resource management process?
        a. training and development
        b. performance appraisal
        c. recruitment and selection
        d. compensation and benefits
        e. labor relations
        (c; moderate; p. 578)

9.   What is the third step in the international human resource management process?
        a. training and development
        b. performance appraisal
        c. recruitment and selection
        d. compensation and benefits
        e. labor relations
        (b; moderate; p. 578)

10.   Which of the following is *not* part of the human resource management process?
        a. recruitment and selection
        b. performance appraisal
        c. labor relations
        d. training and development
        e. all of the above are part of the process
        (e; moderate; p. 578)

11.   From what group can international firms hire?
        a. parent country nationals
        b. host country nationals
        c. third country nationals
        d. both a and b
        e. all of the above
        (e; easy; p. 580)

12.   Which group tends to earn the highest total compensation from the parent
        company?
        a. parent country nationals
        b. host country nationals
        c. third country nationals
        d. both a and b
        e. all of the above
        (a; moderate; p. 590)

13.   Mercedes sent a team of executives from Germany to oversee the start-up of its
        U.S. operations. Mercedes chose _____ to manage this operation.
        a. parent country nationals
        b. host country nationals
        c. third country nationals
        d. all of the above
        e. none of the above
        (a; easy; p. 580)

14.   _____ are residents of the international business's home country.
        a. Parent country nationals
        b. Host country nationals
        c. Third country nationals
        d. All of the above
        e. None of the above
        (a; easy; p. 580)

15.   When a firm uses a home replication strategy, which group of employees is best
        suited for international positions?
        a. parent country nationals
        b. host country nationals
        c. third country nationals
        d. all of the above
        e. none of the above
        (a; moderate; p. 580)

16.   When a firm uses a multidomestic strategy, which group of employees is thought to be at a disadvantage?
        a. third country nationals
        b. host country nationals
        c. parent country nationals
        d. all of the above
        e. none of the above
        (c; moderate; p. 580)

17.   Mercedes hired managers from the local community in Kentucky as operations managers in its plant there. Mercedes used _____.
        a. parent country nationals
        b. host country nationals
        c. third country nationals
        d. both a and b
        e. all of the above
        (b; easy; p. 580)

18.   _____ are residents of the host country.
        a. Parent country nationals
        b. Host country nationals
        c. Third country nationals
        d. All of the above
        e. None of the above
        (b; easy; p. 580)

19.   When a firm uses a multidomestic strategy, which group of employees is best suited for managerial positions?
        a. parent country nationals
        b. host country nationals
        c. third country nationals
        d. all of the above
        e. none of the above
        (b; moderate; p. 580)

20.   _____ are those employees who are not citizens of the firm's home country or of the host country.
        a. Parent country nationals
        b. Host country nationals
        c. Third country nationals
        d. All of the above
        e. None of the above
        (c; easy; p. 580)

21.   Which group of employees may also be known as expatriates?
       a. parent country nationals
       b. host country nationals
       c. third country nationals
       d. both a and b
       e. both a and c
       (e; moderate; p. 580)

22.   What term refers to people working and residing in countries other than their
       native country?
       a. host country national
       b. expatriate
       c. non-patriot
       d. green card resident
       e. none of the above
       (b; easy; p. 581)

23.   Michael is a United States citizen who was sent from the U.S. headquarters to
       Italy to oversee procedural changes in one of the corporation's manufacturing
       subsidiaries. Michael is a(n) _____.
       a. parent country national
       b. host country national
       c. expatriate
       d. third country national
       e. both a and c
       (e; moderate; p. 581)

24.   Mick is a native of South Africa. He works for a company named Octagon that is
       based in the United States. Next week, he will move to Japan to work in
       Octagon's Japanese branch. Mick is a(n) _____.
       a. parent country national
       b. host country national
       c. expatriate
       d. third country national
       e. both c and d
       (e; moderate; p. 581)

25.   Firms using a(n) _____ primarily use parent country nationals to staff higher-level
       foreign positions.
       a. ethnocentric staffing model
       b. polycentric staffing model
       c. geocentric staffing model
       d. expatriate staffing model
       e. all of the above
       (a; moderate; p. 581)

26.   Samsung tends to follow an ethnocentric staffing model. From which group will it
        tend to hire for upper-level management positions?
        a. parent country nationals
        b. host country nationals
        c. third country nationals
        d. both a and b
        e. both a and c
        (a; moderate; p. 581)

27.   McDonald's uses a geocentric staffing model, which fits well with its emphasis
        on standardization. McDonald's will likely hire _____.
        a. parent country nationals
        b. host country nationals
        c. third country nationals
        d. both a and b
        e. all of the above
        (e; easy; p. 580)

28.   Firms using a(n) _____ primarily use host country nationals.
        a. ethnocentric staffing model
        b. polycentric staffing model
        c. geocentric staffing model
        d. expatriate staffing model
        e. none of the above
        (b; moderate; p. 581)

29.   Firms using a(n) _____ may staff from all three sources of employees.
        a. ethnocentric staffing model
        b. polycentric staffing model
        c. geocentric staffing model
        d. expatriate staffing model
        e. none of the above
        (c; moderate; p. 581)

30.   Microsoft tends to follow a geocentric staffing model. From which group will it
        tend to hire?
        a. parent country nationals
        b. host country nationals
        c. third country nationals
        d. both a and b
        e. all of the above
        (e; moderate; p. 581)

31.   When selecting an employee for an international job assignment, what is the most critical skill or ability needed?
        a. skills/abilities to do the job
        b. skills/abilities to work in the foreign location
        c. knowledge of the language
        d. knowledge of the culture
        e. both a and b
        (e; difficult; p. 581)

32.   What skill or ability is necessary to work in a foreign location?
        a. adaptability
        b. location-specific skills
        c. personal characteristics
        d. both a and b
        e. all of the above
        (e; easy; p. 582)

33.   What form of managerial competence will a strong candidate for an international management position have?
        a. technical skills
        b. formal education
        c. knowledge of the host market
        d. knowledge of culture
        e. language competence
        (a; difficult; p. 584)

34.   What type of adjustment must an expatriate be able to make?
        a. adjusting to a new work environment
        b. adjusting to a new job
        c. adjusting to working with host country nationals
        d. adjusting to a new national culture
        e. all of the above
        (e; easy; p. 584)

35.   _____ is the early return of an expatriate manager to the home country because of an inability to perform in the overseas assignment.
        a. Culture shock
        b. Expatriate return
        c. Expatriate failure
        d. Managerial incompetence
        e. Repatriation
        (c; moderate; p. 584)

36.   The cost of expatriate failure includes _____.
       a. training
       b. moving expenses
       c. lost managerial productivity
       d. both a and b
       e. all of the above
       (e; moderate; p. 584)

37.   Which country has the highest expatriate failure rates?
       a. South Korea
       b. The United States
       c. Germany
       d. Japan
       e. India
       (b; moderate; p. 584)

38.   What are the expatriate failure rates for U.S. firms?
       a. 10%-15%
       b. 20%-50%
       c. 20%-30%
       d. 50%-60%
       e. more than 60%
       (b; easy; p. 584)

39.   Danielle accepted a position with the Boston Consulting Group in South Korea
       and moved a few weeks ago. Now, she plans to return home because of her
       difficulty in adapting to Korean culture. Danielle is experiencing _____.
       a. repatriation
       b. expatriate failure
       c. culture shock
       d. all of the above
       e. none of the above
       (d; moderate; p. 584)

40.   What indicator can be used to estimate the likelihood of expatriate failure for a
       job candidate?
       a. language proficiency
       b. motivation for the foreign assignment
       c. interest in the foreign assignment
       d. personality
       e. all of the above
       (e; moderate; p. 584)

41.   _____ is a psychological phenomenon that may lead to feelings of fear,
        helplessness, irritability, and disorientation.
        a. Expatriate failure
        b. Repatriation
        c. Culture shock
        d. Stress
        e. Depression
        (c; moderate; p. 585)

42.   John has been transferred to an office in Japan for a year. In his first few weeks,
        he began to feel confused and rejected as well as a sort of mourning for home.
        John is experiencing _____.
        a. expatriate failure
        b. repatriation
        c. acculturation
        d. culture shock
        e. home sickness
        (d; moderate; p. 585)

43.   Which of the following is *not* a phase in the process of acculturation?
        a. honeymoon
        b. acceptance
        c. disillusionment
        d. adaptation
        e. biculturalism
        (b; difficult; p. 586)

44.   Which stage of acculturation do most people remain in?
        a. honeymoon
        b. acceptance
        c. disillusionment
        d. adaptation
        e. biculturalism
        (c; difficult; p. 586)

45.   After several separate assignments in Russia, Tim feels as comfortable in Moscow
        as he does in his hometown of Chicago, Illinois. Tim speaks Russian fluently and
        his family practices cultural traditions from both Russia and the United States.
        What stage of acculturation is Tim experiencing?
        a. honeymoon
        b. acceptance
        c. disillusionment
        d. adaptation
        e. biculturalism
        (e; difficult; p. 586)

46.   Which method can reduce the level of culture shock an expatriate is likely to experience?
        a.   predeparture language training
        b.   predeparture cultural training
        c.   brief assignments initially
        d.   explanation of the role the assignment will play in the expatriate's career
        e.   all of the above
        (e; moderate; p. 586)

47.   Mirta has been transferred from Germany to the United States. She has been in the U.S. for a few weeks and finds the environment exciting and stimulating. She loves such things as the shopping in the U.S. and feels certain she will adjust to this new environment easily. Which stage of acculturation is Mirta in?
        a.   honeymoon
        b.   acceptance
        c.   disillusionment
        d.   adaptation
        e.   biculturalism
        (a; moderate; p. 586)

48.   In the _____ stage of acculturation, the new culture seems exciting and interesting.
        a.   honeymoon
        b.   acceptance
        c.   disillusionment
        d.   adaptation
        e.   biculturalism
        (a; difficult; p. 586)

49.   In the _____ stage of acculturation, the differences between the new and old environments are blown out of proportion.
        a.   honeymoon
        b.   acceptance
        c.   disillusionment
        d.   adaptation
        e.   biculturalism
        (c; easy; p. 586)

50.   Patricia moved a few weeks ago to South Korea to accept a promotion. While she was initially excited about the move and found many Korean traditions interesting, she is struggling with the language differences and different foods available. Which stage of acculturation is Patricia in?
        a. honeymoon
        b. acceptance
        c. disillusionment
        d. adaptation
        e. biculturalism
        (c; moderate; p. 586)

51.   In which stage of acculturation does the expatriate begin to understand the new culture and gain language competence?
        a. honeymoon
        b. acceptance
        c. disillusionment
        d. adaptation
        e. biculturalism
        (d; moderate; p. 586)

52.   After more than a year in Germany, Carol has become fluent in German and admires the workplace traditions of caution and attention to detail. Carol is in the _____ stage of acculturation.
        a. honeymoon
        b. acceptance
        c. disillusionment
        d. adaptation
        e. biculturalism
        (d; difficult; p. 586)

53.   _____ refers to bringing a manager back home after a foreign assignment has been completed.
        a. Expatriation
        b. Repatriation
        c. Culture shock
        d. Expatriate failure
        e. Acculturation
        (b; easy; p. 586)

54.   As many as _____ of all repatriated employees leave their employer within a year after returning home.
a. 10%
b. 25%
c. 50%
d. 75%
e. 90%
(b; moderate; p. 587)

55.   What term refers to instruction directed at enhancing specific job-related skills and abilities?
a. training
b. teaching
c. development
d. screening
e. practicing
(a; easy; p. 587)

56.   _____ is general education concerned with preparing managers for new assignments and/or higher-level positions.
a. Training
b. Teaching
c. Development
d. Screening
e. Practicing
(c; easy; p. 587)

57.   Where do training activities take place?
a. classrooms within the firm
b. on actual job sites
c. in conference centers
d. in hotel meeting rooms
e. all of the above
(e; moderate; p. 588)

58.   What instructional method is usually used for training?
a. lectures
b. assigned readings
c. videotapes
d. role-playing
e. all of the above
(e; easy; p. 588)

59.   A _____ is the process of assessing how effectively people are performing their
        jobs.
        a. performance appraisal
        b. job review
        c. job audit
        d. developmental audit
        e. all of the above
        (a; easy; p. 590)

60.   What is the measure used to assess a manager's actual performance?
        a. sales
        b. profit margin
        c. market share growth
        d. both a and b
        e. all of the above
        (e; moderate; p. 590)

61.   Expatriate managers generally receive differential compensation to make up for
        dramatic differences in _____.
        a. currency valuations
        b. standards of living
        c. lifestyle norms
        d. both b and c
        e. all of the above
        (e; moderate; p. 590)

62.   The idea that a manager who accepts a foreign assignment is entitled to the same
        standard of living the manager enjoyed at home is the basis for _____.
        a. premium expatriate salaries
        b. cost-of-living allowances
        c. hardship premiums
        d. foreign-service premiums
        e. tax equalization
        (b; moderate; p. 590)

63.   In which city listed below is the cost of living the highest?
        a. Tokyo
        b. Moscow
        c. New York City
        d. London
        e. Milan
        (a; moderate; p. 591)

64.   Smith Enterprises seeks to entice one of its star managers to move to Iraq to
        oversea its negotiations for Iraqi oil. The firm will likely need to offer a _____ to
        a manager's base salary.
        a.   cost-of-living allowance
        b.   bonus
        c.   hardship premium
        d.   tax equalization adjustment
        e.   all of the above
        (c; moderate; p. 591)

65.   What is the term for a supplement used to induce individuals to accept an
        international assignment?
        a.   hardship premium
        b.   foreign-service premium
        c.   cost-of-living allowance
        d.   both a and b
        e.   all of the above
        (d; moderate; p. 591)

66.   A(n) _____ is a means of ensuring that the expatriate's after-tax income in the
        host country is similar to what the person's after-tax income would be in the home
        country.
        a.   tax assessment system
        b.   tax equalization system
        c.   equality in taxes and tariffs system
        d.   hardship premium
        e.   foreign-service premium
        (b; easy; p. 591)

67.   In addition to salary adjustments, expatriates also get adjustments in _____.
        a.   housing
        b.   spousal job location assistance
        c.   private schooling for children
        d.   medical benefits
        e.   all of the above
        (e; moderate; p. 592)

68.   _____ is the extent to which a firm is able to keep valued employees.
        a.   Turnover
        b.   Employee occupancy rate
        c.   Retention
        d.   Repatriation
        e.   Compensation adjustment
        (c; easy; p. 593)

69.   _____ is the rate at which people leave a firm.
        a. Turnover
        b. Employee expulsion rate
        c. Retention
        d. Repatriation
        e. Quit factor
        (a; easy; p. 593)

70.   Which term refers to the process used to make agreements between management
        and labor unions?
        a. labor management
        b. collective bargaining
        c. negotiations
        d. labor allowances
        e. none of the above
        (b; moderate; p. 598)

71.   _____ refers to the requirement in Germany that unions have input into how firms
        are run.
        a. Codetermination
        b. Collective bargaining
        c. Workers' rights
        d. Union power
        e. None of the above
        (a; easy; p. 599)

72.   Which of the following countries does *not* follow a model of industrial
        democracy?
        a. Sweden
        b. Germany
        c. The United Kingdom
        d. Norway
        e. France
        (c; moderate; p. 599)

73.   Which of the following countries prescribes to a model of industrial democracy
        that includes some level of codetermination?
        a. Italy
        b. Ireland
        c. Spain
        d. France
        e. Greece
        (d; moderate; p. 599)

74.   The EU seeks to implement a(n) _____ to standardize such practices as maternity leave, job training, and pension benefits.
        a. social balance sheet
        b. social charter
        c. codetermination treaty
        d. equality act
        e. all of the above
        (b; moderate; p. 599)

75.   The EU's social charter includes the attempt to standardize _____.
        a. maternity leave
        b. job training
        c. pension benefits
        d. both a and b
        e. all of the above
        (e; moderate; p. 599)

True/False

76.   Toyota wants only those employees who will conform to its emphasis on teamwork and corporate loyalty. (T; moderate; p. 575)

77.   Because the cost of living may vary dramatically by country, international HR managers must often tailor compensation systems to meet the needs of the host country's labor market. (T; moderate; p. 577)

78.   Staffing issues confronting international HR managers can be divided into two broad categories: parent country nationals and host country nationals.
        (F; moderate; p. 578)

79.   If a firm is at the export department stage of internationalization, its manager is likely to be a host country national. (F; moderate; p. 579)

80.   Decentralized firms tend to prefer home country nationals in international assignments. (F; easy; p. 580)

81.   Parent country nationals (PCNs) are commonly used to fill lower-level jobs abroad. (F; easy; p. 580)

82.   The primary advantage of using a HCN is that the HCN already understands the local laws, culture, and economic conditions. (T; moderate; p. 581)

83.   HCNs and TCNs are collectively known as expatriates. (F; moderate; p. 581)

84.   In a geocentric staffing model, the firm will prefer host country nationals to either parent country nationals or third country nationals. (F; moderate; p. 581)

85.   When Upjohn and Pharmacia merged in the 1990s, they moved their headquarters from London to New Jersey in order to be near a pool of managerial and technical talent. (T; moderate; p. 583)

86.   Some firms rely on fortunetellers to predict the success of candidates for international positions because of the high cost of expatriate failure and the difficulty in predicting success through other measures. (F; easy; p. 584)

87.   "Can you imagine living without a television?" is one of the questions on AT&T's screening questionnaire for overseas transferees. (T; moderate; p. 585)

88.   Repatriated managers experience change and uncertainty as they adjust to returning home after a foreign assignment. (T; easy; p. 586)

89.   Acceptance is one of the latter stages in the process of acculturation. (F; difficult; p. 586)

90.   An expatriate adjusts to everyday living in the disillusionment stage of acculturation. (F; moderate; p. 586)

91.   Culture shock affects an expatriate's job satisfaction level but does not tend to affect his or her effectiveness and productivity at work. (F; difficult; p. 586)

92.   Development is the general education concerned with preparing managers for new assignments and/or higher-level positions. (T; easy; p. 587)

93.   A repatriated executive who leaves the firm after returning from four years on an overseas assignment could represent the loss of a million-dollar investment to the firm. (T; moderate; p. 587)

94.   Samsung sends some of its younger managers abroad with no specific job duties for as long as a year so that they will be able to function in those countries more effectively when they are in higher-level positions at later points in time. (T; moderate; p. 589)

95.   The cost of living in Moscow is higher than in New York City. (T; difficult; p. 591)

96.   New York City is the most expensive city in the world to live in. (F; moderate; p. 591)

97.   Expatriate managers may receive private schooling for their children and additional weeks of vacation to allow for time to come home. (T; easy; p. 591)

98.   The compensation package offered a host country national is equivalent to that offered an expatriate manager for a position of roughly equal responsibility and power. (F; moderate; p. 593)

99.   Training for manufacturing positions abroad is not necessary because the employees are host country nationals. (F; difficult; p. 595)

100.   Wages account for a higher percentage of the total compensation package for workers in many low-wage countries compared to industries elsewhere. (T; moderate; p. 596)

Short Answers

101.   What is the meaning of human resource management? Answer: Human resource management is the set of activities directed at attracting, developing, and maintaining the effective workforce necessary to achieve a firm's objectives. (easy; p. 576)

102.   What kinds of tasks and functions are included in human resource management? Answer: HRM includes recruiting and selecting nonmanagers and managers, providing training and development, appraising performance, and providing compensation and benefits. (moderate; p. 576)

103.   What challenge do U.S. firms experience when female executives are considered for managerial positions in countries like Saudi Arabia? Answer: The U.S. firms are faced with prohibitions against gender discrimination and faced with a host country culture that restricts the role of women. (moderate; p. 576)

104.   What are the basic elements of the international human resource management process? Answer: Recruitment and selection, training and development, performance appraisal, compensation and benefits, labor relations, and contributions to organizational effectiveness. (moderate; p. 578)

105.   What are the two broad categories for staffing issues among international HR managers? Answer: Recruiting, training, and retaining managerial and executive employees, and recruiting, training, and retaining nonmanagerial employees. (easy; p. 578)

106.   What source of managerial talent will a decentralized firm use? Answer: Host country nationals. (easy; p. 580)

107.   What are the three groups from which firms can hire? Answer: Parent country nationals (PCNs), host country nationals (HCNs), and third country nationals (TCNs). (moderate; p. 580)

108.   What are the three staffing models common among international firms? Answer: Ethnocentric staffing model, polycentric staffing model, and geocentric staffing model. (moderate; p. 581)

109.   Do polycentric firms tend to hire PCNs, HCNs, or TCNs? Answer: HCNs. (easy; p. 581)

110.   What kinds of skills and abilities are necessary to work in a foreign location? Answer: Adaptability and location-specific skills (eg, language, personal characteristics). (moderate; p. 582)

111.   Explain the meaning of expatriate failure. Answer: Expatriate failure is the early return of a expatriate manager to the home country because of an inability to perform in the overseas assignment. (easy; p. 584)

112.   What characteristics are present in the most promising candidate for international assignments? Answer: The most promising candidates share the following characteristics: managerial competence, appropriate training, and adaptability to new situations. (moderate; p. 584)

113.   What is the primary cause of expatriate failure? Answer: The primary cause of expatriate failure is the inability of the managers and/or their spouses and families to adjust the new locale. (moderate; p. 584)

114.   What is culture shock? Answer: Culture shock is a psychological phenomenon that may lead to feelings of fear, helplessness, irritability, and disorientation. (easy; p. 585)

115.   What are the four phases of acculturation? Answer: Honeymoon, disillusionment, adaptation, and biculturalism. (moderate; p. 586)

116.   Explain the meaning of repatriation. Answer: Repatriation means to bring an expatriate manager back home after a foreign assignment has been completed. (moderate; p. 586)

117.   What is the purpose of a cost-of-living allowance? Answer: This allowance is intended to offset differences in the cost of living in the home and host countries. The premise is that a manager who accepts a foreign assignment is entitled to the same standard of living as the manager enjoyed at home. (moderate; p. 590)

118.   What is the purpose of a hardship premium? Answer: A hardship premium is an inducement to an individual to accept an international assignment in a relatively unattractive place. (moderate; p. 591)

119.   Explain the purpose of a tax equalization system. Answer: A tax equalization system is a means of ensuring that the expatriate's after-tax income in the host country is similar to what the person's after-tax income would be in the home country. (moderate; p. 591)

120.   What is the purpose of an exit interview? Answer: Its purpose is to find out as much as possible about why the person decided to leave the firm. (moderate; p. 594)

Essay

121.   How does the scope of internationalization affect the recruiting, training, and retaining of managers?

Answer: When a firm is still in the export department phase of internationalization, it will tend to staff international concerns with a parent country national. As export sales increase, the firm will tend to hire specialists in export documentation, international trade financing, overseas distribution, and marketing. As the firm evolves to the use of an international division, it will house a separate division at headquarters that will be headed by a PCN. Managers of foreign subsidiaries will be either HCNs or PCNs. As the firm develops into a global organization, the specific knowledge a manager possesses will become more important than his or her citizenship. In this case, the firm may hire PCNs, HCNs, and/or TCNs. (difficult; p. 579)

122.   What are the advantages and disadvantages of using parent country nationals in international assignments?

Answer: PCNs typically share a common culture and educational background with corporate headquarters staff so they are able to facilitate communication and coordination with corporate headquarters. They are also adept at introducing techniques from home to the host country setting. However, PCNs typically lack the knowledge of the host country's laws, culture, economic conditions, social structure, and political processes. These weaknesses can be overcome with training but such training is expensive. Further, it is expensive to relocate PCNs and maintain them in the host country. (moderate; p. 580)

123.   How are experienced managers recruited by international businesses?

Answer: A common source of recruits is within the firm itself–among employees already working for the firm in the host country or those who, although currently employed in the home country, might be prepared for an international assignment in the host country. A company may dip into its pool of retired executives to fill short-term international assignments. An international business may also attempt to identify prospective managers who work for other firms. They may rely upon headhunters to locate prospective candidates. A firm may also locate its facilities near a pool of qualified employees. (moderate; p. 582)

124.   What challenges face repatriated managers when they return from a foreign assignment?

Answer: Repatriated managers may not know what their new job back home will entail. They may have enjoyed considerable authority abroad that will not continue at home. They may feel out of the loop on changes that have occurred at the home office. They and their families may have enjoyed a higher social status in the host country than they will enjoy after returning home. (moderate; p. 586)

125.   What factors increase the likelihood of managers being successful at an overseas assignment? Which of these is the most critical?

Answer: Research indicates that the likelihood of success increases if the managers
   • can freely choose whether to accept or reject the expatriate assignment,
   • have been given a realistic preview of the new job and assignment,
   • have been given a realistic expectation of what their repatriation assignment will be,
   • have a mentor back home who will guard their interests and provide corporate and social support during the assignment, and
   • see a clear link between the expatriate assignment and their long-term career path.

The last is the most critical in determining expatriate success.
(moderate; p. 587)